THE
OLD MAN
AND ME

THE
OLD MAN
AND ME

A Gangster's Life. A Son's Journey.

JASON WILSON

MIRROR BOOKS

MIRROR BOOKS

All of the events in this story are true,
but some names and details have been changed
to protect the identities of individuals.

© Jason Wilson

The rights of Jason Wilson to be identified as the author
of this book have been asserted, in accordance with the
Copyright, Designs and Patents Act 1988.

1

Published in Great Britain and Ireland in 2022 by
Mirror Books, a Reach PLC business,
5 St Paul's Square, Liverpool, L3 9SJ.

www.mirrorbooks.co.uk
@TheMirrorBooks

Print ISBN 9781913406882
eBook ISBN 9781913406899

Page design and typesetting by Danny Lyle

Printed and bound in Great Britain by
CPI Group (UK) Ltd, Croydon, CR0 4YY

Photographic acknowledgements: Jason Wilson.

CONTENTS:

1.	Murder in Amsterdam	1
2.	At Death's Door	6
3.	Why A Criminal?	16
4.	The Recovery	23
5.	Pursuing An Answer	31
6.	The Smuggler On The Run	41
7.	The Young Entrepreneur	55
8.	Arrested In Barcelona	65
9.	Leyhill Prison	77
10.	The Smugglers' Consortium	88
11.	Prisoner To Millionaire	97
12.	Nowhere To Run, Nowhere To Hide	111
13.	Bank Robber	126
14.	Back Inside	137
15.	HMP Long Lartin	151
16.	Dutch Justice	161
17.	The Dollar Counterfeit	171
18.	Like Father, Like Son	186
19.	Rise Of A Drug Importer	195
20.	The Dam And The Supply	215
21.	The Network	228
22.	Beating The Enemy	240
23.	Building Of A Question	255
24.	The Road To Amsterdam	268
25.	Return From Spain	283
26.	Operation Downpour	293

27.	Underground Safes And Roving Bugs	306
28.	The Final Showdown	318
29.	At The Crossroads	330
30.	The Final Year	343
31.	Discovering Rosebud	352
32.	The Final Piece	363
33.	Choices	371

CHAPTER 1:
MURDER IN AMSTERDAM

25TH MAY 2001

I FLEW INTO AMSTERDAM on the Wednesday morning, accompanied the Old Man to a few meetings, imparted some advice, thought he had listened, and returned on the last flight home. I'd only been gone a day when he did what he always did and went his own way. He discarded all I said bar the one detail: *"Hoffmans, the late-night deli, has no security cameras"*.

This, he filed away for later.

A tall broad-shouldered man with handsome features, my father was a drug importer who had been on the run from British police for more than a year. Charged with heading a drugs conspiracy, he skipped bail and resurfaced in Amsterdam. There he operated under the alias of 'English John'.

His true name was Anthony Spencer, Tony to his friends, but he was someone who used many names.

In the UK he was known as 'Pat', in Spain as 'Graham', and amongst our group as 'the Old Man', though he was barely 50 years old.

What happened after I had left Amsterdam the Old Man would recount the following evening. He would tell us the story whilst lying on a stretcher bed, unsure whether he would live or die, recalling every detail, explaining what had occurred the night before.

He had arranged to meet the 'Soldier' at *Hoffmans* – the deli without cameras. At ten o'clock it was raining hard. He stood beneath *Hoffmans*' narrow green canopy as customers without coats or umbrellas waited for the rain to pass. The Soldier was likely driving, and so the Old Man stood to the rear of a thickening

1

crowd, backlit against the store windows, patiently observing the people coming and going, watching the traffic on the roundabout, looking for a British number plate, for a car changing its speed – any sign of an inquisitive driver.

Then he saw it.

A car dropped its speed. The driver's head turned. It gazed at the store.

That was him!

The car's tail-lights turned a corner. The Old Man made a call, "He's passed me. I'll be in touch."

He returned the mobile to his jacket pocket and felt the reassuring weight of a gun he had concealed. He hoped it would not be needed but as he told me later, the signs were all there.

They'd been planning this meet for more than three weeks. The Soldier had £190,000 to return – a large amount he was reluctant to part with. However, just a few days before, he'd been oddly keen to hand it back.

The car's headlights reappeared in the distance. The meet was on.

Into loud rain, the Old Man stepped out to the curb as the car pulled over. Its driver lowered the window, leant across, yelled over in a thick northern accent:

"Are you Spencer?"

"That's me. You the Soldier?"

For a moment they held one another's gaze.

"Right," the Soldier said with a frown. "Hop in."

He climbed in. They pulled out.

"The paperwork on you?"

"It's a few minutes away," the Soldier said. "My worker just got it together. It's all there, minus the thirty we agreed upon."

"Fair enough."

"I'll drive around a little first," the Soldier offered, "check no-one's with us."

They accelerated north out of the area as the rain slowed. Passing through a busy intersection, the Soldier checked his mirrors. "I think we're good," he declared.

He swung down a dark side street, checked his mirrors once more and midway down, U-turned the vehicle in one swift movement. They returned to the main road, heading south from where they came.

"Not far now. Be five minutes," he said.

He drove speedily, south towards the docks. One quick acceleration and they skipped through a final red light, checked for the beam of a tailing car, and turned down a series of side streets. Circling the block, he slowed some more, wound his window down, scrutinised the passing road signs, muttered quietly to himself.

"You know where you are?" The Old Man said.

"Yeah, no worries. Just looking for the turn."

"Where's your Man?"

"Parked up – just a minute or so away."

They passed a series of derelict factory buildings before the Soldier spotted the opening. He swung in onto some wasteland where an abandoned warehouse building stood in blackness. He knocked off the lights, slowed to a crawl and circled around to park at an angle, their backs to the road.

Still and silent, they waited.

A minute passed.

"Not long now," the Soldier remarked.

The Old Man nodded, rolled down a window, looked for anything amiss or a clue as to where they were. His front view was blocked off but on either side he saw crumbling factory buildings long deserted. Beyond one, he spotted a canal and could hear the distant sound of the river nearby. Checking the side mirrors, he noted far off to their rear, some residential houses, their view obscured by trees. Either side were some street lights, but neither working.

Just a coincidence?

He began to wonder.

They waited some more. No-one appeared.

"I'd best call him," the Soldier said. "See where the fucker's got to."

The Old Man nodded and subtly rolled his shoulder a little to feel the weight of the revolver against his ribs. Meets in dark backstreets were not unusual in his line of work, but this one didn't feel right.

The Soldier dialled and cursed, "For fuck's sake. He told me he was actually here… It's ringing now." He smiled broadly, raised his brows. "Okay. Two minutes it is."

The Old Man smiled and played along. More seconds passed. Suddenly, a noise from the right. The door flew open.

A masked man stood clenching a gun between both hands.

"GET OUT OF THE CAR OR YOU'RE FUCKIN' DEAD."

The Old Man didn't move. He studied the gunman, considered his options, looked the shooter in the eyes, noted the inexperience, the nervousness.

"OUT OF THE CAR I SAID."

He still didn't move.

The gunman stepped forward, aimed the gun to his head. A second masked figure appeared waving an automatic.

"Come on Dickhead. Get moving."

The Old Man frowned hard. He had little choice.

He lowered his eyes, considered his options and in an instant decided he had just one. Reluctantly he swung each foot, right then left, out of the car. Grabbing the top of the door with his left hand, he looked up.

The gun still aimed at his face.

Pulling himself up, he rotated his body slowly, blocking his right side, allowing his right hand unseen to slide up for the gun. He gazed at the gunman, sensed his unease, nodded softly to hold his attention. But then, for no reason, the gunman glanced down, saw something and panicked.

A round exploded.

The Old Man's chest snapped back with the blast.

The gunman retreated a few steps, shocked maybe, waiting for the Old Man to fall, except... he stumbled forward, grabbed the door to steady himself. And then without warning, raised his head, swung out a gun, and fired.

The first gunman went down. The second sprinted into darkness.

On the driver's side, the Soldier was slow. Scrambling from the car he found the Old Man barring his way – square on. The two men's eyes locked; the Soldier froze.

The Old Man raised the gun, frowned hard, and pulled the trigger. It was a direct hit to the chest.

The Soldier jolted back, staggered to the side, fell to one knee, paused briefly, and collapsed silently to the ground, onto his side, until almost still. Then a violent jerk and he rolled onto his chest, gasping for air, trying to breathe, wheezing and rasping.

The Old Man watched on. The seconds ticked away quickly.

Crawling and twisting, choking for air, the Soldier fought to breathe until his strength drained away and there was nothing. Finally, he slumped onto his back and stared silently up at the night sky.

The Old Man looked down, waited 'til the Soldier moved no more and was still. It was only then he lowered his gun.

He stood still for a moment, breathed deeply, staggered to the side, and leant on the car's bonnet. After several deep breaths, he looked up and scanned the darkness for an idea of where he was and what to do next.

There was a long cold silence. Then, with effort and difficulty, he moved.

He staggered diagonally away from the river.

Heading northwards.

CHAPTER 2:
AT DEATH'S DOOR

26ᵀᴴ MAY 2001

SOME HOURS LATER, I eased myself into another slow Saturday
by reading the sports pages.

Coventry City, my home team, had been relegated that week.
It didn't make for pretty reading, though I was no longer one of the
faithful. In recent years, a wife, a newborn daughter and a job with
unpredictable hours meant my football interests had long fallen by
the way.

This job, with its unpredictable hours, was that of being a
'driver'.

I was the Old Man's driver to be exact, which meant I collected
and delivered money. Most days, this would equate to a few hours
a day of running around but other days, I'd be out all day, zipping
up and down motorways, collecting 'paperwork' as we called it,
perhaps driving it abroad if required.

On that particular morning, I had been taking my time until
I noticed it was almost 10am. The Old Man would be phoning in
soon and as relaxed as I was, it was time I got moving.

Forcing myself up, I headed across to the spare room. In the
corner stood my old animation desk, an angled drawing board with
a large rotating disc at its centre. I removed the disc and from the
papers, passports and bundles of money inside, retrieved a burner
phone. Shoving in its battery, I held the switch down. It took a few
seconds to light up – *NOKIA*.

Immediately it rang.

I picked up, "Hello?"

There was no response.

Instead, the sound of the phone being dropped, some scuffling, a clunking sound. Then his voice, albeit slow and quiet.

"Hello?"

"Yeah, hello."

A pause, "It's me..." – another pause – "I've been in an accident."

My eyes narrowed.

He took a deep breath and continued, "A car's hit me... just didn't see it coming." Another deep breath, "I'm in a bad way."

A slightly awkward silence followed, and as always on the phone, I remained guarded. All I could offer was, "You alright? You going to be okay?"

"Should be okay... but I need you to do me a favour," he paused another breath. "Go grab Blondie and maybe the lad... bring them over as soon as you can." Another pause. "You've got some float... watch who's with you and keep it to yourself... I don't want anyone panicking."

"Okay," I answered. "Will be with you tonight some time."

"Right... just as quick as you can."

The call ended.

* * *

BY NIGHTFALL, we breezed into Amsterdam. It had been 12 hours and 500 miles since the call. I'd told my wife something had occurred with the Old Man and I might be gone a few days. She understood.

"I'll call you once I know what's happening," I said, and headed off.

I had grabbed young Blondie (his girlfriend) and B.T. (her kid brother) on route. They knew less than I did. Our journey had been filled with speculation and long concerned silences. We sped our way into Amsterdam, weaving by cyclists, taxis, and trams – our minds on what might lie ahead.

As per usual, I parked up in the city centre. We then walked some, checked for tails, zigzagged through the crowds at Central Station, caught a ferry, walked some more, entered the Ijplein estate, checked for tails one last time, and arrived at the apartment.

A ground floor flat, this was the Old Man's main base – his 'safehouse' – and few people knew of its location. We exchanged apprehensive glances. Blondie, cold faced with hair tied back, shook her head in anticipation; B.T., sullen faced and measured, stubbed out a half-smoked cigarette.

I knocked the door.

A gaunt man with large black eyes answered. This was Sowerby, ex-heroin addict, one of the workers. He ushered us into a small entrance hall and cut straight to it: "Your dad's been shot," he whispered. "Through the chest… at point-blank range."

He watched for my response. I was too stunned to speak.

He looked to Blondie and B.T. before continuing, "He nearly died… but he's hanging on."

A silence followed.

"Any questions?"

We looked to one another. No one said a word.

"Ready to go in?" he asked.

I looked to Blondie, then B.T.

"Are we good?"

B.T. looked back , solemn and calm, "Yeah. I'm good."

Blondie's blue eyes glistened.

"You okay?" I asked.

She raised her eyes to me, pursed her lips, nodded her head.

I pushed open the door slowly. We entered a dimly lit room.

Sowerby flicked on a lamp which illuminated a large stretcher bed, upon which lay the Old Man, his chest and ribs wrapped tightly in large white bandages. A chevroned grey blanket was draped across his legs and his sockless feet hung over the bed's end. Within his reach a tall side table, upon which sat glasses of water with straws, surrounded by piles and piles of used up medical foils.

Our arrival stirred him.

He moved slowly, eyes flickering, face in pain. He acknowledged us one by one in a quiet, tired, raspy voice.

"How's the journey been?... Any problems?"

"Fine... fine. No problems," I muttered, noting how his skin was pale, his eyes small and grey, his movement old and slow. He pulled himself up, coughed painfully and paused a moment. I glanced to Sowerby and back again. The Old Man continued.

"You checked for trackers?"

"Yeah, yeah. A few times."

"Good, good..."

Another silence followed. We stood around, hushed and uneasy, exchanging glances. After several empty seconds, I spoke up, "What the hell happened?"

His eyes lifted to meet mine.

"A week ago, you were telling me how you had everything under control, and now...?"

A small smile appeared, "I had some bad luck."

"Yeah, I can see that."

His smile widened. Then some seconds passed, and his eyes closed, his head sunk, and his smile faded to nothing. *Is he going back to sleep?* I wondered.

Sowerby grabbed a blue remote from the bedside and pressed a button. A motor trundled away, and the bed's head slowly raised itself. I glanced across at Blondie, white with shock. B.T. appeared calm; he just watched on. After thirty long seconds, the bed came to a smooth halt, but the Old Man remained still, his eyes closed.

I motioned Sowerby to follow me out to the kitchen. Once there, I knocked on a light, pulled the door to and got to the point.

"What the fuck happened?"

He grimaced, tapped out a fag. "Things with that Soldier messed up," he said.

I looked across, raised a brow.

"It never did feel right," he frowned. "You recall how the guy was delaying and delaying, making promise after promise."

I nodded.

"Well, on the Friday, he agreed to a meet…"

He paused to light his fag, "Your Old Man knew there was something wrong and we all told him not to go. The Dutchman advised against it. So did Ryan. I even offered to go in his place, but he refused."

He took a drag and exhaled.

"Then, at the last minute, I persuaded him to take a gun – just in case."

I nodded patiently, "And…"

"They meet up at the Deli – the place without the cameras, just the Soldier and your Old Man. He says the money's offside, so your Old Man hops in the car. They drive down to the docks where the Soldier has a few men waiting – masked and tooled up with guns. They order your Old Man out. Your Old Man sees what's going on, steps out of the car, pulls his gun, and then… Well, all hell breaks loose. They're shooting at him. He's shooting at them…"

He shook his head, smiled to himself, "He got the Soldier though."

"Got him?"

He flashed an evil lob-sided grin: "Shot him dead."

I frowned, and didn't smile. *What did that matter now?*

Sowerby shrugged and smirked to himself, switched on the kettle, lined up some mugs and searched the cupboards for some sugar. He seemed unaffected.

I paused a moment, trying to think of something to say. I could think of nothing. A minute passed in which my mind stumbled blindly. I shook my head, sighed deeply and inhaled the aroma of bleach, strong throughout the apartment. I looked around and noted that every surface was clean, wiped down.

Sowerby had been thorough.

I stepped away, peered into the living room where the Old Man had re-awakened. He was reassuring Blondie that he would be fine, "It's not as bad as it looks," he was insisting but his voice was weak, and she looked far from convinced.

My attention returned to Sowerby, "So, what happens next?"

He returned a blank look.

Holding back any frustration, I kept my voice down, made my words slow and clear: "Are we just going to sit around, and wait to see whether he dies or not?"

There was little response.

"Or is it too late to move him to a hospital?"

He looked up.

"No point," he shrugged. "Everything's been done."

My mouth dropped.

A silence followed and I watched on as Sowerby poured drinks and busied himself with sugar and powdered milk. Suddenly, he stopped and turned to face me.

"A 'Doctor' has examined him."

I said nothing and waited.

"He reckons that a hospital can do him no good at this point. It's a waiting game. Forty-eight hours he gave him. If he survives the next 24 hours, he'll be through the worst of it."

He looked indifferently at me as I thought this through.

A few seconds passed, then some more. I found myself nodding in agreement. They'd done all they could; the decision had been made. There was nothing we could do but sit and wait. Reluctantly, I grabbed some drinks, returned to the living room, steeled myself for a long night.

* * *

THE LIVING ROOM was dark and quiet. At the back end of the room, a small TV sat muted, tuned to the local news station. Across from it on the corner table. Several phone chargers sat in a line, all empty. Tonight, the Old Man held just one mobile phone; our only connection to the outside world, its number known only by the two Dutch men who had brought him here.

We settled down at the front end of the room where two large chairs with a sofa in-between faced across to the Old Man on his stretcher bed. The floor lamp behind provided the room's only light. The Old Man lying semi-upright, now appeared alert, his spirits lifted by our presence.

"You should see the other guy." he said in a dry attempt at humour.

"He's dead, I'm told."

"I should hope so," he said, his voice still struggling,"… I shot him so… so…" his voice trailed off as he became distracted by some discomfort. He frowned, pulled himself up into a more comfortable position, and after several deep breaths, began to talk.

He spoke wearily of the night before. He described the shooting from its roots with just another drug deal to the killing of the Soldier. Moment by moment, detail by detail, he elaborated, and after twenty minutes or so of talking, he was exhausted and done.

We had listened quietly throughout.

A reflective silence followed. It was clearly self-defence. They had tried to kill him. He had done what anyone would have done given the situation.

"What about the Doctor's visit?" I asked.

This was the most relevant part.

We listened closely.

The bullet had ripped through his chest, some fragments exiting, others embedding themselves in his lower back. This suggested a 'dum-dum' bullet – designed to break up on impact to cause maximum damage. It seemed certain that some metal fragments had struck or brushed by the walls of his lungs, and these were giving him the problems. We exchanged glances. It did not sound good. And he did not look well at all.

The voice was weak, the eyes grey, and his discomfort increasingly evident. Adjusting his position on the stretcher, his face contorted whilst he fought to breathe. He winced sharply, "I've got some pain," he said, and grabbed a bottle of meds from the side table. His large hands attempted to unscrew its top, but he lacked the strength and paused for breath.

Sowerby hurried over and opened the bottle. Blondie, B.T. and I exchanged concerned looks as the Old Man swallowed a small handful of painkillers; this was followed by another small handful of coloured capsules from one of the neighbouring bottles. He spent the following few minutes breathing loudly and deeply until the pain subsided. Then he drifted into a coma-like sleep.

We sat in a dark silence. Digesting the details.

Blondie had said nothing for a long time. I glanced across and noted her face pale, her eyes reddened, mouth tight and silent. She looked old and scared. Abruptly she stood up, announced she was off outside for a fag. A minute later B.T. followed.

I remained, and with Blondie gone, turned to Sowerby.

"What happened to the Old Man's clothes?"

He looked up, "Burnt straight away."

"The gun?"

"Threw it in a canal."

I nodded thoughtfully, that was good. "And his phones?"

"The same."

I looked to the floor, Sowerby knew what he was doing. I thought some more.

"What about when he leant on the car?"

He shook his head slowly, "Your Old Man's left a print. But later it did rain."

"Could that have ruined the print?"

"Fuck knows."

I dwelled on this for a few seconds, could think of nothing more and sat watching the Old Man sleep for a few minutes. Forty-eight hours, the Doctor had said. The next twenty-four hours would prove crucial. I watched some more; his breaths were long and deep – steady. After several minutes, I headed outside for some fresh air.

* * *

THE YARD WAS FENCED and slabbed, small and private. No more than a smoking area really. The kitchen light shone softly over Blondie, who sat on a bench taking long drags on a fag, face in a frown. She said nothing, finished her fag, stubbed it out and lit another.

B.T. stood away, smoking slowly, eyes deep in thought.

I sat down to the side, back against the wall, and stared at the floor. The night air was cool and calming. At last, B.T. spoke, "You think he's going to be alright?"

I shrugged, "We can only hope."

Blondie said nothing. She took another long drag, exhaled quickly. We watched on. Finally, she spoke.

"This has got to stop," she snapped, her voice hard and angry. "He needs to be thinking of other people now. He has a daughter to think of. Where's this leave her?"

Neither of us spoke.

"No point having all this money if you can't enjoy it," she continued, angrily stubbing out a cigarette. "He needs to grow up and stop all this shit." And with that, she got up and strode inside, leaving us to reflect on those final words.

The minutes passed in silence. B.T. smoked another; my coffee went cold.

He looked over to me, asked matter-of-factly: "Think he'll make it?"

I pondered a moment. "Fifty-fifty from what I can make out," and on quick reflection added, "Can't be much better than that."

He said nothing in response but took a final drag, stubbed out his cig, strolled back inside.

I didn't follow.

I sat for a while, contemplating the situation, entertaining the worst, and pondering a past long gone. Thirty years back, the Old Man had been a successful businessman, wealthy and celebrated, until a bank robbery ended it all. Since then, he had evolved into a criminal, internationally connected but strikingly different from most criminals. An anomaly. He dealt only in softer drugs, despised violence, made millions, spent it all, saved nothing. He resembled more a businessman than a criminal, a bootlegger more than a drug dealer. I often recalled events of old and recent years, trying to make sense of it all. Thinking and wondering, but as ever returning to that same question which refused to go away: why?

Why would such a smart man become a criminal?

CHAPTER 3:
WHY A CRIMINAL?

1949-66

IT HAD TAKEN many years to accept the Old Man was no longer a businessman but a criminal.

This difficulty lay largely with the impact his early business career had on me. It was all I really knew of him until he went to prison when I was eleven years old. He then spent thirteen of the following fifteen years inside. During those years, he and Mum divorced, and I heard many rumours as to the Old Man's earlier criminal escapades and business deals. He appeared to be a complex man, both a talented entrepreneur and notorious city villain. Some thought he'd been unlucky, others thought he'd merely got his comeuppance.

When he was released from prison, I was 26.

Gradually, and only by working for him, I had got to know him once more. I found he was still the same businessman of old, except his business was now crime. Whilst I could accept this, why he had become a criminal was still something I could not quite grasp. It was a question that had puzzled me throughout my teenage years and now I was an adult, still confused me.

I had come to the thinking that an explanation as to why he became a criminal could only be explained by his upbringing, of which I knew little. The divorce had cut off contact from his family and they were rarely mentioned in our house. Furthermore, the Old Man never spoke of the past and when I had raised old memories, he had been completely uninterested, unable to see what point there was to such conversations.

Nevertheless, I never stopped wondering, arriving at no answers until that was, a few months before the shooting in Amsterdam.

When the Old Man had gone on the run in late 2000, he had put me in touch with his sister, my Aunt. She would prove a fountain of knowledge regarding the Old Man's early years. Her name was Margaret and she lived not far from me. She was a tall, dark-haired woman of 50 with bright brown eyes and a warm eccentric smile, "Kettle's on," she would call from the kitchen. "I've biscuits and cake somewhere. Just give me a sec…"

That day, I was sat at the table, holding a news cutting I needed to see her about. But before we spoke of that, she took a seat, poured the tea and began with the usual question.

"How's your dad doing? Is he in touch?"

She was aware he had gone on the run to Holland.

"I spoke to him last night," I answered. "He's doing well."

"Good! Good. As long as he's staying out of trouble. I do worry about him… he does need to be careful. It is dangerous over there. I saw something on the BBC the other day… what was it…?"

I nodded ironically.

She never seemed to accept that he was a criminal. To her, he was simply her hard-working little brother, a businessman, who over the years, had repeatedly got mixed up with the 'wrong people'. That was her answer to all his troubles, including the event that she claimed had started it all.

"It was the Spencer Club. That and those friends of his!"

The Spencer Club referred to a burglary the Old Man carried out as a seventeen-year-old. I had come to learn that my grandparents blamed that event for the life he'd led, but I could never uncover the details. Margaret was reluctant to discuss the matter; I suspected there was more to it. For a long time, we would stay off the subject and stick to discussing my grandparents, of whom I knew little.

My Grandad came from a poor mining village in east Wales, my Grandma from the wealthy farmlands of Lincolnshire. They met during wartime, married immediately, had three children in four years, the Old Man being the youngest. Once my Grandfather was demobbed, they migrated south to the booming city of Coventry.

There, they lived in a red bricked terrace of the leafy suburb named Earlsdon. It was on the well-to-do side of town, where there was little crime. Like most working men, my Grandad would work a nine-to-five factory job, whilst Grandma accepted the role of housewife, though she would encourage both sons to be ambitious. They would be taught their father's military discipline but instilled with her own sense of entitlement. For her, both sons' potentials were unlimited. However, of the two, it would be the Old Man who would shine.

He would have a charm and charisma his brother lacked.

By sixteen, the Old Man stood six feet three, broad and lean, strikingly handsome. He was known locally for winning boxing trophies and art prizes, for fixing up motorbikes on weekends, for knowing everyone and being rich in friends. It was this last quality that most impressed Margaret. "Tony was everyone's favourite," she said proudly. "He was good at everything. So smart and popular, so good-looking…"

When she was in full flow, I would lean back in a state of puzzlement. Her words more described the upbringing of a saint rather than a criminal. Given his future in crime, you would expect to hear stories of a dysfunctional home, but there were no such tales. He came from a disciplined household with hard-working parents.

Naturally, I wondered when she would arrive at the subject of this burglary referred to when we first met, but now rarely mentioned. I had waited patiently, but she failed to raise the subject.

In the end, I took the matter into my own hands.

I visited the city archives and trawled the newspapers from the year 1966, the year of the burglary blamed for the Old Man going down the wrong path in life.

Could this one event have made all the difference?

As the story, if covered at all, would be small and not worthy of a headline, I had scanned every edition of every newspaper, hour after hour, skimming every story, slowly losing hope. Then at the very point, when I thought I'd missed it, there it was!

9th January 1967
YOUTH IS FINED FOR RAIDING STORES
An 18 years-old youth broke into four stores in the city and stole property worth £260, Coventry Magistrates heard. Tony Shipley, mechanic, pleaded guilty[…] he also admitted receiving stolen goods…

It outlined how the Old Man and two accomplices had burgled local shops and sold the proceeds in nearby social clubs. The Old Man, with the longer list of charges, had been hit hardest of the three. He was ordered to pay legal costs and compensation totalling £175, or £2,500 in today's money. A great deal to any teenager. To cap it all, he was given two years of probation and two months at a young offenders' institution (Borstal) if all monies were not paid within twelve months.

I resolved to show the article to Margaret.

* * *

THAT DAY when I dropped by with the cutting, by coincidence, Margaret had dug out a handful of family photos I'd never clapped eyes on before. She spread them out across the table.

They were as she had been describing them all these months.

The earlier black and white pictures were of a confident young family – handsome parents with well-presented children. With little staging, each picture captured a sense of the personas I had come to expect.

They flowed into a second batch of colour photos from the mid-sixties.

And here there was a noticeable shift. The clothes changed as they became teenagers, conscious of the images they wished to project. The Old Man, with a Tony Curtis haircut, opted for poses that exuded a quiet confidence. There were pictures of him at parties, with old mates and motorcycles, in their terraced street, with neighbours and friends.

She talked excitedly of these years and described how, at fifteen, they would leave school on the Friday and begin work on the Monday.

All except the Old Man.

Offered a scholarship to study art, a grander future beckoned. However, perhaps seeing no future in art, he attended just a few times. He switched to an apprenticeship in electronics, stuck at it for a year, then jacked it in. Refusing all notions of factory work, at seventeen he announced he would work for himself repairing motorcycles.

By now, motorbikes had long been his passion. He rented a nearby garage and, to his parents' despair, lived what to them seemed an undisciplined life, out at all hours with his mates Pip Wells and Rod Pepper, testing bikes, fixing them up, crashing them – rebuilding them. Out most week nights, he would disappear entirely on weekends. Even so, he managed to earn good money.

Nonetheless, he was often broke.

"Spent his money on helping out mates and on girlfriends," Margaret remarked with a shake of the head. "He'd earn it and waste it."

Which is why, she explained, such generosity meant he was broke going into Christmas. "He'd spent all his money, flittered it away. Mam and Dad had to buy him his drinks that weekend. He had nothing.

"So... as I understand it..." she paused to choose her words carefully, "he decided to burgle the social club over the Christmas weekend."

"The club you all used to drink at on weekends?"

"That's the one."

She paused and cleared her throat. It was clearly something she found difficult to talk about, even after some thirty years or more. She took a deep breath and forged ahead.

"Apparently, he returned in the early hours with his mates. Tony bypassed the alarm and they cleaned the club out." She shook her head slowly, "A week later, a local bobby who knew the family and thought the world of Tony, arrived at the house. He was acting on a tip-off and I suppose had little choice," she bit her lip and frowned. "He searched our home and uncovered some of the stolen goods amongst Tony's things. We couldn't believe it."

She gazed away in disbelief, "They took him away in a police car. Immediately, the whole street knew – neighbours, shopkeepers, family and friends. They gossip:

'You heard young Tony's been arrested!'

'You're joking.'

'No. Took him away in a police car earlier. Been thieving, they say.'''

Margaret paused a moment, still ashamed.

I felt my conscience sinking. I knew that rather than a one-off burglary, there had been much more. I had to show her the article. She might have seen it before, but… I passed her the cutting.

"I found this a few days back."

She took it, put on her reading glasses, and examined it.

Two minutes passed slowly.

She set it back down, leant back and sighed to herself.

"He was surrounding himself with such bad influences – bikers and the like. Never stood a chance."

I winced but said nothing.

"He covered for them all," she said, shaking her head. "There were others, but it was always him. He'd take the rap for them all. One of them grassed him; I'm sure. But you know your dad, he always sees the best in people."

I nodded in agreement.

We talked some more. She underlined the view of her parents, that this was what changed him: bad friends, biker mates and greedy girls. Then after a while, our discussion wound down and melted into silence.

There was nothing more to say.

I drove home, pensive and pondering, asking myself: *Can this really be the answer?* That this one event, or at least a crime spree during his teens, acted as some sort of critical crossroads?

Was it really that simple?

Or was Margaret deluded? Kidding herself? Not wanting to see anything that portrayed her little brother in a bad light.

No. A few burglaries when he was seventeen couldn't explain what came later. No doubt there were other reasons that led him into crime, that explained the later robberies I'd heard of, the counterfeiting case I knew of, and the large-scale drug dealing I'd seen.

No, there had to be other reasons.

And that was how I had left it. That was until the shoot-out in Amsterdam. That event would refocus my mind and raise the question once more: why?

Why would such a smart man become a criminal?

CHAPTER 4:
THE RECOVERY

MAY 2001

I HADN'T SLEPT LONG; a few hours maybe.

The sound of footsteps, the smell of coffee, morning sunlight everywhere. Disorientated and blurry-eyed, I sat up, realised where I was, and squinted ahead at the still figure of the Old Man.

Was he okay?

I leant forward to listen but detected nothing. *Had he made it through?* It was several seconds before I heard breathing.

He'd made it. *Could it be the worst was over?*

Maybe.

Minutes later, he awoke in a stuttery fashion. Managing to sit upright, he asked for some food and a coffee. I watched on as he ate cereal with trembling hands. Shortly after, he attempted to stand but gasped in pain and slumped back. He looked across to me, "It isn't the wound," he insisted. "It's the ribs." He gave up and sat still for a while, gazing into space, clearing his thoughts, pondering what lay ahead.

A sleepy B.T. stumbled into the room and halted at the doorway: "Fuckin' hell Tone!"

The Old Man looked up.

B.T. offered a rare smile, "Thought you'd had it Tone."

The Old Man laughed to himself, "That was a close one."

He sounded better. His voice soft and deep once more. Like his old self.

* * *

IT WAS TO BE A DAY unlike any other.

I spent the first hour following the Dutch morning news, hoping for an update on the shooting, but there was nothing. I looked across to the Old Man sat on the stretcher bed, staring into a small shaving mirror with an unsteady razor, pausing whenever his hand trembled for no reason. Slowly he shaved, concentrated and patient. As he neared the end, he looked my way.

"You getting cleaned up?"

"In a minute."

"It's gone nine," he reminded me, meaning I needed to get moving. He had little patience for slow people in the morning.

Once cleaned up, he requested another coffee, some pens and paper, his phone numbers. Using his side table as a desk, he proceeded to map out the day by drawing up several lists, something he had done each morning for as long as I could remember.

"You can't even stand yet," I reminded him.

"I will later," he murmured, and carried on compiling lists.

By ten, Sowerby returned with a fresh set of mobiles. I don't think he'd slept for two days, but he was indifferent. He spent half an hour setting them up. Within the hour, they began to ring.

"Is this not all a little too soon?" I cautioned.

The Old Man didn't look up, "No, I need to get talking to people. They need to know everything's okay. That business is good."

At that point, Blondie appeared, long hair tumbling down, no make-up, no smile. She made herself a coffee, strode back to her room. He paid her no attention. They'd had words; she failed to understand he had things to do.

"She's concerned," I said.

"She doesn't get it. If people think I'm out of the game, then we really will have problems. Where does she think the money comes from? No, we must keep confidence up. This is merely a delay."

As the morning progressed, I watched on as the Old Man, unable to sit up for long, lay across the stretcher bed making calls and scheduling visitors.

Visitors?

"I need to know what's going on. I need for people to actually see for themselves that I'm good. And then I need to make plans for getting out of the area. The police suspect I'm housed up nearby. They visited the bar this morning. They know I'm injured."

"I know that but…"

"I wish I could sit around getting the fuck better, but there's no time," he snapped, and met my eyes with a brief frown. "I can't just sit here waiting for shit to happen. Waiting for them to come and find me." He swigged down some warm coffee and turned to Sowerby, "Get me Albert (Spain) on the phone and then Jerry (Belgium)."

I watched on in resignation. Not a lot I could do. Just go along with it.

* * *

IT RAINED TWICE THAT MORNING. The first time was just a brief shower, but the second time it hammered hard and loud for twenty long minutes. It emptied the streets outside and provided cover for the first of the day's visitors: Veltman and Jansen, two Dutch manufacturers of amphetamine. They drank coffee and after hearing the Old Man's account of the shooting, extended offers of help: "You only have to ask John," Veltman said. "We can get anything you ask. You want away from here; we can arrange it today." I would hear many such promises throughout the day to come.

From his stretcher bed, the Old Man thanked them and moved onto the business at hand: their "lab" in North Amsterdam was ready to go. They could supply 50,000 pills a week. The project had been in development for some months, but now, with the clock ticking, they had to wrap up the details.

Whilst they negotiated, two bearded faces – Gerry and Ivan – from the bar dropped by to update us on the police enquiries. Detectives had visited that morning, probing and questioning. They would return, perhaps with a warrant. It was thought the Old Man had just a few days at best. He needed to move. As this was considered, more visitors arrived – Gent and Christiaan – who, like those before, offered to move him that night, this time to Breda. As this was discussed, more visitors arrived, who, due to the numbers, sat out in the kitchen and awaited their turn.

The apartment resembled a social gathering for a while, a funeral or christening maybe, where everyone knew everyone, but all were sober and serious. There was no panic, but all were aware that time was of the essence. The police could arrive anytime, if not today, tomorrow; and if not tomorrow, the next day. Consequently, there was an urgency to every conversation, a desire for deals to be completed.

Through the morning and into the afternoon, I followed the deal making as all purchases and shipments were rescheduled; locations changed; credit terms altered, and less trusted contacts deleted from all deals. People came and went, the phone calls continued, news trickled in; the Old Man recounted the shooting for any new visitor. Eventually I tired of it all and stepped out for some fresh air.

In the backyard, I found B.T. sat alone on a bench, smoking a rare joint. He looked up.

"Greedy fuckers aren't they?"

"Who?"

"Those in there – the Dutch people. Like fuckin' flies."

I looked to the doorway, "I know what you mean. It's all business and money with them."

"He'll be alright now, though. Take more than a bullet to stop Tone."

I took a seat and we sat in silence for a while. B.T. smoked another before heading back inside.

I held back, reflecting some more. I ought to have gone back in but saw little point. Each new set of visitors would prompt the Old Man to recount the shooting, he would oblige, they would talk deals. I could only watch on.

It began to rain once more. I took shelter under the guttering, supped my coffee, watched it lash down for a while, and gave thought to the question that had been gnawing away at me for many years now.

Why had he become a criminal?

It wasn't what the Old Man's family had claimed. It could not have been down to that one burglary or criminal phase. If that were so, there would be hundreds of thousands of people like the Old Man all over the country. Many youths who experienced brushes with the law adapted their behaviour, grew up if you like. His co-accused on the teenage break-ins – Pip Wells – had changed his ways. He had devoted himself to hard work, invested in property, and become a local millionaire. He was now a tax exile on the Isle of Man.

It was clear there were differences. The Old Man would go on to make far more money than Pip Wells ever did, but he would waste it and return to crime again and again. Something about the Old Man meant he did not learn from his early mistakes. If anything, they seemed to have spurred him on.

So, if it wasn't the early bad luck that pushed him this way, what was it?

By late evening, no police had broken down the doors. The Old Man sat up eating bread and soup whilst taking calls. He sounded tired and weak, though he remained focused. The last few Dutch visitors travelled up from the south and left a few hours later promising to have him in Spain by the week's end.

By quarter to midnight, the apartment was quiet once more. The Old Man, still on his stretcher bed, took a small handful of tablets. Whilst he waited for them to kick in, he paid some attention to the brooding Blondie.

"Told you I'd be okay," he laughed.

She frowned and looked away.

"How's Nellie? How's the dog?" he continued to tease. "Is Nellie doing well at school?"

"It's not funny Tone," she said, glaring his way. And for the umpteenth time that day, disappeared out for a fag.

With her gone, he turned to me and asked about my family: how was my wife, how was my daughter, how was the car running? – he always asked about the car.

"How's David and Kate getting on? How's your mother?"

"Fine, just fine," I offered.

He never mentioned my mother when Blondie was around.

"Remember it's her birthday soon. You must get her a good card," he reminded me, as if I might have forgotten. "It's the card that matters," he added, "She cares about the words... I'll get her a card before you go."

They'd been divorced for almost twenty years now, but he never forgot her birthday, regardless of which wife or girlfriend he was with. I watched on as he sank back into his pillows, closed his eyes and murmured quietly, "Remind me later... it's the words she really cares about... I mustn't forget."

And within just a few seconds he'd fallen into a long, deep sleep. I shrugged inwardly.

This was the only sign of sentiment he'd expressed in more than twenty-four hours. The night before, when he'd been at death's door, there'd been nothing.

* * *

BY DAY THREE, the Old Man was up and moving, albeit slow and with care. That evening the "doctor" visited. He applied a fresh dressing, left a pile of meds and warned about not moving anywhere too soon. The Old Man agreed and within minutes of the doc leaving, finalised his plans. He would be out of the Netherlands within the hour.

Spain was his destination.

And with that, it was time for Blondie, B.T. and me to make tracks, back to the car, to the motorway, and the long journey home. We grabbed our bags; the Old Man cracked a few jokes and a handshake later, we were gone. Back on the road.

The mood was pensive as we drove south into Belgium and along into France. No-one spoke. We were weary and there was no more to say, though much to think about. As we clocked up the miles, one thought kept returning to me over and over: *he was supposed to be a businessman, not a criminal.*

That's who he'd been when I was growing up. He ran businesses, made a lot of money, dabbled on the side buying and selling with an array of city businessmen. I understood him to be mostly legit. Except over the last year, thanks to Margaret, I'd learned that there was a great deal more to him than I'd originally thought.

Now I didn't know what to think.

Over a twenty-year period, he had moved from being acclaimed thirty-year old businessman and 'Cooker King' Tony Shipley – his original name – to becoming fifty-year-old drug smuggler and crime boss Tony Spencer.

Was he a businessman, or a criminal? One or the other? Or simply both.

The late ferry was tired and ghostly, the drive back to the Midlands long and silent. We exchanged few words over the hours. I dropped Blondie and B.T. off and headed home. Across a darkened countryside and into the stillness of a sleeping city, I thought some more.

I recalled the night after he'd been shot. How I'd sat there in the early hours, anxious and worried. Worrying he might die; aware I might be out of time – that after years of trying to understand him, I had gotten nowhere. To the question as to why he, a successful businessman with the world at his feet, became a criminal, I had no answers.

Without answers, I had no hope of understanding his past or mine. His life had defined my own, and yet he made no sense at all. He came from a good background and a decent part of town. As I understood it, Coventry's criminals came from the sink estates of the city with none coming from leafy green Earlsdon, apart from the Old Man.

It made little sense.

I traipsed up the stairwell to the flat, fumbling for keys. Stepping inside, I paused a moment and listened to the long empty silence – no-one up yet.

I slumped into the chair by the window, thinking, wondering.

And then I had an idea.

CHAPTER 5:
PURSUING AN ANSWER

1967-72

MUM HAS ALWAYS taken photos from right when we were small. Scores of photos of us kids, family pictures, some of the Old Man when he wasn't working. She documented our childhood with care and pride; however, once the Old Man went away in '81, those photos ceased.

I balanced a torch between beam and gable, and treaded carefully across ceiling joists, passing by boxes of comic books, bags of clothes, an old film camera, more bags of clothes, and then I halted, and leant down to rip open a large cardboard box. I peered inside to find several bags inside.

They were here after all!

The bags sprayed up plumes of dust as they landed on the dining table. I carefully slid out the tired and frail photo albums so as not to disturb any order. I figured that to understand the Old Man's move from business to crime, I needed to know his story from the very beginning.

And to do that, I needed a chronology.

The oldest album I opened with care. Dried out pages allowed its photos to slide out from under their acetates. It had been a long time since they'd received any attention. The first photos were in black and white and taken during the Sixties.

The summer of '66, Mum had met the Old Man one quiet morning on the Albany Road. A bike roared by, skidded and flipped. The driver, wearing no helmet, was thrown clear, landing hard on his back.

She rushed over.

"You okay?" she asked.

"Of course I'm bloody not," he smiled.

She gazed down on him; his face looked familiar.

The Old Man had recently rented a garage off the high street. She had seen him out and about, always with one bike or another. He was good mates of Pip Wells and Rod Pepper from down the road. She'd keep an eye out for him.

Soon enough, they were mixing in the same circles.

She liked dancing, he liked films. They dated for a while, going to clubs or the cinema. She met his parents, liked his father and was fearful of his mother, for whom no-one was good enough for her son. Before long, Mum fell pregnant.

Shortly after, they were married.

Here, there were plenty of pictures. She dressed in white and slightly pregnant; he suited, tall and assured. Both had a glint in their eye as they smiled and laughed at one another over wedding cake. Only eighteen, they had little, but were optimistic.

Unfortunately, from the earlier burglaries, he was still on probation with large court fines to pay.

With his parents offering no support, the Old Man was on his own. He hadn't helped matters by racking up a long list of motoring offences. Several court appearances would leave only one option. The Old Man shrugged and joked; it was no big deal. He would serve the two months.

Whilst away, their son David, my brother, was born.

Released in early '68, the Old Man had a new family to support. A run-down out-building on some wasteland is where he began by trading as *Tony Shipley Motorcycle Repairs*. He worked alongside a biker named Fudge. The pair worked long hours, made a good living, but then it came to an abrupt end.

Out of the blue, a new housing development forced them to relocate, and they did so, choosing the rough and ready Harnall Lane in Hillfields.

PURSUING AN ANSWER

A sprawling district of low-grade housing, Hillfields, with the building of several tower blocks, had accepted thousands of new residents. Overpopulated, its busy streets became home to a scattering of second-hand shops selling everything from used clothes and jewellery to washing machines and televisions. One that was prospering was owned by Robert Shipley, the Old Man's elder brother.

A young man of ambition, Robert had gone self-employed, buying and selling from a multitude of sources. Soon after, he established a second-hand shop selling household furniture. He made a good profit, worked long hours, and didn't suffer fools. At twenty-three, he was a slender, good-looking suit and tie business-man with a hard attitude. Margaret frequently described him as "Hard on the outside, soft on the inside."

Others simply described him as a nasty sod.

Robert cultivated the persona of a refined businessman, with a middle-class accent and an air of authority. Behind the scenes, though, he was a sadistic hard man without scruples. Within a few years, deal by deal, contact by contact, he had established himself as a reliable fence amongst the city's more serious villains.

I spread some photos across the table, brushed away some dust, and wiped away a few marks. There was one early picture of Robert with the Old Man at a wedding or something. He's grinning as he ruffles the Old Man's hair. They look close, but unlike their earlier pictures, Robert's older confidence dominates the picture.

There is no doubt he would have had a great influence over his younger brother. An older brother is more authoritative than a younger brother. This perhaps evens out when they become adults, but to begin with, that relationship and age difference matter.

I think in the Old Man's early teens, it greatly mattered.

* * *

HIS arrival on Harnall Lane proved a poor move, I'm told. He'd rented a shop, but few neighbours would tolerate the loud and dirty bike work he liked to conduct through the night-time hours. Increasingly, the Old Man looked for other ways to earn money.

It was natural he would turn to his brother.

In the late Sixties, Coventry was a thriving city of a thousand factories and warehouses. Thieving was rife and if you had friends on the inside and knew the right fences, you could make more money than any nine-to-five job. Before long, the Old Man was robbing on the side, with Robert fencing the spoils.

Even so, by all accounts, it was clear that Robert took the lion's share. As the elder brother, he may have felt entitled. But also, he was the one with the shop and the contacts, and to begin with at least, the ideas.

It was on his initiative they moved into thieving scrap metal. An uncle up north owned a scrapyard, and they sold off any scrap they could thieve to him. It proved a lucrative sideline for a while, but then something happened.

The details are vague, but I had heard the Old Man went to prison about this time, something to do with scrap metal. A few people said the Old Man had gone away to protect his brother. Furthermore, their recollections were that in return for going away, Robert had set the Old Man up with his first shop.

With enough of an idea, I checked it out for myself.

I spent a grey morning combing the city news archives. The Courts section was not printed during this period, so I spent a few hours scanning weeks and months of stories until I reached the August editions.

Then it appeared.

December 11, 1970
MEN CAUGHT BURNING COPPER 'TO DISGUISE IT'
Two men who handled stolen copper bars were ordered at Coventry Quarter Sessions to pay £400 compensation to an electronics firm.

Both had been caught 'red handed' by police at Hunningdon burning copper to disguise it, said the prosecution. The copper is said to be part of a haul worth £2,400 stolen from Micro Electronics, Bodmin Road, Wyken, Coventry.

Tony Shipley (21), of Kingsland Avenue, Coventry, was sent to prison for 18 months for handling the copper, which weighed three tons four hundred weight.

Paul Connelly (24) of George Street, Coventry, pleaded Guilty to handling the copper found at Hunningdon. He was sentenced to 12 months imprisonment, suspended for two years, and ordered to pay £10 compensation.

Mr David Jones defending said Shipley accepted having physical control over the stolen copper. Shipley made nothing out of the offence.

The timing was spot on, as was the crime. The Old Man took responsibility for more than three tons of copper when he could have claimed to be just a worker. It kept his accomplice Paul Connelly out of prison, but it also cut off any further enquiries, perhaps heading in Robert's direction. The rumour appeared to be right.

I slid over a later photo of Robert. By his late twenties, he supported a thick black beard beneath sharp, piercing eyes. "So clever he was," Margaret would say. Later I would ask her about this article and what others had said. She denied all knowledge but conceded that Robert was "not perfect".

Others since have described him as evil, though this does seem harsh.

On release, the Old Man named his new shop Lloyds – after the bank. It faced one of Robert's shops and the idea was that they would complement one another, except as the months passed it didn't work out that way. Whilst Robert ran his shops like a fence and kept a low profile, the Old Man worked obsessively and within just a few months set up a second shop further down, and then a few months on, a third.

He installed a manager at each shop, who did little aside from collect money and organise deliveries. The Old Man would then be free to head out buying and selling, and throughout the day would call by each shop several times to deliver new stock, to conduct business out back, or simply to use the phone or cash up. Occasionally there would be a routine visit by local detectives, browsing and checking stock, but little more than that. Any dodgy business was done offside.

On the evening, the Old Man continued working, but the nature of the work would change.

With Robert's contacts and his own, he had an address book full of small-time villains to trade with. Many ran legal businesses and bought and sold on the side – counterfeit, fraud, stolen goods – the opportunities were endless. Evenings were spent attending meetings at various pubs, clubs and car parks around the city. For a young man with few scruples and a way with money, there weren't enough hours in the day.

Once asked what his ambition was, he smiled and responded: "I'll be a millionaire by twenty-five."

It seemed reasonable. I suspect many of his friends held a similar ambition. Some, over the future decades, by investing in properties, running clubs etc., would indeed become millionaires, but some would simply become villains.

The Old Man stood alone in becoming both.

Towards the back of the first album appeared some colour photos of my brother and me with the Old Man down the park. I'm two years old, my brother six. We stand either side, holding hands with our dad. He's tall, lean and broad shouldered with thick black hair. By this point, he'd served two terms inside: three months for a burglary and one year for melting stolen copper.

Both sentences had been avoidable.

As far as I know, Robert had never been to prison. Margaret said he was not a reckless man. He proceeded with care in business, was ruthless when he had to be, and trusted few people. In this respect he had all the virtues of a good villain.

The Old Man, I would later learn, couldn't be more different. He dealt with most of the city's villains and before long was teaming up on 'robberies' from the city's warehouses and factories. Most of these robberies, of course, were hardly robberies at all, but inside jobs where you were simply removing goods without detection from the security guard, caretaker, or driver you'd paid off.

More often, he would sell off such stolen goods not through the shops but via the classified ads of the local paper. For instance, one person at home with twenty televisions apiece in their back room, would advertise a second-hand TV in excellent condition via one classified ad. With a TV working in the front room, as if it were their own with maybe the kids watching, the seller would organise one buyer every half hour and work through the stock. Naturally, several sellers could easily sell a hundred televisions within just a few evenings.

In contrast, a credit scam would be a good example whereby the proceeds could be cleared through the shops. For example, one finance company offered £500 credit on the proviso the lender bought a £250 sofa from a national retailer. Thereupon, the Old Man organised hundreds of purchases from derelict addresses fronted by a team of just five people. The money was all profit and the sofas, as they had paperwork, could be sold through the second-hand shops. The scam proved baffling to visiting detectives, suspicious at the deluge of brand-new sofas.

Speaking to ex-workers, there were numerous tales, all revealing great ingenuity and a disregard for the law. "If your Old Man had a choice between making £10,000 legally or illegally, he'd be drawn to the latter," I was told. "He couldn't help himself."

This was borne out, for as I combed the archives, more and more articles appeared. Within a year or two, the Old Man was fleeting in and out of the courts on a regular basis. Usually, the charges were for receiving and he would be fined, but on other occasions it would be for thieving and conspiring. But then suddenly such headlines came to an abrupt halt.

The reason, I'd learned, was because he'd been involved in a serious motorbike accident.

One wet Sunday morning, racing down winding lanes at high speed, a car pulled out from nowhere and the Old Man lost control. The bike skidded away and shot him into the path of an oncoming truck. Spinning low and fast, he caught its wheels, which – and I'm assured this is completely true – actually went across his legs, chest and helmet.

He was left at the roadside writhing in pain.

At the hospital, he was critical. The helmet had saved his life, but his chest was crushed and both legs mangled. Amputation was discussed, however, due to his age, the decision was held off and time granted. Finally, a series of metal rods were inserted in both legs. They would provide him with a lifetime of arthritis but more pertinently, the occasional inconvenience whenever he passed through a metal detector at a prison or airport.

Several weeks later, he was discharged in a wheelchair.

At this time, I was three years old, my brother six. Apparently, this would be the only time he would spend time at home. People would often describe the Old Man as someone who could never sit still, but as he recuperated, he had little choice. Housebound, he ate with us, watched TV with us, played games with us, watched me during the day whilst Mum was out and my brother at school.

Unfortunately, I can recall none of this golden period and can't imagine it lasted long.

As soon as he was able, he returned to work on crutches. He wouldn't quit riding bikes entirely, but would favour cars in future, and like many villains, opt for Jaguars. The choice underlined his membership of the criminal community.

Over the previous few years, many of the city's top villains had become his contacts and friends. He dealt and dined with the club owners, the robbers and thieves, the loan sharks and racketeers. His name had become known and with it he had a reputation.

Now when you heard the name 'Shipley', villains and police alike knew you were referring to Tony Shipley, businessman AND villain.

I now wonder how much of this reputation had been enabled by his brother Robert?

He was certainly a critical influence.

If it weren't for Robert, the Old Man wouldn't have joined this circle of villains, wouldn't have returned to prison, wouldn't have met other criminals inside, wouldn't have become the bank robber, counterfeiter, and drug smuggler of his later years.

But then, who knows?

It might not have made the slightest bit of difference.

I added the photos Margaret gave me of Robert to the albums. He was an important influence, but not the only one; there would be many more. Intermittently, in the months and years that followed, I would discover this as I continued to gather more photos, news clippings and prison letters; as I talked to more relatives and friends to develop the chronology, nailing down the geography, the locations and people.

The albums would prove an invaluable tool I would develop whenever there were breaks in the driving work. However, after the shooting, within just a few months, things had returned to normal.

* * *

ONE NIGHT, I arrived home with a small bag of money. This was not unusual, and my wife did not comment. She knew I was back driving for the Old Man. I headed through to the bedroom to check the count. I spilled the bundles of notes onto the bed and began counting.

There was £46,000 in all.

I retrieved a black jacket from the wardrobe and lay it on the bed. Its linings had been adapted to carry money. The money I divided into slim bundles and fed them into the inside arms of the coat and horizontally along into the lower back. At £26,000 I tried it on, to see how it felt. I looked in the mirror, light from a lamp would highlight any bulges.

It looked good.

Of the remaining £20,000, half was in Scottish notes, the remainder made up of £10 notes and was unduly bulky. Two grand I stuck in my wallet, four grand I slid between the absent pages of two paperbacks. That made £32,000.

Around to the spare room, I lifted the disc of my drawing board, placed in the remaining £18,000 and retrieved my passport. The following morning, I had an EasyJet flight to catch from Luton.

I was off to see the Old Man.

CHAPTER 6:
THE SMUGGLER ON THE RUN

OCTOBER 2001

LOOKING BACK, it's difficult to believe how often I passed through British Customs and how unaffected I appear to have been by the experience. I can only believe that as a young man, I was highly confident.

The pat down at Heathrow was the one point of concern I had. However, half the time, queues crawled along and from far back I could observe the pat downs, scrutinise the officers, and switch queues without drawing attention. Stepping through the metal-detector, there were roughly two passengers to each customs officer, so only half of passengers would be patted down. A turn of the back, or a pause to check a bag or a pocket would allow another passenger to leap-frog ahead and face a pat down, meaning I could stroll through unchecked. However, if unavoidable, most officers merely carried out a lazy pat down of the torso, outside of the legs and arms only. The insides of arms were routinely missed as were the backs of jackets.

Once through, I would be relieved. 'Another clean sheet' I would think. I was ever fearful of the day when I couldn't switch queues or avoid an officer, who, for whatever reason, was being thorough. That day was yet to come, but if it did, I knew it wouldn't be the worst thing.

The risk I was running here wasn't arrest, but confiscation.

The legal limit per person for exporting cash was £10,000. Found with a pound above this amount, all the money would be confiscated and you'd be given ninety days to provide evidence of its source. If you could not manage this, the money would be lost.

The Old Man had met such occasional losses with a shrug. The important thing was the worker was safe and hadn't talked. He could always make more money.

I strolled through unchecked and killed some time in Duty Free, browsed the book stands, grabbed some newspapers. In the event I was being watched, I needed to appear casual, as if on holiday.

Finally, I headed to my gate.

In just a few hours, I'd be landing at Barcelona.

* * *

ON SCHEDULE, I stepped out from the Arrivals building to be greeted by an intense blue sky and burning sunshine. I breathed in the warm air, felt the heat off the concrete, squinted at the brightness. Spain was a welcome break from the grey skies back home.

At the taxi rank, a handful of holidaymakers sat waiting, surrounded by bags and cases. All taxis were out, so there'd be a wait. I sat at the end of a bench and rummaged in my travel bag for a paperback, surveying those waiting as I did so: a pair of pensioners, a loved-up couple with a baby, an old frail Spanish man mumbling to himself.

None could be undercover.

Such a look was a long-practiced habit. Airports were the easiest places to pick up a tail. To locate the Old Man, I would be the one to follow. To blend in and stay in role, I opened my book, tried to read a page or two, but then stopped as a question sprung to mind: *How have you ended up doing this?*

It was a good question to which I had no clear answer.

The most obvious answer was the money. It paid well, but so did other jobs, and this particular job was one I would only ever do for the Old Man. It was on the one hand, a way to earn a wage, and on the other, a way to see the Old Man.

I looked across to the car park opposite. A little activity, few people about, no-one I would recognise. I returned to my book, still unable to read much.

Circumstance was another reason for doing this job. Truth was, I was in limbo. I had been working as an animation artist, but the arrival of CGI had consigned me to the scrap heap. I was a thirty-year-old pencil artist with no desire to change. The future had arrived in the form of software, screens and styluses, but I had no wish to be involved. Consequently, I had no career, no future, little appetite for this modern world. We were effectively in a stand-off: it insisted I change, I insisted I would not.

Working for the Old Man was preferable to all other options. He was stubborn, like me. An idealist like I had once been. He got up each morning, determined to take on the world and make a fortune.

I admired that. Always had.

After struggling through a couple of pages, I again looked across to the car park. There on a low wall sat a red, spikey-haired Dutchman with glasses. He was swigging a coke and smoking a fag as he watched people come and go.

This was Dennis, an ambitious weed grower from Belgium.

As per usual, he had been observing the rank for some time. Once confident no-one had tailed me, he nodded and disappeared to the car park. I allowed a few minutes to pass and followed him over.

We scooted along a shimmering highway, the radio blasting, windows down. Dennis shook a fag loose from its pack, lit it up, took a drag and exhaled with a frown as he checked his mirror – a brown Renault was sat back a quarter mile. I had noticed it too.

We observed it for a while; after a few miles it turned off. Nothing replaced it, and the road behind remained clear. With our minds at ease, Dennis delivered an update.

On the last trip, the Old Man had been organising shipments of hashish between Spain and the UK, whilst taking control of the boat work from Morocco. This would assure a lower purchase price and cut out the Spanish middleman. To traverse the Mediterranean, he was developing three options; a fishing boat at Gibraltar; a rib boat at Benalmadena, and a small cargo ship moored at Alicante.

It was presumed only one would be employed, but the Old Man favoured investments in all three. For Dennis, this made no sense.

"Why three schemes? Why not just one? It would be less risk and less work. But for your father, everything has to be big! He is not happy with one transport, he wants three. And he does not want to run every few weeks but every ten days. It is crazy!"

This was of no surprise to anyone who really knew the Old Man. Relying on one scheme was not his way. He thrived on options whether it be supply, storage or transport. For these reasons, their days were long as they attended meetings and dealt with locations often hundreds of miles apart.

I didn't think Dennis really appreciated the plan they were working to.

"And the spending is just reckless!" he continued, "He has put in a quarter of a mill into that cargo ship, but he has not paid me my wages for three weeks. He says we must all wait for the next load to land. But he still pays for all these women of his to come out – Blondie, Irish Ange, the Red Head."

I was yet to meet the Red Head. Apparently, she was a dancer.

"I have no time to see my girlfriend, but *his* we make time for. Blondie is down here now, staying at the apartment."

"She doesn't get in the way of work, though, does she?" I reminded him. This was always the Old Man's counter-argument. Work carried on regardless whether Blondie was here or not. He made few allowances.

"Maybe not. But why does she have to come here at all? He is on the run from not just England but Holland now! And what does he do? He brings his girlfriend and daughter out here during the school holidays. Who does that? It is a risk to us all, I tell you.

"Money comes in and he spends it. We work long days, but they are never enough. He talks about security but has people flying in every day. I don't know anymore…nothing is ever enough."

Some silence passed. I checked the mirrors and Dennis shook his head some more, "I'm thinking of going back home."

He looked my way for a response, but I said nothing. It came as no surprise as few workers lasted more than six months. They'd quit and be gone, replaced by someone equally naïve.

We exited the highway for the coastal road south. Moments later, the bluest sea emerged between passing hills to run alongside us. I gazed at long stretches of empty white sands which gave way to scores of ornate villas followed by a flurry of beachside restaurants.

This was Castelldefels.

A wealthy commuter resort, Castelldefels saw few tourists and out of season was two thirds empty. We checked our mirrors one last time and turned into the gardens of a stilted apartment building surrounded by manicured lawns and tidy palm trees.

To those who lived here, the Old Man was business executive Graham Penney, who worked for a large British company based in Barcelona.

He occupied the second-floor apartment.

We strolled through to the rear L-shaped living room where the Old Man sat at a dining table surrounded by mobile phones, immersed in calls. His daughter Nellie, my half-sister, was sprawled at his feet surrounded by bright colouring books and crayons; her mum Blondie sat across the room, bag in hand, wearing an impatient frown. Slumped down next to her, reading *The Sun,* was parked a stocky little Scotsman with a thick black beard. He'd been on the run for a few years and had recently joined the group. He used the name 'Glasgow'.

"A' right son?" he called.

"A' right," I nodded.

He returned to his paper.

The Old Man clocked me, continued to talk 'paperwork' (money) with someone in the UK. Seconds later, a second mobile rang. He grabbed it, closed off the first call, and spoke to the 'Brighton Man' in their familiar code of cigarettes (*product*), Embassies (*hashish*), and Super Kings (*amphetamine*).

I exchanged looks with Blondie.

She shrugged and shook her head.

I shuffled on by, dropped my bag in the spare room and got changed. Minutes later I emerged in shorts, sandals and t-shirt, listening to the Old Man making promises on fifty Embassies for Sunday. Then a third phone rang.

Blondie glared in my direction, "It's been like this all morning. This is what he's like!"

I wanted to offer some conciliatory words but was interrupted

"Sam!" he barked, handing a phone my way. "It's Linx. He's got paperwork sitting there – around seventy pages (£70,000). Needs to know when you can grab it. He's off away at the weekend."

I took the phone and stepped into the kitchen. There, fixing a round of coffees, was Roma, Dennis's red-headed Romanian girlfriend. Young, fit and with the longest smooth legs, she favoured short skirts which antagonised Blondie, who wasn't one to flaunt anything.

Her sweet green eyes flashed my way, and she waved a cup, "Coffee Sam?"

Sam was my nickname here. Few knew my real name.

I nodded and returned to the living room, where Blondie looked more annoyed than when I arrived. With the pick-up details agreed, I passed the phone to the Old Man who wrapped it up, "Alright mate. It's all under control, he's with me now. Just that seventy and you're all done".

Call over.

He turned to his desk, placed two of the phones on charge along-side three others, browsed down one of his lists, crossed out several items and wrote down two more. For a minute, there was complete silence in the room. He studied another list for several seconds, tore it off, fed it through the shredder, and turned to face me.

"How was the trip?" he asked.

"Yeah – easy. Customs were straight forward."

"Good. You got the paperwork?"

"Yeah."

I grabbed my coat and pulled out paperwork from its lining. "There's £32,000 there, most of it in twenties."

He looked surprised, "It's more than I thought."

"You said bring what you can."

"You really should have split it with someone else. If you'd lost it…"

He palmed the bundles, re-stacked them into fives and placed them at the far side of the desk where other piles were lined up.

"Right, we're almost there," he murmured to himself.

"Are we going or not?" Blondie asked sharply.

"Yeah… we're about ready now," he remarked as he wrote a few figures down at the bottom of a list. He then stood up and dropped his reading glasses to the table.

Turning towards his daughter, he smiled, opened his arms and she immediately charged towards him. Sweeping her up, he playfully threw her in the air and caught her in his arms; she giggled uncontrollably.

"Will see you in a few weeks, Nell," he said, pinching her nose as she laughed. "You keep working at school and I'll see you in a few weeks, you little stinker".

She giggled again as he put her down.

Blondie glared at him, "Can he take us now?"

"Yeah." He turned to Dennis, "You okay to get her to the airport?"

"I'm ready John," Dennis said, and snatched up their bags.

The Old Man kissed Blondie briefly, assured her that next time he would find time, but right now, as she could see, he had a lot on.

She looked unimpressed.

I watched on.

"It's always next time," she complained loudly. "You say that every time we come. Nell's at school now. We can't just drop things and come over whenever you want Tony."

He appeared to listen and reiterated his promise. "Next time will be different. In a few weeks, I will take some days off and we'll go off somewhere for a few days. Promise."

"I hope you're right Tone," she murmured and disappeared out of the door with Dennis in tow dragging her cases.

The tension in the room immediately lessened. Roma's long legs emerged from the kitchen. "Is everything okay now John?"

As in Holland, all the workers called him 'John' as opposed to Tony.

"Yeah, fine," he replied, his face frustrated. "She just doesn't understand. Expects me to spend all my time with her. Doesn't think where the money comes from." He put on his glasses and referred to his schedule. "Got to meet the Moroccans in ten minutes. They're just down the road. Right. We best get moving".

He gulped down a coffee, grabbed his phones from the table, arranged them in his shoulder bag, folded up his lists and placed them in a side pocket. He looked over to me, "You ready?"

"Yeah, sure."

"We'll be about an hour," he called to Glasgow, who lowered his paper. "Take Roma down to the car hire and have her pay everything up to date. And then get on with that other thing we talked about before Peiter arrives. He's in at midday."

"Ay. I got it," Glasgow said and returned to his read.

The Old Man watched him for a moment and then grabbed a light jacket.

We exited the apartment.

Outside, Dennis was pulling away and Nellie watched us through the rear window. The Old Man smiled her way and waved.

She smiled happily and waved back. We watched them disappear into the distance.

The Old Man frowned, "She's better off at home. Can't be having all this shit whilst we've got work on."

He glanced at his watch and strode on ahead.

Seconds later, I followed.

* * *

WE CROSSED OUT of the shade onto the seafront, strolling by warm empty beaches and the sound of surf. He walked at his usual brisk pace, and though I sensed he had much on his mind, I knew this was the only chance to talk about the one subject that was being ignored.

"Any news from Holland on the Soldier thing?"

He responded with no surprise that I'd asked.

"They're still looking," he answered. "My name's been mentioned. They have my prints and DNA – off the palm print and blood at the scene. Now they'll be patient. Wait until I surface."

"And if you don't?"

"Then they'll have to step things up and come after me".

For a moment I contemplated what this might mean.

"You'll need to be careful," he continued. "They'll drop on you first – your house, your car, your phone."

This was just what I'd been thinking.

"Be careful, like I've shown you. That's all you can do."

"I'm doing all the normal things."

"You check your car?"

"Every few days. It's parked away from the house. Nothing's in my name."

"That's good. And your phone."

"Only you come in on it. Switched off at night. Changed every two to three weeks."

"It needs to be more often. Change it when you get back."

I nodded in agreement and we walked on.

IN SPAIN, he was ever careful with whom he met. Some old British contacts would visit him on business, but away from Castelldefels. They were kept at a distance, few were trusted. What face to face meetings there were, he restricted to foreign contacts who were unaware he was on the run. Often, I would accompany him on such meetings, especially with the Moroccans whose mouthpiece would also be accompanied by family.

The Moroccans were the main suppliers for the new venture, which promised to smuggle tons of hashish to the UK. That I was such a casual participant underlined my lack of concern by this point. For the most part, I was relieved that he was alive from the shooting, living safely in Spain, and only dealing in hashish.

It was not a drug that would trouble my conscience anymore, though it had initially.

Before working for the Old Man, I had been dismissive of all drugs, regarding them all as one and the same. However, once working, I had learnt to make distinctions. He dealt in soft drugs – cannabis and amphetamine – which few people at the time saw as particularly harmful. Most of his peers dealt increasingly in cocaine. The Old Man would not. This had allowed me to nurture the idea that we were bootleggers rather than drug dealers, leaving me with a clearer conscience for the most part.

We would meet the Moroccans at a seaside restaurant we called the 'Blue Chairs'. They were backed by the Moroccan Mafia. The older was the spokesperson, the younger, his minder. Adaptable to any of the three methods proposed; they just wanted regular sales. To begin with, the cargo ship was favoured due to its large capacity, but its purchase was still some weeks away.

Once up and running, the Moroccans, thanks to their navy contacts, could guarantee safe transport out of Morocco. Therefore, there was a fortune to be made. However, there was one obstacle; the Old Man needed finance and since moving to Spain, what capital he did have, was tied up in Holland. Therefore, whilst he stalled the Moroccans, he arranged to meet Albert.

A couple of hundred yards up the coast at the 'White Chairs' we met Albert, a semi-retired Midlands villain. He'd been on the run for more than a decade and survived this long by seeing few people and dealing with less. He and the Old Man went back decades and their meetings were conducted one to one whilst I read the papers at a nearby table. Albert trusted no-one, even if they were family. They talked for almost an hour and he agreed to chuck in a hundred grand but not a penny more.

Once done, we strolled towards the apartment via a series of public call boxes that lined the ocean road. It was from them, each morning and evening, the Old Man would make what you might call his 'sales calls' into the UK.

He would spend the best part of an hour bouncing in calls to his customers – the wholesalers in the main cities. These were his most trusted contacts – buyers of twenty to a hundred kilos – whom he would notify of future parcels and prices.

Whilst he worked his way through calls, I would chill out, maybe walk down the beach, take some time to reflect a little. These short trips had become so frequent they now felt normal; what the Old Man traded in was easily forgotten. The days were all meetings and phone calls; I never saw any drugs. It didn't even feel like work, more a weekend break in which I was doing my father a favour.

I would almost have done it for nothing if he'd asked, for I liked Spain. I liked the sunshine, the blue skies, how cheap everything was, but above all, I liked how safe it felt. Up in Holland, I had been highly aware of the business he was in. Amsterdam was packed with CCTV and police surveillance. Whatever the deal, undercover officers, phone taps, bugs and wires were all factors to be considered.

In Spain, not a worry.

To be arrested, you had to be caught hands-on with drugs. There were no conspiracy laws, and therefore phone taps and wires were unheard of. You simply had to watch you weren't being followed or set up.

I walked down to the surf, removed my sandals and walked a while.

Driving money to Holland was the only activity that involved any risk for me. Once a month I'd make a couple of drives with around £70,000 a time. I would deliver it to Amsterdam and scoot straight back. I'd be searched by British Customs almost every time, for I was flagged on their system. Even so, they could never figure out why the son of a drug importer kept driving through, but concealing nothing in his vehicle. They'd pull my car apart, convinced something was stashed away. I would sit and drink cold coffee, read a paper, work to appear unconcerned.

Looking back, this might seem foolish, but at the time I saw it differently. I appeared to be taking risks but in reality, was not. As my car was clean, there was nothing they could do. Nevertheless, the adrenalin was enticing, the feeling I'd put one over on them, that I'd outsmarted them. I could understand how some people enjoyed this feeling.

The Old Man, for instance.

I looked up the beach to the call boxes. He was wrapping up and waving me over. I walked up and joined him. Running late, we headed back to base at speed. There in private we would meet his transport contact – Dutch Peiter.

MEETINGS WITH transport contacts were always held in private. The 'transport' was simply the means to move the drugs between countries, but it was imperative that few people knew who was doing this. A bleach-haired bodybuilder called Dutch Peiter wished to work exclusively with the Old Man. His transport ran between Spain and the UK with the concealment details exclusive to just Peiter, the Old

Man and the workers used on the day. Even the driver would be ignorant of where the drugs would be concealed.

They settled down to business; I made some drinks and joined them. The Old Man summarised our position regarding the Moroccan suppliers, the extra cash injection from Albert, and the volume of cash still to be collected in the UK. He assured him that at a push, there was £260,000 available.

They discussed dates, drivers and drop-offs. The parcel after landing in Spain would be removed from the cargo ship and driven to a 'warehouse'. There it would be repackaged to blend into the goods on Peiter's transport. After, they would link up with Peiter's transport and conceal the parcel. It would then continue its journey to the UK via Holland. Arriving in the UK, only Peiter, the Old Man and the key workers involved would know which vehicle it was on. The transport, once checked for tails and trackers, would pull off the motorway and the parcel would be removed and sent onto a warehouse in preparation for distribution. A small team of drivers would take care of this and seven days later the money would begin pouring in for collection. The bulk of this money would be returned to Spain to pay for further loads.

The question was how to get this cash to Spain without using the normal channels, which had been riddled with distrust and the suspicion that certain drivers were developing sticky fingers.

This is where I came in.

"Sam's off in about an hour," the Old Man declared. "He'll start collecting and in two weeks' time – three at most - the cargo ship and the Moroccan suppliers will be fully paid off. Then the larger loads begin. Every 10-14 days, regular as clockwork. Again, Sam will collect paperwork."

Peiter smiled and turned my way, "You okay with that, Sam?"

Given the Old Man hadn't mentioned this so far, I guessed I had little choice. There was no-one else they could trust, I nodded, "Sure. No problem".

"There's nothing to worry about", added the Old Man. "Sam's moved millions over the years without a loss."

It was a rare compliment, but he was correct in what he said. For almost six years, I had been collecting money and in all that time hadn't lost a penny, stole a penny or miscounted a single pound.

Peiter grinned, "He is right. For you, it will not be a problem."

I smiled thoughtfully, thinking forward to the weeks ahead. I hadn't collected such a large amount for some time. It was a lot of money to collect, a lot of money to move. A quarter million to collect by road, to wire by Western Union, to deliver by flights when all the false names were exhausted.

There would be some hectic weeks ahead, but I wouldn't let them down.

CHAPTER 7:
THE YOUNG ENTREPRENEUR

1972-75

EVERY NOW and then I read that the boys of fathers who have spent time in prison are five to ten times more likely to serve time themselves. I am not surprised. You are conditioned from early on to accept the most unusual things without judgement or surprise. This might mean accepting and being desensitised to violence or vice, fraud or theft, yet for me, it was about accepting a father who made an abundance of money. As a kid, the Old Man had always dealt in large sums of money, to the extent that years later, I had simply come to expect it.

One important thing was different, though.

He hadn't started out dealing in large sums through crime, but rather by legitimate business. The Old Man, whilst still in his early twenties, had killed the second-hand business in the city for a while, such was his domination. People would tell of his fleet of shops, the high volume of stock he turned over, the bags of money he'd gather up each day, bundles and bundles of cash.

Whilst I awaited news on the cargo ship deal, I was reconstructing this early part of his life, organising the albums, speaking to relatives, uncovering more pictures, but keeping it quiet. I had adopted a strategy of investigating matters on the quiet. I couldn't imagine the Old Man would see any point to my interest. He rarely referred to the past, always he lived in the here and now, ever looking towards the future.

Me, I was different. I'd always looked back. And thanks to this tendency, I had gradually established a timeline that gave order to all the story scraps I had amassed.

Within a few months of the bike accident, he returned to work on crutches. By then he had built up four second-hand furniture shops – Lloyds, Barclays, Royals and Westminsters.

Over the next few years, he expanded these to five, six, seven and eight, some specialising in second-hand furniture, others in white goods such as washing machines and fridge freezers, others electric goods – TVs, lamps and radios. The Old Man would spend his days hopping between shops, organising deliveries of fresh stock, out on meetings. At the day's end, he would drop in to cash up for his evening deals.

More often, into the evening and early hours, he pressed on, meeting and dealing with an assortment of businessmen and villains from all corners of the city. He seemed unrestricted in whom he dealt with, a straight property developer one minute, a notorious city gangster the next. Some deals were straight, others crooked, but all were cash deals where one's word was everything.

The result was he drew more and more attention.

Police visiting the shops with warrants became increasingly common. At such times, thanks to being tipped off, the Old Man's whereabouts would be unknown. Often, he would avoid such police visits for weeks and months until one or two officers would turn their attention to his brother Robert.

With a couple of tightly run shops, Robert was horrified to see hostile CID visiting his businesses, poking around, waving a warrant to arrest his brother. Desiring respectability, Robert had ingratiated himself with various lodges to raise his standing. He dressed middle class, lived middle class, even took elocution lessons to sound so. Whilst the Old Man took police visits in his stride with a typically dark sense of humour, Robert saw it as no laughing matter.

He and the Old Man had different ways of operating. The Old Man, as well as dealing with many of Robert's contacts, now dealt with many of the villains Robert chose to avoid due to an air of distrust, dislike or fear. Furthermore, the Old Man's contacts had broadened and now took him further afield. Often, he would disappear up to Glasgow or down to London for a few days and return with a case of money and orders for goods. He'd spend his evenings on a 'safe landline' organising deals and then disappear again 'on business' for a few days. Occasionally he would return to establish an alibi and head off enquiries concerning local robberies of warehouses and factories.

Combing the news archives, I noted how, alongside the masses of job losses, robberies, heists, and burglaries dominated the headlines. Amongst them, I had, of course, uncovered various articles featuring the Old Man's court appearances, but had been reassured that none could be considered heavy or violent. That was, until one afternoon, I uncovered an article that would provide a fresh perspective.

It was from the summer of '76.

The Old Man had sold some stolen bikes to some London contacts, who refused to pay. In retaliation, he had threatened one of them at gunpoint. I instantly recognised the tale, recalling a story he had told just a couple of years back.

The Old Man rarely socialised, but as he'd not long been released, I'd tempted him to drop by his old neighbourhood one night. There, he quickly bumped into a series of old schoolmates and by the early hours, we sat drinking, them wanting to discuss crime, its truths and fictions, the myths perpetuated by books and newspapers, each encouraging the Old Man to be forthcoming. The conversation flowed through his encounters with modern criminals – John Haase, Curtis Warren, Charles Bronson et al – before moving onto the classic London villains of the Sixties.

"Weren't you friends with the Richardsons?" one asked.

"I know Eddie," the Old Man answered, "but not Charlie."

"And Frankie Fraser?"

"His son I know very well, but not the father. He's the older generation."

"And the Krays?"

"Just before my time, though I know many that knew them. Few criminals liked the Krays; they weren't businessmen as such. They were really just bullies – scaring people who couldn't fight back. Anyone can do that. Most London villains were glad when they were put away."

"But you were down there in the Seventies?" I interjected, "I remember being told that…"

"In the early and mid-Seventies, yeah. Back then I…" he paused a moment, glanced around the room, noted how all eyes were waiting for him to continue, expecting something. He nodded to himself, "I used to deal with a few of the people in East London," he began. "Then one day I had a problem."

He was sat on the floor, back against the sofa, Bacardi and coke in hand. Scattered around the room, several bodies sat in the shadows, nursing drinks.

The room was silent.

"A man owed me some money but wouldn't pay up," he continued. "He'd had some stock off me – bikes they were – and he'd took them, sold them, refused to pay. He owned a clothes factory off Bethnal Green, and in the afternoon was to be found at the factory. Out front, his Bentley was parked up as usual, so I knew he was in. He was considered a big name, a friend of the Kray twins, who were locked away at this time.

"I drive by and check it's quiet and park up a few streets away. Under my seat I've taped an automatic. I pull it out, unwrap the tape and put it in my left inside pocket. I'm wearing a leather jacket, so it doesn't sag, and is unnoticeable.

"I walk swiftly down a side street and along a series of ginnels and emerge outside the side entrance of the factory. The side doors were left open on hot days such as this. I enter, walk down a long corridor. On my right is the factory floor and the noise of sewing machines. His office is to the left and as I walk along, I gaze down the blinds of the office and see him sat at a large, cluttered desk with a cigar in one hand and phone in the other. He is alone.

Without knocking, I go in, pull the door to softly, and step in front of the desk and look down at him. He doesn't look up, but he knows someone's there. After a minute or so, he glances up, sees it's me, covers the phone's mouthpiece with his palm, 'Hi there Tone. Won't be a minute. Take a seat'.

"I remain standing, watching him. He was a large man, in his fifties, with long grey hair greased back. It was hot in there and he'd loosened his tie, so he was already sweating. He looks back at me and I meet his eyes full on. He knows why I'm there.

"I say nothing but wait.

"He rounds off the call, 'I'll call you back, something's just come up' he says, and places the receiver slowly in its cradle and looks up at me and smiles, real friendly like. He puts his cigar in the ashtray – all calm. 'So, what can I do for you?' he asks.

"I say nothing.

"He rolls his tongue along the cheek of his mouth, leans back in the chair, takes a long drag on his cigar – holds it a second or two. His forehead furrows in thought, and he blows a long plume of smoke across the desk and looks at me through squinted eyes. 'Is everything alright, Tone?'

"I say nothing... for three, four, five seconds... then I reach into my pocket and pull out the gun and aim it at his head. 'I've come for my money?' I say.

"His jaw drops, just a little. He remains poker-faced, and his eyes look from the gun to me and back again, evaluating whether it is real or not. Then he looks down at his desk for a moment, sighs loudly, looks up at me with a glare of impatience.

"I don't move.

"He swallows once... collects his thoughts.

"The room is silent but for a fan that hums away on top of a filing cabinet. Outside, the sound of machines are rattling away, but I don't really notice them. I'm just looking at him.

"Him at me.

"A whole minute passes and then another. He folds his arms, strokes his lips with his teeth, and finally speaks, 'Right. I think I explained the situation, Tony. We did not get the goods. There is no money.'

"'No. I'm told you had them. You've a bill to pay!' I keep the gun aimed to his head. He stares hard at me, with these steely blue eyes, trying to intimidate me. 'Why don't you just put that down?' he says.

"'I'm here to collect,' I say. 'Three grand.' And I stare down the barrel, lower the gun a little, so it's aimed at his face. I see a flicker of fear. He knows I mean it, but to his credit he does remain calm. He won't be scared and after a few seconds he clears his throat, delivers his words slow and clear, 'Okay then son... Have it your way'.

"He leans forward, stares at me beyond the gun, and without blinking... jabs his forefinger, 'Look here son. I don't have your money and I'm not paying you A FUCKIN' PENNY!'

"His face trembles and he holds me in an ice-cold stare, allowing the words to linger, for the words to sink in. And then, still staring, he leans back in the chair, folds his hands behind his head, and smiles all wide.

"The gun remains steady and I'm thinking it through. Before I do anything, though, he shakes his head slowly, 'You know the people I know. You are not going to shoot me. SO WHY DON'T YOU PUT THAT FUCKIN' GUN DOWN.'

"I don't flinch. He studies my face for signs of doubt. I lower the gun a touch and feel my finger tightening on the trigger. More silence as he watches me. My finger is pulled as far as it can without firing. Just a little more...

"'Easy Tony' he says firmly. 'There's really no need for this.'

"'I want my money – three grand. It's what you owe.'

"'You know you're not getting it.'

"I study him. He watches the gun. All is quiet. The fan still hums away in the corner, the only sound now. Nothing else. And then after a few seconds I realise – I can't hear any sewing machines.

The factory floor is an empty silence. He also notices this. His eyes crawl to his left – to the windows and door. He pauses a moment, and then looks back to me and the corners of his mouth rise.

"We are being watched.

"I look right and see them also – all the machinists – watching us through the office windows; stood back watching as if it's a movie. All are still, no-one moves. A smile creeps across his face. He thinks I won't shoot now, that this changes things, that help will be here soon. 'Three grand!' I remind him. He gazes back at me, slowly shakes his head.

"My finger tightens back on the trigger some more. No-one knows me here. I can shoot him no problem, be out of there within seconds. A minute ticks by, and I'm just stood there, arm outstretched, gun aimed, people watching. And then another minute. However, he doesn't flinch. He just sits there.

"The workers watch and wait – waiting for something to happen. He says nothing. I hold my position, finger pulled on the trigger. Then the silence is broken by the phone ringing. He looks at the phone and back to me. His hand reaches across to answer, but then he pauses, looks to me, and I shake my head slowly.

"It continues to ring.

"We watch one another.

"I weigh up what to do. If I shoot, I must be able to get out. The workers will disperse as soon as I fire – it's what people do.

"It continues to ring. And then I think of the money. I'm not getting any. And if I shoot him, it'll be for nothing.

"It continues to ring. I stare at him and think, *I have to shoot him? I look weak otherwise.*

"Finally, the ringing stops.

"The room is silent. He manages a fake smile, 'C'mon Tony. This is just business!' he says.

"The trigger's on the edge, needs just a little more. But something is holding me back. I'm not sure what. I glance over at his staff gawping at me like statues. They all know my face. They've had time. I look at him one last time and ask: *Is he worth it?*

"I need to decide. The workers watch on. I allow more and more seconds to pass until I can allow no more. I lower the gun."

The Old Man looked up, shook his head slowly. The room was still. It had been silent for more than ten minutes.

Some seconds passed.

Finally, I spoke, "Why didn't you shoot him?"

A brief silence.

He shrugged, frowned in thought. "I was just a kid!"

Another silence.

He glanced my way and added, "You learn as you get older."

It was the final story of the night. Dawn was breaking, we were winding down, but it was something I would later reflect on: *"You learn as you get older."*

What did he mean by that?

That experience teaches you not to mess with such people, or it teaches you not to hesitate? Or as I later believed: he wasn't cut out to kill anyone. That whilst he knew many hard men, he was no hard man himself.

Of course, this wasn't quite the end of the story.

The factory owner did two things. Firstly, he made some calls, found out more about the Old Man. It would be a few days before a brown parcel was delivered to our address. As we rarely received parcels, Mum rung the Old Man at work. He ordered her to place it at the top of the garden and get us kids indoors. He raced home, and cautiously opened the parcel to discover... A dummy bomb!

Just to let him know he could easily be reached.

The second thing the factory owner did was call in the police. A warrant was issued for attempted murder. Days later, police carried out raids, but the Old Man had been tipped off and slipped away. He grabbed whatever money he could and went on the run. Weeks passed and the police visits persisted. There would be no let up. The Old Man established a hideaway up north, made fly-by-night visits home, continued to wait for the heat to die down.

However, it never would.

And as the weeks turned into months, his fleet of shops suffered. In his absence, they haemorrhaged money. Eventually, one by one, he had little choice but to sell them off. The ten shops become eight which become six and four, until just two, and then one remained – Lloyds, his first shop.

With almost a year having passed, police eventually received a tip-off and captured him at his hideaway in Sheffield. The charges were for attempted murder, possession of a firearm, theft, receiving etc. In order to keep the London gangster out of it, they offered the Old Man a plea bargain. He had little choice.

The article I'd dug up told half of the story:

26th October, 1976

CASH TROUBLE MAN 'INVOLVED' WITH CROWD OF CRIMINALS

A MAN whose second-hand furniture business were running down found himself in financial trouble, Coventry Crown Court heard.

So, he got himself involved with a crowd of criminals to help pull him out of trouble said his counsel, Mr Kenneth Clark yesterday. But after receiving 99 cycles, knowing them to be stolen, he was let down by his professional contacts in London who were 'too sophisticated for him'. And when he produced a gun to try to get his money for the bikes it did not have any effect.

Tony Shipley (27), formerly of Broomfield Road, Earlsdon, Coventry – and latterly said to be living in Sheffield – was jailed for a total of four and a half years.

He admitted dishonestly receiving 99 cycles knowing them to be stolen [...] Shipley admitted everything and directed the police to premises in Lower Ford Street, Coventry, where the gun was found. Mr Clark said Mr Shipley had built up 10 second-hand furniture businesses in Coventry but because of financial pressures he had to sell them.

This article prompted a rethink on my behalf. Whilst I had considered his brother to have dragged him onto a criminal path, I could now see that wasn't entirely so. The Old Man was unlike his brother. For Robert, business and crime were about the money, whilst for the Old Man it seemed to have been about something more. If it had been about the money, he would have had a few shops like his brother, dealt a little on the side, accumulated cash reserves and maybe bought some flash cars and a fancy house. But he hadn't done this at all. He would invest all he had in the next venture, and then into the next, and the next after that. Some businesses would prove to be gold mines, others, money pits. Nevertheless, he had to expand and go bigger. Like Dennis had said, with the Old Man everything had to be big. Not one shop but ten. Not one transport but three.

If it wasn't about the money then, what was it?

CHAPTER 8:
ARRESTED IN BARCELONA

JANUARY 2002

WORKING FOR THE OLD MAN, risk was always on one's mind, but the people we were in fear of, the police, the undercovers, the Crime Squad, were very much out of sight. Day by day, we strived to minimise the risk from those people we never saw. But we knew they were out there somewhere.

Sometimes, the 'other side' as we called them would reveal themselves.

The weeks before the deadline had seen me collect more than £400,000. A chunk of this I delivered to Gibraltar, another chunk up north, and half a chunk to service local expenses, wages and debts. This left £230,000 towards the cargo ship.

I moved to a hotel for the final count.

The night passed slowly as I counted into the early hours. Inevitably my mind drifted, and one question of concern arose: *If I were to be discovered in a hotel room with close to a quarter of a million pounds, would I have a problem?*

Finding the receipts to cover £20,000 as payment for a car was one thing, but what if I was stopped with a sizable amount of money. Would the Old Man find the paperwork to cover it?

I believed he would.

I trusted the Old Man. In working for him, he had never let me down. His guidance was crucial. Whilst his peers treated their drivers as disposable, he did not. In the years I'd worked for him, he hadn't lost a single driver.

I couldn't see me being the first.

I spent the following day visiting branches of Western Union, where under a series of aliases I wired a score of low, five-figure chunks to Spain. Even so, another thirty was required and collecting it late on the final night was cutting it fine. With Western Unions slow to open most mornings, I offered to grab an early flight.

"You on your own is too risky; the deadline's midday our time, eleven yours, and we need time to collect. If we were to lose it...." The Old Man paused, "Tell you what – ten's the limit per passenger. Grab two other bodies and split it."

Reluctantly, I agreed.

* * *

WE TRAVELLED SEPARATELY. The legal limit was £10,000 apiece, so we each carried a few pounds under. We ignored one another at every stage. It was vital, in the event of a pull, neither brought attention to the others. However, all went well. One, two and three – we eased our way through customs at Heathrow, a few hours later, the same at Barcelona.

Out of the Arrivals building, the Spanish sunshine was ruthless. I removed my black jacket, strolled along to the taxi rank at Terminal Four, took a seat, and awaited the others.

First to arrive was my uncle – the Car Man – an overweight ex-biker dressed casual in shorts and t-shirt. It was his fourth trip carrying money and he'd been getting into the swing of it. He took a seat, "Where's Murray?"

I glanced over his shoulder.

Swaggering our way, a scrawny figure decked out in an England top, baggy shorts and oversized sunglasses; Murray was my ex-brother-in-law. It was only his first trip and he stood out a little, but he was keen.

"That was a piece of piss!" he laughed.

"Told you it was easy."

"So, we're done then?"

"Just a quick cab ride, drop the money and we'll get off for the day."

We hopped a taxi, gave no address, just the district. Pulling away, whilst Car Man and Murray discussed our plans for the day, I quietly checked our mirrors, watched for a tail. We were clear. I sat back and studied the driver – a middle-aged Spaniard with family photos stuck along the dash. Seemed genuine.

We arrived in Rubi, an industrial district.

Dropped at the kerb, we watched the cab vanish into the distance before making a move. We strolled around the corner to a narrow four-storey office building in brown marble and glass. This was the new 'warehouse' where the drug shipments passed through after they landed.

I cast a final look around as we approached. Nothing! The area was deserted. I rang the bell and waited patiently – unaware we were being watched.

Unaware, a large police surveillance team were studying us.

They had been observing the warehouse for several days now. Already that morning, they had noted a step-up in activity. Two Brits and the Dutch woman had been joined by two Spanish men, and shortly after by us three, carrying shoulder bags, evidently from the airport.

It was obvious what they thought.

A bored-looking brunette answered the door. It was Janette, the Spanish translator. She mumbled for us to follow her up to the third floor where, in a long narrow corner room, we found the Old Man and the Boatman studying maps and diagrams. To their side, watching on, sat a slender bald man in a suit – Sergi – the Boatman's brother-in-law. He offered a wide toothy smile our way, "Hello Sam!"

Murray frowned in surprise; he hadn't gotten used to my being called 'Sam'.

"Alright Sergi. We have the rest of your money here," I gestured.

He smiled and waved to the floor.

At his feet, running towards the window, were several rows of money, amounting to some £230.000. At one end sat the Scotsman Glasgow, and across from him, new man Tiff, an ex-middleweight boxer.

He and Glasgow were our muscle.

I cleared some floor space, and for the benefit of Sergi, began counting the thirty to be added.

He watched me closely.

Meanwhile, the Old Man, realising that nine people in a room with more than a quarter of a million pounds was not a good idea, ordered Glasgow to take Murray and Car Man off to a local bar. I would join them shortly.

Minutes later, Glasgow drove out of the car port with two of the three new arrivals. Several seconds later, an unmarked car with a single driver followed on behind. A minute later, a second car carrying four armed officers departed.

The rest of the team remained in position.

Inside, Sergi was carrying out a recount of the new bundles. I watched on, frowned impatiently to the Old Man. He nodded calmly. Once Sergi was done, I bundled the money in a hold-all and Sergi made for the stairwell, except the Old Man stopped him. Rather than leave via the stairwell, he directed him to the roof, where he could use the fire escape and leave unnoticed from the street.

With Sergi gone, he turned to the Boatman.

"So, we're all done here?"

"*Si, si...*" grinned a happy Boatman, who asked to wait for Sergi's return. The Old Man agreed, and suggested Tiff and I go on ahead and join the others. Minutes later, we pulled out of the car port. Seconds later, two unmarked cars followed.

* * *

THE OTHERS HAD DRIVEN out to a large retail park rumoured to have a few bars. Tiff drove swiftly and noted I was still checking mirrors, "No worries Pal. It's all done."

I nodded and stopped looking.

We swung into a sprawling car park where lines of cars fried in the sunshine and streams of shoppers lumbered back and forth with noisy kids and shopping trolleys. We found Glasgow's car and pulled up alongside.

I climbed out into a fierce heat.

It was too hot to do much other than find a bar and drink. We looked around and spotted Glasgow, Murray and the Car Man walking our way, their faces unduly serious.

"There's fuck all there," declared Murray. "No bars, pubs or nothing."

This gave us a dilemma.

Should we head into the bustle of Barcelona, where trendy tourist bars were aplenty, or down the coast to the beach bars near the apartment? Either way, as we discussed and dithered, we dropped our guard and a police unit surrounded us.

A few minutes passed.

We tossed a coin, and Barcelona it was! Glasgow would drop us; Tiff would drive our bags to the apartment. We stepped to the cars, popped both boots, grabbed our bags and heard rising voices.

Within seconds, a rabble of twenty officers fell upon us waving guns, shoving and screaming "DRUGAS POLICIA! DRUGAS POLICIA!"

There was little we could do; they corralled us tightly between four parked cars. Armed officers blocked either end. Voices left and right barked orders. I stood feet back, head down, hands on the car hood as I was frisked. Outnumbered five to one – all armed, scruffy and unshaven.

Not what I expected.

Against the yelling, they went straight for our bags. Officers rummaged through, emptying out socks and pants, tops and shorts but finding nothing. They examined the bags more closely, pulling at the seams, tugging hard at the linings. A large hand shoved my head down.

"Eyes down señor."

I faced down, my eyes still darting here and there, taking it all in, noticing the holsters and body armour, how most wore leathers and sunglasses, had ponytails, beards or 'taches. Some even had tattoos and earrings, I was impressed. They looked more like criminals than police. A few of them began to bicker back and forth; they appeared to have found nothing.

Then their attention switched.

A senior officer with a grey ponytail fed their findings across a walkie talkie and listened intently to the information being relayed from the other end… where something important was occurring.

* * *

OUTSIDE THE WAREHOUSE, the Old Man, Janette and the Boatman sat cuffed against a wall. Two armed officers stood over them as a search team entered the building.

The warehouse had a car port, four floors and a roof top; it would take some time. A dog unit arrived; within minutes they were at work. The Boatman and Janette exchanged anxious glances whilst the Old Man directed Janette to translate what she could hear off the police radio. She relayed how they were holding us nearby, that the warehouse had been under surveillance for a few days, that a man was missing – a Spaniard (Sergi). They figured he was hiding in the building.

Had he escaped with the paperwork?

He was either clean away, or this was a set up and Sergi and the Boatman had been working with local police. In time it would become clear, but in the meantime, the Old Man's greatest concern was not the money but his passport.

What sort of check would they run on it?

It would pass any regular check unless his identity was already known. If so, they would be running his passport via Interpol.

* * *

AT THE RETAIL PARK, Murray, Car Man and Glasgow had given up their passports and been placed in separate cars.

Then it was my turn, which was a problem.

An officer thrust his face inches from mine, "You. British passport!"

I looked down. My passport was concealed in the lining of my jacket, and I didn't want to give it up.

"PASSPORT!" he spat out. "You. Passport – NOW!"

I spoke clearly, "I leave – passport – at hotel."

He held still, not understanding a word.

A second officer intervened and produced a notepad, thrust a pen in my hand and gestured I write down my name and date of birth. I stepped back and scrawled down in capital letters: '*JASON JONES*' – the name of an old enemy from school. I then made up a birthdate.

He took it, studied it and placed it in his pocket. Waving two large officers over, they frog-marched me twenty yards to an unmarked car. I climbed into the rear seat; they slammed the door. I sighed, looked out at the large police team assembled and wondered where they had come from.

Had I brought them here? Had they dropped onto us from the airport?

I replayed our movements, convinced I'd been careful. We'd taken the second cab available; I'd checked for a tail, the driver appeared kosher. There was only one answer:

They were at the warehouse waiting.

I looked up ahead; Tiff was busy provoking one officer who had to be pulled away. Two attempted to frog march him over my way, but he shrugged them off, took his time, casual and unhurried. At the car he halted and smiled, waited for an officer to open the door, which one did. He thanked him and climbed slowly into the passenger seat in front of me.

The officer swore and marched off.

Tiff sat quietly with an aura of inner calm. After a minute or two, he reclined his seat, tucked his hands behind his neck and closed his eyes.

"What do you think?" I asked.

He thought for a moment, "Must have been on us."

I shook my head.

"It'll be that Sergi," he added. "Your Old Man never trusted him."

* * *

THE DOGS BEGAN on the first floor and worked their way up slowly. The search team bristled with confidence. Outside, the Old Man, Boatman and Janette remained cuffed against a wall. Two officers watched over them, smoking cigarettes.

Janette sulked. She had tried to explain that they ran a transport business for other expats. She had produced some paperwork which they refused to read. She cursed them in Dutch.

The Boatman was less cool. He asked Janette to assure the Old Man that his brother-in-law could be trusted. The Old Man shrugged, remained patient and pressed Janette to translate any news coming over the radio. She relayed how we were being held, but their search had proved fruitless. They were pinning their hopes on finding some drugs in the warehouse.

There was no mention of his passport.

Two hours later and little had changed. I sat exchanging thoughts with Tiff as we watched the officers milling around in the sunshine, circling the cars where Car Man, Murray and Glasgow were being held. The senior officer – 'Ponytail' – checked his radio every ten minutes or so, and in-between, the fringe officers would wander over for news.

Otherwise, all around us, people carried on shopping, cars drove back and forth, the sun grew hotter, the air warmer.

For a while my mind withdrew and rued my misjudgment. For a long time, I had believed that by staying in the background, by sticking to paperwork, I could stay on the periphery of the Old Man's business. I was not greedy. I wanted to earn just enough and no more. Yet despite the best of intentions, I had gotten in too deep, trusted the Old Man too much, not thought for myself.

My thoughts rushed back to life at home with my wife and daughter. We lived happily in a cosy flat on a friendly street. Life there was suddenly perfect, and I wondered how this situation might affect them both. My wife would be distraught, my daughter unaware. But if I were sent to a local prison, the legal process would drag. In Spain a person could be held for months before being released without charge, or worse than that, a person could be found guilty on next to no evidence.

I cursed myself.

How naïve I had been. Driving here, there, and everywhere, catching flights whenever; how long had I thought I could go without a problem?

Where had I thought this was going to end?

My thoughts returned to my daughter, just eighteen months old, walking and gargling, calling me 'Daddy'. What a start for her? Father in prison! The Old Man had been inside when I was her age. Back then, he'd trusted his brother and been let down; here I was trusting my father and being let down.

Suddenly, I was filled with resolve.

If we make it out of here, I'll be done with the driving. That'll be it. Enough for me. I'll simply tell him I can't be doing this anymore.

I looked across at the officers in the distance, drinking coffee, engrossed in chatter. I began to bargain with myself, to make promises.

If we make it out of this situation, things will change! If we make it out, I will…

And it was just as I began to make these grand promises, that something appeared to be up.

In the mid-distance amongst the officers, following a phone call, a series of conversations were taking place. There were lots of shrugs and shaking faces as Ponytail related news from the other end. Officers paced and gestured wildly. Something had gone wrong. Tiff called over our guarding officer, "What's going on pal?"

He shrugged, rolled his eyes, muttered a few words and walked over to the main group. He stood listening, nodded several times, shook his head and walked back before abruptly turning his back to us.

"They've fucked it up!" declared Tiff.

"You think?"

"Yeah. We'll be out of here soon."

We continued to study them closely and several long minutes later they began to move. A few climbed into their cars and sped away. Then Murray and Car Man emerged stretching legs and shaking heads, as did Glasgow. One officer strode across to us, opened the car door and held out Tiff's passport. As before, he moved slowly, climbed out and accepted his passport with a smile.

The officer glared down at me, "You have no passport."

I thought for a moment, prepared to say something, but was interrupted.

"You go too."

My brows rose, "I go?"

He marched away, waving his arms and yelling aloud, "You go!!"

* * *

MOMENTS LATER, a small convoy of cars sped away in a cloud of dust. We watched on as they disappeared from sight. I turned slowly and faced Car Man, Glasgow, Tiff and then Murray. No-one said a thing. There was a relieved silence for several seconds until at last someone spoke.

"A great fucking idea this was!" announced Murray, looking in my direction.

I shrugged with a grin.

"Yeah, 'Easiest three hundred quid you'll ever earn!'" he added. "Last time I listen to you 'Sam'!" And with that, his smile turned to laughter.

I shook my head and laughed along, but was far from happy.

Shortly after, we linked up with the Old Man and Janette. Whilst she was unimpressed, the Old Man found it funny, "Shake you up did it?"

"Just a bit."

"That's how they come at you. If they're any good, you just don't see them."

"We never did. They were just there!"

"It's good experience for you," he added with a smile. "Maybe next time you'll spot them – or not. These were good, but there are much better. I've seen them coming down on wires, over walls... unbelievable stuff."

He shook his head with admiration and moved on, apparently unconcerned.

They had only missed the money by minutes. Sergi, who we'd all been doubting, had moved quick. The search of the warehouse produced nothing. Passports were returned. And whilst for me this had felt like a near fatal disaster, for the Old Man it was nothing of the sort. He took it in his stride and, if anything, seemed to have enjoyed outfoxing the undercovers. I would even say it made him happy.

Almost arrested and he was happy!

And perhaps this was a difference between him and me, between him and others. Most people would not have enjoyed what we'd just experienced. Exhilarating as it was, it would be something they would swear never to repeat.

That evening, Car Man, Murray, and I settled at a bar, drinking whiskey and replaying the day's events into the early hours. We laughed at our inept foray into international crime and looked forward to home and the lives we knew and the places we belonged. Except for me, there was a crucial difference.

I was set to carry on. The boat venture was at its beginning and the work was set to continue over the months ahead. For the foreseeable future, my fate was tied up with the Old Man's. Driving paperwork was my job. I couldn't just say no.

I couldn't abandon him.

On the flight home, I reflected on how this had come to be.

My brother and sister had stopped working for the Old Man some time back. Only I had carried on. For one thing, my options to earn were limited. But there was something more, something deeper and less logical.

Looking back now, it is obvious.

Since being a small kid, I'd dreamt of working with my Old Man, of helping him to make a fortune. As it turned out, this business of his – dealing, importing and smuggling – was it. I was in a strange way living that boyhood dream of mine. However, through that process of abnormal things being normalised, it had drifted far, far away from what I'd originally envisioned.

As a kid, I had imagined something entirely different to this.

CHAPTER 9:
LEYHILL PRISON

1976-78

EVEN TODAY, I look back at our visits to Leyhill Prison with great affection. Strange as it sounds, it was on prison visits where I had first gotten to know the Old Man. I was seven years old and was told we were visiting him at 'college'. Whilst most other fathers were working nine 'till five, my Old Man had sacrificed time with family, devoted himself to education in the belief it would pay dividends in the long run. That was the story I believed or had constructed for myself. Throughout his two years there I did not doubt this tale for a minute as he often talked of his studies.

We would rise early on those days. A bath was demanded with orders to wear our best clothes – trousers, shirt and polished shoes. It was as if we were going to church, though we were never a church-going family.

Mum would be ready early – makeup on, hair down. She would tug a brush through my thick blond hair, and it'd hurt and I'd yell; she'd take a damp tissue and wipe sleep from my eyes and curse me for not washing. I couldn't understand why all the bother as other kids would be dressed scruffy in jeans and T-shirts. It seemed unnecessary.

My three-year-old sister Kate, dolled up in a brand-new dress with pigtails, would take the front seat. My brother and I sat apart in the back, trying not to argue for the hour or more it would take to arrive. We would read books, play 'I Spy', look out for farm animals appearing once we pulled off the motorway. Down hills and lanes, we passed farms and villages before turning down a long-wooded lane to arrive at a grand, rustic stone wall entrance. To the side, a large sign pronounced *'Welcome to HMP Leyhill.'*

I was yet to understand what 'HMP' meant.

At the security barrier, a guard checked our paperwork, assigned us a number and pressed a button. Like magic, the barrier rose unaided and triggered butterflies of excitement as we swung into a vast empty car park. My older brother David – a ten-year-old skinny boy with a large head – was charged with carrying the large picnic bag. I hurried ahead, happy we appeared first to arrive.

Across the car park and past some swings were two long clapboard huts. I climbed the steep steps of the first and walked into a narrow, dimly lit room. Several lines of bare wooden tables and chairs were arranged in lines. A guard sat at the desk supping tea, and despite us being the first arrivals, would make us wait. On the hour and not before, he would give us a table number and check our bags. My brother and I would rush over, locate the table and drag chairs either side of where our dad would soon be sat.

We'd wait impatiently for him to arrive.

Over the following half hour, other tables would fill with smoking wives and screaming children whilst we remained ordered and restrained. Most of the mothers smoked, a few swore quite openly, many made no effort to dress up in any way whatsoever; I felt overdressed. Eventually the inmates would trickle in and the noise level would rise to a cacophony as dozens of conversations filled the room. Often the Old Man would arrive late due to 'classes' having run over; like the other 'students' he'd be dressed casually.

He wore the usual trainers, jeans, and T-shirt they all seemed to favour. Arriving with a smile, he'd offer handshakes to my brother and me, kisses for our Mum and sister. Sitting down, he'd check his watch, apologise for the delay and my sister would climb up on his knee.

"How are you buggerlugs?" he'd ask, playfully gnawing her neck as she giggled away. We'd exchange happy glances.

Each visit began with small talk, him asking about our journey – the car, the roads, the traffic and so on. Mum would then talk of family whilst my brother and I listened and fidgeted. Once the family talk was done, he would update us on his studies, the qualifications he'd gained, and in doing so impressed upon me at least, the importance of books and learning. It was then our turn. We'd offer some words concerning school and he'd take the keenest interest. He'd reiterate that we work hard, and then, with a glance towards our Mum, ask how we were behaving at home. My brother and I would nod guiltily, hoping Mum hadn't told him about our constant misbehaviour. He'd frown a little and I'd suspect she had said something. Our behaviour had deteriorated in recent months. My brother and me fought most days. When warned or promised that Dad would be home soon, I realised that I could not recall him clearly. My memories of him, given my poor eyesight, were of a dark and blurry figure, always on the move, dashing in and out of the house, off to work or somewhere. It was only at the prison that I could ever recall sitting up close and speaking with him.

He'd move the conversation over to work, how was the shop doing, was Mum seeing any money; we'd listen for a while before exchanging impatient glances as we shuffled to the edge of our seats. After being on best behaviour all morning, my brother and me were bursting to get outside to play on the swings; plus I would notice the long lists of small blue biro writing running up his arms, and knew he and Mum had much to get through.

These lists would dominate prison visits in all the years to come; fifteen minutes of small talk would be followed by an hour or more of discussing lists, with each item requiring a conversation of its own. As kids, their significance was unappreciated; we just wanted to go out and play.

The prison had a series of swings which the inmates had made in the workshops. They were box swings where two children sat opposite one another pulling on a rope in turns sending you up higher and higher. My brother, being older, would insist on going as high as possible; so high, in fact, that at the highest point of the swing I could squint and see the 'college' buildings in the distance. They were stood back behind a long, tall fence with razor wire along its top. It was where the 'students' returned after the visit. A few times we'd hung on and watched the students being marched up the gravel track towards its gates. I often wondered whether he'd ever take us for a look around one day. I had asked, and he had promised, "One day." And then looked to our Mum and they had both laughed.

By the time we returned, he'd still be working down his lists – erasing each one with a damp thumb as he went or adding a word or two in black biro. He would try and save his lists for when we were outside, but sometimes there was too much, especially when they ran onto his second arm: *jobs to be done and jobs that have been done; messages to relay and messages to collect; requests to make and things to collect; information to gather and questions to ask.* Scores of people would be mentioned, and it went on and on and on and on. We would know to sit quietly and be patient. He had so little time, he'd tell us.

Prison visits would ever be this way. Never enough time. So many lists.

After an hour, he'd check his watch, wind down and take a break. Mum would get the "picnic" out and we'd eat together – sandwiches, cake and even chocolate for after. There would be no more list talk, and this was without doubt the highlight of the visit. We would eat, share and gulp our food down happily with any bad manners ignored. My sister still sat on his lap as he talked and joked with us throughout. Occasionally there'd be an interruption.

A guard would ask him to sign for something – a present for one of us. It would be something he'd had made in the workshop – a hand-crafted jewellery box for our Mum one week, a large and cute stuffed cuddly dog for my sister's birthday the next. I was impressed that with all his studies he could find the time and hoped he'd still be here when my birthday came around.

After we'd eaten, my brother and me would return to the swings one more time. More often, we would ask if he could come out to watch us for a while, but he never would. Even when the lists were complete, he'd say there was always next time. It was the same on every visit. He'd stay firmly seated, and they'd talk and talk about things I rarely understood or often misunderstood, smoking being one thing.

He detested smoking but was always organising for more cigarettes to be sent in. I'd asked him why and he'd explained with a straight face, that as I could see all around me, other students did smoke and if he could help them, he should.

To me, it seemed a kind thing to do.

For the final part of the visit, the room darkened as they locked the doors to check the register. The Old Man would run over jobs to do once more and talk of when he would be home. Apparently, many people were offering to help with the new business. Even so, rather than come home now, he insisted they'd have to wait a few more months as he'd be a while — perhaps another six months.

"But that's ages," I'd said.

"No worries. It'll fly by," he'd insisted with a smile.

I nodded in agreement and looked forward to the summer when he would be home. For some reason, I believed everything would change when he returned, that the businesses he discussed would happen, that the future would be a wonderful place.

I saw his enthusiasm and had no doubt.

MOST SATURDAYS, Mum worked half-day at a local bakery. My brother, sister and I would stay with our Grandparents for the morning. They lived just a few streets away in a three-bedroom terrace. If I wanted an insight into the household my father grew up in, this was it.

Mum would walk us up, dressed smartly, one toy apiece.

Tall, dark-haired and formal, our Grandmother had a royal demeanour that expressed little warmth. On arrival, she would remind us of the usual conditions: no going upstairs unless you needed the bathroom; no going in the front room as that was for best; no visits to the garden as it was muddy out there, and, of course, do not go in the kitchen. If we wanted something, we should ask.

We would spend the morning watching TV, the BBC that is; ITV met with her disapproval, as did most things we enjoyed. Following the Old Man's arrest, we had lost our house and been taken in by an aunt and uncle who had a laid-back approach to life. We were left to play, to have fun, to be messy and be kids. We watched *Tiswas* in their house, had water fights, listened to loud music, spent hours playing in the streets, creating a mess wherever we went; all things which met our Grandma's silent disapproval.

She was houseproud, liked order, and wished to avoid any mess. Consequently, we rarely left that small living room and the times I dared look in another room it would be neat and polished, untouched and unlived in. It was something I came to notice, that their house was immaculately ordered, but somewhat lifeless. It was a home without books, without games, without play. Boring to my mind.

Our Grandfather worked half day at the factory on Saturday and would arrive home early to watch *Grandstand* or *World of Sport*. His arrival would break the monotony for a while. A tall, lean man of fifty, he could be warm and good-natured but more often was short-tempered, insisting on peace and quiet whilst he watched his TV. He would sit in his armchair with a newspaper, following the racing, as did Grandma.

They rarely talked during programmes.

Occasionally, when they did talk, I would be reminded of how judgmental Grandma was. She was hypercritical of their daughter Margaret, said little of the Old Man, and lavished praise upon their son Robert.

Of Robert, my Grandma was most proud. She would often refer to the wealthy uncle with the posh family we never saw; the point being, as far as I could make out, that his money made him important. He had just bought a large expensive house, was sending his kids to private school, had joined a few private clubs, and now spoke with a posh accent. A cut above, us it seemed; we were the riff-raff. Later, I would be told that to distance himself from the Old Man's so-called reputation, he had changed his name by Deed Poll from Robert Shipley to Robert Scholtes.

To me, it seemed a particularly cold thing for a brother to claim. But then I noticed the family was quite cold. Affection wasn't demonstrated, emotions were dismissed or mocked, there was little empathy.

* * *

THAT SUMMER CRAWLED by slowly, the Old Man remained at college, Mum continued working at the bakery. I continued at school, a Catholic school where I was undergoing my Holy Communion. I prayed the Old Man would be home shortly, but nothing happened except our visits stopped. Apparently, he would be home soon, whenever 'soon' was.

I took to pilfering sweets for a while, and within a few weeks had stepped up to apples and oranges. Me and my brother still fought every day, but once I was seven, I could walk home alone. It was then, without his supervision, I was caught red-handed stealing an orange.

It had become a daily habit. Unfortunately, as I rounded the corner and begun peeling it, I was nabbed by the owner's son, who manhandled me home and pounded the door. Fortunately, Mum was out and my laid-back Uncle Bill answered.

"What's up?" he said, eyeing the boy.

He had me gripped tight by the jumper.

"He's stole an orange from my dad's shop."

Bill dug into his pocket, "Ten pence will cover it. Now hop it"

The boy took the money and scuttled away.

I stepped inside. My uncle shrugged, gave me some money to buy him some fags and a bag of chips for us both. I ate guiltily. That night I prayed he wouldn't tell Mum, and she wouldn't tell the Old Man. The Old Man would be disappointed if he was told.

It seems, even then, I feared disappointing him.

* * *

TWO WEEKS INTO the new term, approaching home, I noticed a large green Bedford van parked outside. As I neared, I noticed a man dressed in overalls washing the vehicle's walls with a mop and sponges. Another man was in front, wearing jeans and T-shirt, hunched over the engine with the bonnet up. I peered around.

It was the Old Man.

"Alright Jason?" he said with a smile. "How's school?"

"Alright," I muttered and then watched him for a while as he wrestled with engine parts, his hands covered in oil, smudges across his face. There was no explanation of what had taken him so long. With no celebrations or fanfare, he was back as if nothing had happened.

* * *

MANY YEARS LATER, I would learn that his release had been delayed a few months. And during those extra few months, he enrolled on a psychology course for which he wrote eight papers on various aspects of practical psychology: the unconscious, conflict and complexes, personality, art, work and money, superiority and confidence. These essays would survive the years and find themselves in Margaret's hands. Some twenty-five years later, on the eve of a road trip to Spain, she would pass them onto me.

I would digest them on the journey down.

CHAPTER 10:
THE SMUGGLERS' CONSORTIUM

AUGUST 2002

FIFTEEN HUNDRED MILES in twenty-four hours was the aim.

We were to deliver an urgently needed Land Rover to the Costa-del-Sol, but by Bordeaux I was already wiped out. Car Man took over and I slept for several hours until a hard sunrise woke me as we wound through the mountain roads of the Pyrenees. It was then, with a fresh head, I grabbed the psychology papers from my bag.

The eight papers of several sheets apiece covered various subjects of practical psychology. They struck me as being very much in line with the Old Man's business philosophy. Perhaps that's why he'd kept them. They covered an assortment of subjects, but within the essays and the self-reflection sections lay his own thoughts on personality, money, and how to treat people.

On **Personality**, he rejected egotism and prized sincerity as the key to being natural. In a nod to his Protestant upbringing, he offered Jesus Christ as an example of a natural, sincere being without egotism. He went on to discuss weaknesses, and in regard to himself wrote:

"I can quite often be over hasty in turning my thoughts into action. I allow my better judgement to be persuaded into doing the wrong things. This is usually done by allowing my 'heart to rule my brains' as the saying goes. Quite often, I am blind to things around me because of my absorption in something that I may be doing at the time."

Both a blessing and a curse, I thought.

Regarding **Money**, he considered ambition and money as the means to gain appreciation. He emphasised that critical to any success was the power of the conscious mind and personal will. In relation to himself, he wrote that:

'I have far more will-power and enthusiasm than anyone else I know. I find that if I can see a use in doing a thing then I can generate far more enthusiasm than the average person. By being able to do this I find that most of the difficult jobs become easy. Simply by telling yourself you are capable of doing a thing you are half-way there'.

That was him; in prison or out, he had absolute confidence.

On **People,** he emphasised how the most important needs of a person are to be appreciated and feel important. He wrote of treating people well, seeing things from their perspective, and employing praise and sensitivity.

I nodded. Regardless of the business, he treated his workers in a way that inspired great loyalty. I read on, until finally, midway down on the final page, he wrote, **"We are today what it paid us to be yesterday."**

I considered this a moment.

Was he a criminal now because it paid to be one yesterday?

Maybe so.

Could that also be applied to me?

I hoped not.

After a score of miles, I put the papers down and after some contemplation returned to the here and now and the work at hand.

Up ahead, he was still on the run, dealing with a diminishing circle of villains and accumulating large debts; even so, he had managed to organise a consortium for smuggling hash from the Moroccan coast into Spain.

It was our sole reason for driving down.

Two four-by-four vehicles were needed for the beach work. From the boat landing, the hash would be transferred to the four-by-fours at lightning speed and driven off across the sands to a safe house for the night. With the sea forecast for calm, the night of the first run was imminent.

This followed just weeks after a major setback when the cargo-ship he'd bought only a few months back was seized by Spanish Customs. The ship had been dogged by a long history of undeclared fines the Boatman had thought best not to mention. The Old Man, with all his money and promises tied up in that enterprise, switched to plan B.

Plan B was old-fashioned rib runs between Morocco and Spain. For this he'd bought in three close allies from London, Brighton and Coventry. Each kicked in finance, resources and manpower in exchange for an equal share. The Old Man would manage the enterprise, provide the hash supplier, the rib boat, and the transport to the UK.

* * *

BY AFTERNOON, we arrived at a quiet fishing village on Spain's south coast. The Old Man and his crew were holed up at a villa overlooking the bay. There, his crew of nine attempted to maintain a low profile.

It wasn't proving easy.

Inside the Old Man sat feet up on the table, mobile to his ear, whilst across the room Paul and a few of the London lads played cards and drank tea, biding their time.

"Alright Sam," Paul said. "He'll be with you in a minute. You stoppin' for the work?"

"No, we'll be off tomorrow. Be leaving you to it."

"Oh, your Old Man thought otherwise."

I smiled and shook my head; I knew too well what the Old Man was thinking.

We chucked our bags down and I slumped in a chair as the Old Man finished some calls. Given the problems of late, he was unusually calm and looked surprisingly well. He wrapped up the call, wrote a few notes and turned to face me.

"Good you made it so quick," he smiled, "Though… we won't be needing the Land Rover for a few nights."

My mouth dropped. *Weren't we told that…?*

"Weather reports have turned bad. It'll be Sunday or Monday now."

I exchanged glances with Car Man. We'd flogged our guts getting it down here and now… My eyes returned to the Old Man, who fired me a familiar question.

"Any thoughts on taking the final spot?"

I knew he'd ask.

"It's easy work," he continued. "Sit up on the cliff edge with a receiver and walkie-talkie. Stepney will be on the cliff edge opposite. There's no risk, really."

"No, no. It's not for me. I just can't be…"

"Yeah, no worries. I'll sort something."

As much as I wanted to help, I'd been a reluctant worker in recent months. Our earlier arrests at Rubi had served as a wake-up call and I'd taken a step back for a while. That was until the cargo ship was seized, and then I offered anything I could do to help.

He leant over his list, struck a cross through a name, then changed the subject.

"We're going over to Fuengirola tonight. Get away from this villa and this fucking village. They're going stir crazy here. Are you up for it?"

This was a rare thing. In six years, I had never known such a gathering of his closest contacts. I was certainly curious.

"Yeah. I'm up for it."

He leafed through some papers and as an afterthought added, "Oh, Ryan ought to be down sometime late. Will be a chance to update him on all that's going on."

I raised a brow. It had been some years since I'd last seen Ryan, though we'd all heard of his progress. At just thirty years old, Ryan had become the multi-millionaire drug dealer widely admired and feared throughout the north of England.

The evening promised to be interesting.

* * *

ON THE SEAFRONT at Fuengirola sat a small Chinese restaurant. The place was less than a quarter full. We commandeered several tables, placed our orders, and settled down to an evening of surprisingly restrained behaviour and informative criminal chit-chat.

The evening warmed up with a discussion of recent mishaps concerning the dry runs to and from Morocco. So far, they'd lost one boat to the tides, recovered it, and then lost it to the coast guard. Then they almost lost the test load to a refuelling error when the Moroccans forgot to supply the return fuel as agreed. Out of fuel a few miles from shore, they'd been forced to swim for it, which left one man drowning. The Old Man and Paul had swum back and rescued him.

Smuggling by rib boat wasn't easy.

The group talked rapidly and drank slowly. When the starters arrived, they switched to talking of the business back home. Such drugs talk I had grown long familiar with; its business jargon, its credit terms, logistics and headaches. Staff, like in any business, would bring problems due to dishonesty. Then there were issues with suppliers and the transport people, and the mid-level dealers who avoided, delayed or cheated on payments. Inevitably, there were fallouts. However, in truth, there was little appetite for violence unless all options were exhausted. More often, it was considered wise to chalk such things down to experience.

Nonetheless, as they exchanged stories, they made the most shocking experiences seem trivial and natural. They tended to be regretful of any violence, *they had no choice*; dismissive of deaths and suicides, *they just happen*; philosophical about the long years spent behind bars, *everything happens for a reason*. No-one mentioned their families. They seemed to treat prison solely as an occupational hazard, costly in terms of time and money, believing the losses would be made up when released.

None betrayed any bitterness.

By the time the mains arrived, they'd moved onto talking of prisons and serving time. Here the Old Man was something of an authority having spent substantial time at dozens of prisons over the years. I listened carefully. His time inside was something I knew little about.

Like them all, he was indifferent to the time he'd served. It is what it is. No point in complaining. He talked of the people, the prisons and the benefits – experiences gained, knowledge earned, contacts found – like he'd do it all over again without hesitation. The highs justified the lows, and the good people excused the worst. No regrets.

No regrets?

I did wonder upon hearing this. How could being locked up, away from your family, your kids especially, not be a regret? Did he not regret his time away when we were kids? Or was it that he had no choice. Perhaps inside, there was no gain in missing your family. It could only make the time harder.

I sat and listened for the most part, taking mental notes, trying not to judge. I had no experience of being in prison other than visiting the Old Man. That had certainly left an impression. Growing up, not going to prison had been an ambition for me. Not that it appeared likely, but my memories of visiting assured me it was one place I was determined never to go.

In contrast, everyone around the table had been to prison. More than once or twice. Furthermore, each one had been a businessman at one time but was now a criminal. They were a similar breed, an unlawful type. True businessmen pulled back from danger; they, like it or not, played by the rules for the most part. None of these men did or would. They considered themselves above the rules and what's more, if challenged, could be quite nasty.

London Paul was such a man, having spent a few terms inside. I recalled collecting money from him one day when he casually told me how he'd been walking his dog that morning and had been harassed by another dog. Its owner failed to restrain it, and this had fired Paul's temper. He pulled a knife and stabbed the dog in the throat, left it gushing blood, its owner terrified.

"Next time, he'll put his dog on a fuckin' leash," he snapped.

I sat stunned, not knowing what to say.

Red, like Paul, had served a few terms. The last one for manslaughter. He and a few others had stomped a rival to death over some petty dispute. Red appeared to be a fearless individual. As did Brighton who, when the cargo ship was seized, pushed for the kidnap and torture of the Boatman so his money could be returned.

"Snap a few toes off and he'll soon be handing us our money," he had stated.

Again, I'd kept my thoughts to myself.

Tiff had also been inside. Violence against two women. He was drunk and failed to recall the incident. One of the conditions of him working for the Old Man was that he stayed sober and clean. Normally he was a jovial kind of guy, but sometimes not, it seems.

And the Old Man?

Tall and burly, he carried himself with confidence, appearing to fear no-one. That he'd killed the Soldier served as a reminder that he wasn't considered a heavyweight criminal for nothing. Prior to that, though, he appeared to have left any violence in the past, though he certainly retained great leverage amongst those who were violent. Names who evoked terror in the city would usually be old 'pals' of his. Mentioning a name notorious for pulling a knife and slashing someone because he didn't like their face would be met with a shrug.

"He was alright with me. We made good money."

I surmised this ease he had was due to his business dealings over the years. Many feared individuals had made more money with the Old Man than they could ever have hoped to make otherwise. He once stated, "You can always buy muscle, but you can't buy brains."

I could see what he meant.

In recent years, I had observed situations with the most arrogant of small-time villains who tried it on. If the Old Man was clearly in the right, he would hold his ground and, knowing he could buy unlimited muscle, would threaten what he had to. Usually though, his name would be enough. His associations with the highest criminals and the largest Mafia organisations were well known.

Nevertheless, for me, in recent years there was a noticeable lack of violence to his reputation.

* * *

BY THE EARLY HOURS, they had moved onto the news from recent drug trials. The entire table were hungry to learn more and each man was generous to pass on info regarding the latest police surveillance. Measures to counter phone taps were of special interest and just as this discussion became particularly fine in its detail, Ryan James rolled in with a few hungry workers in tow.

I looked over. He'd changed little.

Slightly short of medium build with a crew cut and a matter-of-fact face, he dressed casual in sportswear, sounding like the typical loud-mouthed Brit abroad. However, underneath, he was seriously switched on.

I'd first met Ryan back in '97 when I'd been driving the Old Man. We'd taken a series of trips up to meet Ryan, who lived on a run-down council estate in the north of England. He'd just been released and was keen to get moving.

"Anything you can get I can shift, but get me the pills and the Charlie," he urged in his broad Notts accent. "They're fuckin' mad for them, mate. I can shift any amount you send me. Anything."

I was driving with the Old Man at my side and Ryan sat in the back, leaning forward with elbows resting between seats. He talked loudly and bluntly, cursing as he went. It was a fresh car and they both felt free to talk.

"I understand what you're saying," the Old Man reiterated, "but if we stick to the Embassies *(cannabis)* and my line *(amphetamine)* there's more than enough to be made. And there's less risk."

"But I've got the fuckin' market. I can sell anything. You've just got to get it me. I *know* you know the right people."

"But you see my point regarding the class As," the Old Man repeated. "Those guys doing them, they get police operations put on them for months and months at a time – and they fall. Stick to the class Cs and you don't have that problem."

I agreed with this reasoning, though to me he'd previously given moral reasons: "Class As like cocaine and heroin ruin people; class Cs like cannabis and amphetamine don't."

Ryan plainly disagreed, but the Old Man held his ground.

As it was, ten and twenty kilos were where they began, and they worked up from there. Over the next eighteen months, the numbers would climb and our trips up to Ryan increased. Sixty grand a week was a standard collection based on just the two lines of Embassies and Super Kings, but it would pass a hundred grand on a busy week. It made Ryan our largest customer and the Old Man's closest ally.

When the Old Man had gone on the run, they'd become partners for a while and Ryan had effectively been tutored by the Old Man in business. He'd brought in new suppliers and customers, scaled up Ryan's set-up, made them a national force rather than just another provincial firm. Later in Amsterdam, he'd provided Ryan with the contacts to step up once more, but the shooting of the Soldier had brought it all to an end.

By that time, Ryan had gained more than enough contacts and know-how. With these contacts he would work tirelessly and by switching up to cocaine would make millions.

He swaggered over to the bar, produced a wad of cash, unpeeled the owner some notes to stay open a few hours extra. Two waiters promptly appeared and adjoined extra tables to ours. Ryan took a seat to my right.

"I'm fuckin starving, mate," he announced. "Been on the road since five this morning."

Like the Old Man, Ryan worked long, intense days. Still, he was ever sharp.

"Alright Sam. How you doin'? How's that brother of yours? And your sister – the younger one. Still doing the horses? Still got that white Volkswagen?"

I hadn't spoken to him for five years, but you wouldn't think so. He was great with details, recalled everything, forgot nothing.

"You need to have a word with your Old Man. He needs to get back with us and forget all this fuckin' boat nonsense. He can make more money with us."

He didn't await an answer. There were a few people here he needed to speak to – deals to offer, favours to offer. He moved around the table several times before his food arrived, and then sat with me and the Old Man, scoffing down a stir-fry, talking fast, referring to a few of the people they knew who'd turned out to be "right fuckin' wankers, mate"; but they'd talk of them later when it was just the two of them.

* * *

OUR CONVOY of cars raced up the moonlit foothills of Fuengirola. With drunken drivers shooting up, down and around its hairpin bends, we arrived at a gleaming white villa nestled between two hills. Here the Old Man and Ryan would have the privacy to discuss the 'wankers' not to be trusted and some deals Ryan wanted to put his way.

The Old Man would listen, but wouldn't commit. He had resolved not to reignite their partnership, although he conceded Ryan had more to offer than ever before. Whilst the Old Man had the greater contacts, Ryan was now his own man. He was also a free man largely unknown to the UK's National Crime Squad, whilst the Old Man was wanted by them, Dutch Police and Interpol.

He was on borrowed time and everyone knew it.

Already, he ran a risk whenever passing through a Spanish toll road or border; airports were firmly off limits, as were trains and boats. The greatest risk factor, though, was that any business rival, enemy or debtor had motive to tip off British Police as to his whereabouts. Consequently, he trusted fewer and fewer people as time passed.

In Ryan's circle, there were too many he could no longer trust at all.

At the villa, as the dawn light appeared behind nearby mountains, the Old Man, Ryan and his workers headed out to the pool. Whilst they splashed, drank and bantered loudly, I left them too it.

This get together had been interesting, but it was not something I would be in a hurry to repeat. I was only accepted amongst them because I was Tony's son. Nepotism, if you like. Normally, these people would not be friends of mine.

They were not good people.

The Old Man was untypical. He may have once been as hard as any in his day, but in recent years I suspected he owed his reputation more to the money he'd made and the people he knew rather than for being violent or ruthless. This was important to note, because if I had noted this, then others might also observe this aspect of his character.

Time would show that some already had.

I found a small empty room and slumped down. Through an open window I listened to the yelling and screaming of Ryan's drunken workers and beneath that, the muffled voices of the Old Man and Ryan sat at the pool side, engrossed in talk of more drug deals.

"We are today what it paid us to be yesterday," the Old Man had once written. Was that his reason for becoming a criminal?

By now, and I had done the calculations, he had served nineteen and a half years inside. And still he carried on: a once talented businessman turned to crime – looking to become a multi-millionaire by making crime his business. Except to me, it seemed unnecessary.

At one time, he'd been a millionaire and made it legally.

I'd seen it for myself.

It was after he was released from Leyhill in '78. I was seven years old, my brother was eleven. We 'd been there and saw how within just a few short years, he'd gone from a man with a prison bag to a millionaire.

Except it hadn't been enough.

CHAPTER 11:
PRISONER TO MILLIONAIRE

1978-80

I WAS ONLY SEVEN years old, but I can still remember the scene vividly.

He emptied his polythene prison bag onto the double bed in the rear bedroom and pulled out several items: an army penknife, a pair of large sunglasses, a maths book, a blue fountain pen, a simple watch with a frayed black strap, some playing cards and a writing pad. He produced a coin from his pocket and tossed it high – spinning fast – and caught it.

"Heads or tails?" he asked.

I hesitated before opting for heads.

His large palm opened wide: tails.

"David can go first."

My brother chose the penknife and I bit my lip: *I wanted that.*

"I'll take the book." I said and realised my mistake; David wanted the sunglasses. It left me with the pen, but an expensive one with a real nib and cartridge – he'd used it when he was away. I reassured myself that my brother had failed to appreciate its value. Plus, I got the watch he'd worn when away, so I was happy.

He had not been home long, but things were already better. Life was moving and the house was buzzing. Something was there which had been missing before – a spark, an energy, and with it a sense of unity. We no longer argued and fought but co-existed in harmony. No longer walking or waiting for buses, we drove once more, here, there and everywhere, the Old Man making lists in his notebook, pen tucked behind his ear, radio blaring. He drove a large green Bedford van, which, as the morning unfolded, from auctions and backstreet deals, he filled with old furniture; "One man's junk is another man's gold", he would say as we headed off to his bustling shop over on Harnall Lane.

A deep and narrow shop, Lloyds was an Aladdin's cave of assorted household furniture, huge televisions, countless lamps, ornate fireplaces, all spilling out onto the pavement where lines of cookers and fridges stood, though not for long. They sold instantly and were the 'gold' he spoke of. From their demand, he had already made plans.

Several weeks after release, he'd leased another shop, a dozen doors up. It would sell solely white goods, but especially cookers. As the Old Man prepared the new shop, his brother Robert – our Uncle – would frequently appear, to offer his thoughts, to chat over some business. I would keep a fearful distance and watch this intense man nodding thoughtfully to the Old Man before speaking his mind.

"No, no, no. You're wrong Tone. It won't work" he'd finally pronounce.

I'd never heard anyone disagree with the Old Man before.

Patiently, the Old Man would expand on his point and Robert would more sharply repeat his own view, "No. Don't see it, Tone." I stood back – watching – making sure I didn't catch his eye. I'd heard he had a temper. He would refer to my brother as 'that little shit'.

Uncle Robert didn't like kids.

* * *

NINETEEN SEVENTY-EIGHT may have been the worst year to launch a business. The Winter of Discontent saw the largest job losses in a generation. Relentless industrial action contributed to a climate of low aspiration. A man just out of prison aiming to make a million within just a few years was a rare thing. Nevertheless, that was the ambition for which the Old Man had a plan.

The Government had deregulated white goods and consequently small second-hand cooker outlets were popping up all around the country. Many of Coventry's second-hand furniture shops were moving this way, and with the Old Man's new shop he was set to follow, except with a slight difference.

He had learned how scores of government departments scrapped thousands of perfectly good cookers each year, from schools, hospitals and the like. They were sent to scrapyards where they were 'decommissioned', which meant their ovens were pickaxed to make them unusable.

Shooting direct to source, the Old Man secured government contracts for these scrapped appliances on the basis that he would strip them for parts. Overnight, he had an annual supply running into the thousands. However, he intended not only to use them for spare parts, but to recondition the cream of the supply and sell them on. For this sole purpose, he set up a company named Mainline Gas.

Within months, this company of a mere dozen staff were turning around hundreds of cookers on a weekly basis. Beat up greasy appliances came in, sparkling and reconditioned they went out. The demand was overwhelming; the cash flowed in and as was his habit, the Old Man invested every penny back into the business. Consequently, town by town, city by city, region by region, he began to flood the market with second-hand cookers.

Meanwhile, we saw him little.

* * *

OUR NEW HOME was a random mid-terraced house in the nearby town of Nuneaton. It was there we would become, as far as I was concerned, a normal family. Mum was a traditional house-wife, the Old Man a typical father. He headed out to work each morning, came home sometime in the evening. We would eat at the table together, though often his space, due to him working late, would be empty. Nevertheless, I for the first time considered us to be a family, just like everyone else.

The only odd thing was the long hours the Old Man worked. He seemed to leave for work earlier than most dads, arrive home later than most. Then, sometimes he wouldn't come home at all, or he'd be away on business. It meant he had no time for the usual father things. Open nights, football games, family get-togethers, he could never make it. I understood he had businesses to run, and they made great demands upon his time.

The odd morning though, if up early enough, I might see him for ten minutes.

On those mornings, I would wake to the pounding beats and screeching fiddles of country records pounding the stereo. I'd stumble down and see him sat in the armchair by the front window, phone to his left, notepad to his right, rattling off calls, making notes, drawing up lists. I'd make breakfast, sit at the table, eat and slurp Sugar Puffs and watch on. He wore a navy-blue pinstripe suit. On his wrist a large gold watch replaced the simple frayed thing he'd given me. He checked this watch frequently, ever racing time. By 7.30 his calls would be done. Chucking the paperwork in his briefcase, he'd grab the massive bunch of keys he carried everywhere, kiss our Mum a brief goodbye, and head out for another long day.

Most nights, he wouldn't return home until I was in bed.

The only exceptions were Sundays. Then he would arrive home early, by six usually, carrying a carrier bag or two, full of crisps, chocolates, a bottle of Bacardi, a couple of videos. Already bathed and changed, we'd greet him excitedly, raid the bags, give him some space. He would still have calls to make, lists to compile. Once done, we'd draw the curtains and settle down to watch a movie on the new video recorder.

As the Old Man was rarely home, the choice of film was his. More often he would opt for a prison or gangster movie: *Papillon*,

Cool Hand Luke, Godfather, The French Connection, The Getaway. Lots of car chases and prisons; I would often smile widely during the car chases. The Old Man could drive like *Bullitt* when he wanted to. We'd been out a few times and once when running late he'd asked me to put on my seat belt, and then we'd shot across the city at top speed through lights and across pavements, down sidestreets, all the while me with a smile on my face, before coming to an abrupt halt at a mate's place.

"Don't tell your mother," he'd said.

I nodded happily.

So, we would sit up past our bedtimes watching these films – Steve McQueen or Paul Newman breaking out of prisons, robbing banks, doing time, never buckling to the man. We laughed and smiled, our family time, watching these movie stars overcame all obstacles, beat any adversary, triumph over authority.

It would be some years before I could appreciate why the Old Man chose such films.

* * *

AFTER A YEAR OR SO, my brother and I began accompanying the Old Man to work on Saturdays. These days would make a great impression on us both, defining the Old Man as a boss, a workaholic, an organiser and thinker, a man to be emulated. It was on these trips I discovered we no longer shared the same surname.

"My name's Spencer now," he reminded me.

"And I'm Shipley?"

"Yes. It's a business decision. Spencer sounds more business-like."

I didn't see it, but I trusted his reasoning.

He had by this time expanded over to Far Gosford Street. A long, sloping thoroughfare teeming on both sides with pubs and pool halls, bookies and pawn shops, it boasted a score of second-hand shops which sold everything from fridges and televisions to bent MOTs and passports. I would later learn it was the premiere stomping ground of the city's villains who operated fronts there, dealing in stolen goods, various counterfeits, assorted drugs, hardcore pornography.

To my young eyes, though, Gosford Street was simply this bustling place where I hung out each Saturday.

Our morning would begin at the Mainline Gas shop, a white Art Deco building which stood on a jagged crossroads. Above the shop, the Old Man's office, a large, curved room dominated by a grand oversized desk. On it, a row of phones in assorted colours, green, black, brown, red, each matched to different pseudonyms. Away to one side against the wall ran a black leather *chaise longue* he slept on when working nights. Against the wall opposite, a large green safe sat, home to the various piles of money I'd occasionally caught sight of.

Settling at his desk, he bounced from phone to phone, keeping his calls brief, usually signing off with a time or place, "I'll be by at ten"; "See you at twelve"; "The usual place." He would scrawl further notes, adding them to the list he'd compiled the night before. As well as the new cooker shops, he had opened up a motorbike showroom, continued with some second-hand shops, rented some flats out, even had a few sex shops for a while. Out of habit, he had his fingers in a lot of pies, hence the lists.

Once done, we'd stroll down the street to the large open doors of a warehouse where a lorry would be being loaded with cookers; either side, cobalt-blue vans parked up on the curbs, their sides emblazoned 'Mainline Gas Services'. Drivers, fitters, and cleaners would be arriving, clocking on, slipping on overalls, setting to work.

The Gaffer at Mainline was Paddy, a stocky, no-nonsense Irishman who had worked tirelessly in building up the company with the Old Man. Loading up a lorry might take the best part of an hour and the pair would stand yapping, planning deliveries, discussing sales and the weekly targets they were striving for. At such times, a few local businessmen might drop by for a word with the Old Man. They'd conduct informal meetings at the kerbside, them chain-smoking fags or cigars whilst the Old Man drank coffee.

Out of boredom, I would disappear inside to explore and wander.

In retrospect, the warehouse was a health and safety nightmare. Acid baths, oily floors, dripping taps, dirty cups and cold offices. I had hoped for something warmer and cleaner. The second-hand shops had been the same – cold, bare and practical. I had spent many hours in their back rooms next to a blow heater, reading comics and drinking hot chocolate. I couldn't fathom why the Old Man had chosen another business with so few comforts.

Once the business at the warehouse was complete, we'd head out for a series of meetings, working down his lists. He'd meet an assortment of businessmen in cafes, in car parks, in their homes or at their businesses. More often, I would be sat outside in the car with pop and crisps watching the minutes tick away, occasionally wondering how we were doing, if we were well off, if he was a millionaire, and if so, why did we live in such a small house?

Some weeks later, sat in the office, my curiosity would get the better of me. The Old Man had left his briefcase behind and his dark blue book on the desk. I dared to open it and saw what appeared to be his accounts, all hand-written in that right leaning cursive writing of his. Even now, the numbers are clear in my mind. He was turning over between £38,000 and £62,000 per week. An incredible amount for the time. My mouth dropped when I read it, and my mind wondered why so little of this money made it home.

However, this did not last for long. One Sunday, the Old Man brought home brochures for two mansions on the luxurious Kenilworth Road.

We were told to pick one.

I went for the larger one: a large thirties mansion with a long, sweeping drive and grand lawns either side. It was massive. Larger than any house I'd ever seen. Larger than any I'd ever visited. Larger than Uncle Robert's, I thought.

I smiled to myself. Our Uncle, that bad-tempered snob, would be seething when he found out.

* * *

FURTHER UP GOSFORD STREET, Robert had moved into pawn brokering. He was reputed to be making a small fortune, his 'swap-shop' a gold mine. All ought to have been good, except it couldn't have been. Around this time, his wife had left him with both children and filed for divorce. Her reasons were many: his domestic abuse, frequent affairs, and drug use being three. Given she was from money and her family knew lawyers, the anticipated divorce threatened to clean him out.

It was the worst timing; his younger brother's fortunes had recently soared.

All around, Robert saw the evidence as Mainline Gas shops, warehouses and offices were expanding up and across Far Gosford Street. He couldn't escape bumping into Mainline workers in the surrounding pubs and cafes, he might even catch sight of his brother who spent his days within that square mile organising shipments, making more and more of those lists of his.

The two brothers had little to do with one another anymore.

It was said they no longer got on, that they simply clashed. I would hear it said later that he and the Old Man were simply different characters. And *character* was the thing. Perhaps, being brothers, their differing nature was to be expected. Though of the two, from what I now hear, it seemed Robert was more suited to being a criminal than the Old Man. Robert was an intimidating figure, tight-fisted and dripping with contempt.

I recall we had been warned to stay away from his shop. Finding my Uncle to be a scary figure, I didn't need much persuading. But later, good reasons came to light as to why that might be: Robert was said to be a drug dealer.

The 'swap-shop' made money, but its main profit came from the drug dealing conducted out back. It enabled him to live an affluent lifestyle, but he had to proceed quietly, not draw attention. Now with a divorce pending, something suddenly changed.

For years, he had cultivated the polished well-spoken persona of the conservative businessman, but that image quickly crumbled as he increasingly hung out with low-level villains, hitting the pubs and clubs, womanising and partying, taking drugs.

Which drugs were unknown, but later it could be inferred: cannabis certainly, cocaine maybe, heroin possibly?

Maybe this was a reason the two brothers no longer mixed. The Old Man, like most people, like most villains, was anti-drugs. Back then, it was considered no respectable way to earn a living.

* * *

BY ITS THIRD year, Mainline Gas boasted a multi-million-pound turnover, two score of workers spread across several sites, a dominating position in the market. Each week thousands of discarded cookers were shipped in, reconditioned, and shipped out to all corners of the country.

As per usual, my Saturdays began at the office, where the Old Man continued to make his calls and scrawl out his lists. Now, though, he was more casual. He dispensed with the suit and briefcase for boots, jeans and black leather jacket – the image of biker turned businessman, a casual boss who everyone called Tony. I'd by now grew accustomed to the office and was looking forward to the day when I might become part of the business.

One morning, that day moved into view.

For once, he ignored his lists; he needed to stay local as an envelope was due to arrive. We spent that morning hanging around the new warehouse, where security had suddenly become a priority. A new caravan, night watchman and guard dog had been installed. Some workers had been instructed to raise the height of the perimeter fence and add a corrugated roof. There had been government officials prying, taking photos, observing the shops.

Late morning, a suited man arrived with a small brown envelope. The Old Man signed for it and marched on ahead.

"Jason, follow me!" he called.

I scampered behind, struggling to keep up as he walked at his usual brisk pace. We marched along the alley, around onto Gosford Street and after fifty yards, turned into a large complex of old derelict factory buildings. It was here that he stopped, and I caught up.

He walked slowly over the broken glass of a large, uneven car park and studied the faces of two large buildings whose windows were smashed and whose walls were graffitied. A stretched two-storey building faced across to a larger three-storey building that climbed across to meet a tall hangar, which contained some smashed-up coaches. The Old Man walked and turned to survey both buildings before arriving at the corner entrance of the three-storey and tearing open the brown envelope to reveal a small bunch of keys. He tried several before one worked, and then shoved the door, which creaked long and loud as it swung open.

We entered a dark and musty hall of bare boards, brown-grey walls and a wide dilapidated staircase which hugged the left wall. We walked slowly, headed right and passed through another door into a larger room and gingerly through a set of doors which took us into a warren of dark empty rooms. Circling around, we arrived back at the broken staircase.

"Stay left," he said.

I nodded and followed.

With no bannister rail, he helped me over the missing steps, up onto the second storey, where the floors were solid and we could stroll from room to room, the Old Man flicking on lights as we went, revealing little of interest besides dirty walls, dusty work benches and the musty smell of time. Finally, we paused at a large and long room lined by tall broken windows. The Old Man paced the room, taking it all in, frowning thoughtfully. He finally stopped pacing and turned to me, "I've bought this."

My eyes widened and I broke into a large toothy smile.

He added nothing, but paced his way back to the previous room. *Wow!* I thought to myself, *This, is ours!*

I followed him into one of the largest rooms. He was absorbed in thought, but broke off and beckoned me to follow him as he marched from room to room, outlining his plans, "This will be the shower room… that the main office… over there the solarium… we'll have sunbeds in those side rooms… there we'll knock through and install a sauna… the gym will be downstairs…" He was transfixed and serious, "It'll be the same in the other building except it'll have a hairdressers… That will be the women's gym, this the men's. The hangar, we'll knock down."

I listened intently.

"There's a lot of money in gymnasiums," he added. "Health and fitness are the future."

I nodded keenly, smiled a little at my Old Man, who could see the future so clearly. It felt like we were on the verge of a new adventure.

THE FOLLOWING MONTHS saw the Old Man throwing every penny into the new gyms. However, he soon began to run low on cash. For the previous three years, he had been reinvesting all his money back into the gas company. As a result, he was asset rich, but cash poor.

But then he had an idea.

He directed his workers to fill the old warehouse with three years of useless stock. Opting for a Saturday night, he engineered an electrical fire and slipped away. Within an hour, the building was a crimson furnace. Inevitably, with acid baths and chemicals everywhere, a series of explosions shook the district as the fire crews arrived. Nearby residents were evacuated. Five fire crews battled the blaze and by dawn's first light, they had finally brought it under control.

Monday morning, the Old Man stood in its smoking ruins explaining to local reporters how the devastation could destroy the company. "It could put us out of business!" he declared whilst posing for photos in the building's burnt-out shell.

He immediately put in an insurance claim for a quarter of a million pounds. He was confident it would go through, except already, CID were encouraging an investigation of the blaze for signs of arson. Officers disclosed the Old Man's criminal record to the insurance company. Furthermore, they informed them of a previous fire some years back at a motorbike garage on Harnall Lane.

The insurance company would use this as grounds to refuse payment.

Unaware of these developments, the Old Man borrowed against the payout. With bank loans and a bloated £200K overdraft, he pressed ahead with the creation of the new gyms. A series of intense months followed, during which he poured all his resources into getting the gyms up and running.

Meanwhile, Robert continued to hear the stories of his brother's ascendency and the predictions for what promised to be his greatest venture. What he thought was unknown, he might not have cared, he may have been bitter, jealous even. My Grandfather would often say they would have owned half the city if they could have worked together, but it wasn't to be and as it would turn out there would be no more time.

* * *

ONE FRIDAY NIGHT, Robert, after a long raucous night, was arrested and thrown in the cells for drunken disorder. Released the next morning, he picked himself up, carried on with his day and by noon suffered what appeared to be a mild heart attack. Rushed to hospital, he had little patience for doctors. At aged thirty-four, he considered it as nothing serious, and discharged himself.

The following morning, whilst lying in the bath, he was struck by the most explosive of heart attacks. An ambulance was called, but it was too late.

At the hospital, he was pronounced dead.

His death would make no sense to the family. They ignored the rumours of his drug use and concocted their own explanation: "He was heartbroken." His divorce, losing his wife and kids, the influence of the people he mixed with, they had all done him.

I asked the Old Man what happened some years later.

"Got mixed up in drugs," he replied without hesitation.

A silence followed before he added: "I tried to warn him – told him he was being an idiot – but he didn't listen."

And he said no more.

Over the years, many had conceded that Robert was a volatile man with a ferocious temper. None could provide answers as to what he was so angry about. Nor answer why the Old Man was his opposite in this respect.

They shared similar childhoods, but couldn't be more different in nature. The Old Man loathed so many of the things that Robert was accused of: the meanness, the violence, the drinking, the smoking, the drug taking.

I wondered whether these were clues. Clues as to why the Old Man was the way he was. Perhaps a by-product of his upbringing was that he'd resolved to be all that Robert was not and held in contempt much of what he was.

The Old Man would ever be gentlemanly and generous, charming and sober.

It was this manner that suggested a softness that was sometimes mistaken for weakness.

And if the Old Man had a weakness as a criminal, it was that he lacked an air of intimidation which others employed. For a long time, I had considered that Robert would have made a better criminal from a financial point of view. He cared about money, had an intimidating air, a ruthless business manner. I would continue to think this for a long time until I took a road trip to Madrid with the Old Man in the spring of 2003. Events on this trip would remind me of how Margaret had once described her brothers: "Robert was hard on the outside, soft on the inside. Your dad, soft on the outside; hard on the inside.

She would be proved correct in her description.

CHAPTER 12:
NOWHERE TO RUN, NOWHERE TO HIDE

5TH JANUARY 2003

"HAVE YOU SEEN it yet?" he asked.

"I'm looking at it now," I said.

The line went quiet.

Splashed across two pages of the *Sunday Mercury* ran a large headline: 'THE FIVE MOST WANTED MEN'. Underneath, a large blown-up mugshot of the Old Man, tagged *'Public Enemy Number One'*. Circling him were a series of mugshots featuring public enemies two, three, four and five.

I took a deep breath and read the blurb.

Elite cops last night dramatically named the five most wanted super-criminals in the Midlands. The crack National Crime Squad – Britain's equivalent of the FBI – is hunting two killers, two international money launderers and a major drugs-dealer.

Public Enemy No1 is Anthony Cyril Spencer, who fled the Midlands as National Crime Squad detectives moved in to smash a multi-million-pound drugs factory at a remote farmhouse in the region.

Spencer, from Nuneaton, Warwickshire, is also wanted for questioning about a murder in Amsterdam during a terrifying shoot out, believed to be linked to a drugs war. Spencer is thought to be living abroad, possibly in Spain...

"Well?" he asked.

"It's two full pages. It covers the UK thing (Drug raids) and the thing up in the Flat (killing the Soldier)."

"And the picture?"

"An old one. The hair's dark rather than grey... it's taken with a flash... some of the features are bleached out ever so slightly."

"Anything else?"

"Picture for number two is excellent – of Red – and number three – Ash's brother is okay. And there is a phone number given (Confidential Hotline)."

A silence passed as he digested the news and considered its effect. This took just seconds. "I'll adjust things up (security) at this end. If you could do the same – have a clear out, and we'll talk when I see you."

"Will do."

"Later."

And with that, the line went dead.

I put the phone down, gazed back at the headline. My Old Man was the National Crime Squad's Most Wanted Man. I felt the strangest mixture of both twisted pride and overwhelming horror. Pride, because the Old Man in a perverse way was being credited for success in his chosen field. Horror, because such acclaim was not good, for it signalled major problems up ahead.

* * *

A MONTH LATER, I flew into Spain more cautious than ever. It seemed an unnecessary risk, but he'd insisted. It was urgent.

I took the usual stringent measures. Travelled under an old passport, under a false address to someone else's credit card. I passed through customs wearing my usual black jacket, cash concealed in the arms and back. No papers on me. No receipts, phone numbers, car keys, anything which might suggest where I had come from or where I was going.

Straight through at customs, I expected a tail, but was ready.

At the airport, I grabbed a taxi into Barcelona. Dropped at *Las Ramblas* I disappeared into the crowds of tourists and after wandering around the city for half an hour, was convinced there was no tail. I hailed a cab out to Rubi where I was dropped short and zigzagged the final quarter mile. Arriving at the tall corner office building on the hill, I rang the bell and waited.

Tiff was quick to the door. He flashed a smile, "Good to see you pal!" I noted his upbeat tone and followed him up. Once upstairs, his manner became clear.

Two new workers, a tall Mancunian and a heavy-set Welsh man, were on their feet.

"Thank fuck you got here!" exclaimed the Manc stepping my way.

"You've got some paperwork then," asked the Welshman, leaning in. "You do have it – I'm desperate for some fags mate."

I nodded and looked across the room to the Old Man sat behind an ordered table of mobile phones, writing some notes. He leant back, chucked his glasses down, stood up and shook my hand firmly as per usual. "Good you made it. You watched yourself coming through?"

"Yeah, no worries… took my time," I mumbled, a little over-whelmed by their response, eyes studying the room for anything out of the ordinary. "So, what's been happening?"

"Got no food, got no fags, got no fuel, got no phone!" announced the Manc, pulling a chair up, "Been like this for fuckin' days now!"

I looked to the Old Man.

"Yeah, it's been a tough, few days," he replied. "Got the money?"

"Sure," I reached for my jacket. "It's just twelve, though."

"That'll be enough".

"I could have sent it sooner by Western Union if you'd said how desperate it was."

"No, we can't be doing that shit anymore," he responded.

This was a reference to how the game had changed. The *Sunday Mercury's* two-page announcement had been followed up by all the region's papers. Full page articles ran in every town and city devoted to locating the five most wanted with a great emphasis on the Old Man. Consequently, he'd cut contact with most in the UK.

There were few he could trust now.

He divided the money into bundles, split them into ones, pulled out a few rolls and chucked one each to Tiff, Manc and the Welshman. Within minutes all three disappeared out to stock up on food, fuel and the desperately needed phone credits. This left just me and the Old Man in a quiet, still apartment.

"Been out of credits for two days," he remarked.

"What?" I answered with incredulity. "You've had nothing?"

"Fuck all."

I considered this a moment and sighed, "So, things are going well then?"

He suppressed a smile, grabbed a pen and switched attention to his lists. He navigated his pen down several lines before frowning and tapping his pen several times as he considered a plan of attack.

I strolled over to the long east facing window and gazed at the skyline of Barcelona in the distance, shaking my head slowly in disbelief.

"Ryan was to send twenty, but that was last week," he called over. "We've heard nothing since."

"He's probably busy," I called back.

A silence passed between us and I ventured with a question that needed asking.

"Shouldn't you think about getting out of Spain?"

He looked up from his writings, "I've thought about it, but it's too early."

"The papers all say they know you're in Spain."

"There's hundreds of people on the run in Spain. Most are in the Costa del Sol. I don't mix down there."

"But you are thinking about getting out?"

"Yeah, but later. I need to keep working. There's debts to square off."

He leant back in his chair, rested an arm across its back, "I'm thinking North Africa. I can get a villa there. Work would be easy. They couldn't extradite me."

"Sounds good," I said. "You should maybe do that."

He nodded, replaced his glasses and returned to his lists.

I wandered out to the kitchen, intending to fix some drinks. I found there to be no coffee, no tea, no sugar, no biscuits. Opening the food cupboard, I counted three tins of tuna, one tin of evaporated milk and half a bottle of olive oil. I paused a moment and called out, "You've been eating well, then?"

"Without the tuna, I don't know how we would have gotten by these last few days," he called back and began to expand upon this, but his voice faded out to nothing.

I squatted down and stared into the fridge: a pair of tomatoes, half an onion and a solitary piece of Garlic. Also, no milk. In comparison, the freezer was a bonanza, with two drawers full of ice cubes. Looking to its side, the water barrels were empty though, "You been making your own ice and drinking the tap water?"

There was no response.

I stepped back to the living room, where he was assigning small piles of money to their respective 'to do' lists. He wrote a few side notes, made two crosses, chucked his pen down and removed his glasses. Pinching the bridge of his nose, he scrunched his eyes and yawned. Then, whilst we awaited for the others to return, he felt compelled to update me on the three schemes he'd been working on:

1) Cargo ship – "is still held by Spanish customs. The two Dutch women were negotiating its return when they stole that large parcel of hashish. Less said about that the better. We'll get the boat released once we're back on top."

2) The rib boats near Benalmadena – "they'll wait until the spring. All's paid for. Just need the weather."

3) The fishing boat in Gibraltar – "All paid. We just need some fresh cash on the table to get it running – pay the exes."

In total, he had spent almost half a million on the three enterprises and had little to show. His rationale was, 'That's the game we were in,' and 'Things take time'.

I disagreed. I was appalled at the waste, but I was used to it.

Ever since I'd been driving for the Old Man, I'd seen how wasteful he was with money. He made a great deal, turned over massive amounts, but saved nothing. At times like this, a little money tucked away would have come in handy.

Finally, Tiff and the Manc returned with supplies, including the desperately needed phone credits. Suddenly we were back in business. Within minutes the Old Man had the phone to his ear, organising payments, making promises, lining up finance. Out in the kitchen, Tiff chewed hungrily on a baguette and fixed some coffees whilst Manc settled down to topping up a row of phones. Meanwhile, I observed, listened and willed the Old Man to get his work back on track.

As the calls flowed, items were either crossed off the lists or added. In the UK, few were willing to send money anymore. Nonetheless, he pressed on, each call equating to a loss or gain: an investment or favour. Things to do were assigned to Tiff, Manc or Welsh, whilst others received a question mark with the words 'Later' scrawled to one side. Midway on the list was the time-consuming task of returning a rental car to Malaga and meeting the Chinaman who arrived in Madrid last night.

Both were circled heavily.

He leant back, arm outstretched, pen bouncing between them once and twice. I could guess what he was thinking. "Do you want to drive over to Madrid and catch the Chinaman?" he asked with a thoughtful frown and smirk. "He's talking about investing."

I lowered my eyes in consideration – *how long could it take? Last time, as well he knows, I was gone five days and my wife wasn't impressed. But then...*

"It'll be a day and a half. You can catch a flight back from Malaga."

I hesitated a further second or two but then the words jumped out: "Alright. Why not?"

* * *

BY LATE AFTERNOON, we left Barcelona under a glaring sun and a sky shimmering blue. It was set to be a hot one.

It would be some four hundred miles to Madrid across long stretches of desert for the most part. I would drive, the Old Man would make calls and navigate when required. The car was a dusty blue Audi saloon with broken air conditioning. The journey would be sweltering.

There promised to be many quiet hours ahead, plenty of time to raise some of the subjects that had aroused my curiosity in recent months. I thought he might welcome something new to talk about. There was plenty to choose from.

It was just a matter of how to get onto these subjects. I would leave it a while, until we were out of the city – there was no rush. He had calls to make, but due to a fear of phone taps was carrying just two phones.

It would make for a quiet journey.

Once out of Barcelona, the traffic lightened and the views flattened. Desert plains crawled by and the highway was clear. A particularly long period of silence followed, and I decided there would be no better time. I cleared my throat, took a deep breath and began casually.

"I don't know if Margaret mentioned it, but she and I have gone through some of the old photos. Doing some family history. She showed me pictures of before you moved to Coventry, when you lived up Horncastle way."

I waited for a flicker of interest, but there was a long silence.

"What about it?" he finally replied and looked down to one of his lists.

"I saw pictures of where you used to live – by the stream – across from the fields?"

"Oh," he said, and added something to one of his lists.

"I drove by there a few months back, coming back from Linx's."

He gazed out the window.

I pressed on, "Took some pictures of how it looks now. Even knocked the door. Explained to the tenants its relevance and they invited me in to look around. Saw where Grandad knocked the two living rooms into one, saw the yard where you Margaret and Robert used to play."

He continued to gaze out at a featureless landscape.

This ought to have been a typical father-son conversation, but it was not. In reality, we never spoke about such ordinary things.

"Mmmm," he said quietly and then added," Yeah…" and then nothing. Nothing for more than a mile.

I glanced across and noted how he couldn't be less interested. I pursed my lips and resolved not to give up. There was no better opportunity than this for us to talk.

"You've never mentioned much about your brother Rob –"

"I need to give Raj a call," he interjected. "Should have done it earlier. When's the next services?"

I didn't know and I didn't answer. He reached into his bag and pulled out an address book and searched for a number. "Keep an eye out for signs, "he said. "Must call Albert also. We might swing down and see him after the Chinaman."

I said nothing. We drove the next twenty miles in silence. Conversation with the Old Man had never been easy, but I had hoped things might have changed. Unfortunately, they hadn't. He had no interest in the past and wandering down family lane. As he sat back and again gazed out at a dull, baking landscape, he drummed his fingers on the sill of the window.

His mind was elsewhere, as was mine. His mind was on the meeting up ahead and the pressures and the problems that had piled up in recent months. My mind was on old questions and how if we could only strike up something like a normal conversation, it would open up some common ground between us.

The following half hour passed slowly, marked by just a handful of short calls. The final silence was broken by him reaching into his bag for a bottle of tablets, muttering to himself as he did so, searching for some water: in the drawer, in the footwell, under the seat, "Is there no fucking water anywhere?"

He leant and twisted over to the back seat and found a bottle, swigged it, and swore at how "bastard warm" it was, then swallowed a series of tablets and waited for their effects to kick in.

Several minutes passed before I dared to ask, "Any better now?"

"Chest and back playing up. Keeping me up all fuckin' night."

It was the first time he'd mentioned this in a while. Following the shooting, he'd rarely grumbled about any after-effects, but just lately he'd been referring to the sharp pains emanating from the path of the bullet. They were usually alleviated by a course of medication, but this time they were having less effect.

"I thought you were going to get that looked at."

"It's easier said than done." he answered, shaking his head in irritation. "There's never the time."

I nodded my concern. The injury, as far as I know, had never been seen by a real doctor.

* * *

FOR HALF AN HOUR we looked out at a burning landscapes with just the rumble of the engine for company. As the miles passed, I scrubbed any ideas for any meaningful conversation. It could wait. Instead, I asked about this trip to see the Chinaman.

"He has his restaurant up and running. It's doing well. He might have some spare cash to invest, but it can't be all talk this time."

It seemed like a desperate roll of the dice. The Chinaman had been low on the list of priorities some months back; now he was top. Suddenly we needed him more than he needed us. These were desperate times.

The reasons were obvious as to why. Being on the run meant the Old Man rarely left the relative safety of Spain. Furthermore, out of wisdom or habit, he had stuck to dealing in hashish and the occasional soap bar, which as events were proving, wasn't where the money was anymore. UK gangs were growing weed better than anything imported from Spain.

And there were other problems.

Being on the run had choked off his finances. He could hardly chase any monies owed; he was too easy to avoid and fob off. Moreover, he could not exert any pressure as it might lose him an ally and gain him an enemy. The drugs business was full of grasses. All he could do was try to deal with the 'good' people, as he called them.

But then the 'good' people also made problems.

The Irish point blank refused to pay for a load of hash. They cited his failure to make good on the money lost to the 'Soldier'. His death had appeased, but not compensated them. Then ten days later, a parcel was stolen by Brighton's people from the warehouse at Girona. He said it paid off his investment in the cargo ship deal. The Old Man attempted to negotiate it back, but it was futile; he was on the back foot, his position weak, the odds stacked against him as many people saw it.

These were desperate times indeed.

WE PULLED INTO A SERVICES. The sun above was fierce whilst the concrete below boiled up in the heat. I peeled myself from the car and fuelled up whilst the Old Man headed across to a call box. He phoned Raj, collected messages from his UK pager and returned any calls.

I found a rare strip of shade, slumped down, drank two ice cokes, and wondered whether I really should have come along.

I had rather hoped that I could engage him in conversation, and he would, in his open blunt fashion, address directly or not, the burning question as to why he'd become a criminal. However, he was overwhelmed with problems and wanted no distractions. And seeing how uninterested he was, left me questioning whether there was an answer, whether it really mattered and whether it could ever be known.

Can you ever know why any person becomes the person they do?

I lifted my head and looked over to see the Old Man arriving back at the car, waving me over. I wearily raised a hand in acknowledgement, slowly got up, trudged on over, and before climbing in, poured a full bottle of water over my head and shoulders.

"You better now?" he said.

"Yeah. I'm good," I answered.

"Good. Not far to go now."

* * *

WE SLOWED to a crawl as we approached the heart of Madrid. The Old Man scrawled some notes, made a call, and then, as was his custom, drummed his fingers impatiently on the windowsill. The sinking sun reddened the sky as we edged forward, a mile every twenty minutes.

Struck by impatience, he finally directed me to park up and we continued on foot.

Marching the last half mile, we followed the foot traffic, weaving through streams of night goers heading to the fiestas. The Old Man marched a few metres ahead, map in hand, until we rounded a corner into an explosion of nightclubs and bars where scores of taxis filled the road, pouring forth hundreds of curvaceous long-legged señoritas and their menfolk.

With no time to stop and stare, we strode onto the grandest and brightest restaurant on the strip, where a score of limousines blocked the road and a long queue snaked its way up the pavement. We ignored the queue and climbed the steps into the bright crystal lights of a grand foyer.

The Old Man engaged the Maître d.

As he did so, I stood marvelling at the surroundings – glass and marble from floor to ceiling and bordered by crowded marble benches of the most beautiful señoritas and their partners. More impressive though, above and around them lining the walls from floor to ceiling and running deep into the restaurant, were tall narrow illuminated aquariums containing fish as large as cats and crustaceans larger than dogs, swimming and hovering amongst thousands of rising air bubbles sparkling like diamonds. On one wall was a large, long tank and within it was an actual shark. I took a few steps forward in disbelief and watched the shark, still alive, unable to move forward or back, doing what it had to do to stay alive.

The Maître d', upon hearing we were here to meet the Chinaman, immediately welcomed us like old friends and led us to our table.

* * *

SOME HOURS LATER, many of those sparkling tanks were emptied of their beautiful crustaceans, though the shark was still alive. We stepped out into the warm night air with the Old Man carrying eighty grand in his shoulder bag. He was satisfied with the night's work; I was less so.

We walked briskly to the car as the Old Man outlined how we'd make our way south. From there, I could catch a flight from Malaga whilst he switched cars and carried onto Gibraltar. With the Chinaman's investment and the promises of more to follow, he anticipated having a parcel landing within fourteen days.

I listened but said nothing. In truth, I was far from happy.

He popped some painkillers, folded his arms and retreated into a deep sleep. As we headed south, I ran my thoughts back to what was bothering me.

The meeting had gone well. The Chinaman I had met before. He was not Chinese but Portuguese; he resembled Al Pacino and fancied himself as something of a flash Latin entrepreneur. He oozed wealth as he discussed his money, the unforeseen problems with laundering through his restaurant, before moving on to the matter of his investment. He was keen to move quickly and wanted to jump the queue.

Could he invest today?

Of course.

The Old Man was beguiling as he outlined the planned schedules, rich returns and how, as the Chinaman had missed out before, he'd allow him to jump the queue of investors. The Chinaman listened, unable to contain a broad smile. It was then that the discussion switched tracks, and I was taken unaware.

"*When are the first loads from South America arriving?*" he'd asked.

My mouth dropped.

The Old Man without missing a beat explained how it would be four to six weeks as there was still a lot to finalise. Plus, he had to fly out, meet face to face with the suppliers in Venezuela and Columbia; tie up the loose ends. These were mere formalities, though.

All became clear.

"You need any more money, just call," the Chinaman added.

I listened and felt my anger simmering.

They continued to talk. The Chinaman smirking and smiling at the thoughts of the grand profits his small investment might lead to; the Old Man stoking his greed with boasts of large shipments and greater profits. I suddenly realised why the Old Man was so unconcerned about his climbing debts and recent losses. Compared to what he would soon be earning, it was nothing.

How had I not seen this coming? Had I simply been naive?

Cannabis and amphetamine had been the two lines he had traded with from the very beginning. He'd dismissed cocaine as a hard drug best left to others. It meant that I was able to consider what we were doing as ethical in its own sweet way, the Old Man a modern-day bootlegger if you will. But to deal in cocaine, that would be a game-changer for me.

Many hours had passed, but my feelings hadn't changed.

For a long time, I had considered him a businessman who had made drugs his business but retained a moral line by dealing in softer drugs. After tonight, this wasn't true anymore.

He was a criminal, no better than any other.

I drove on with just a quarter tank, not wanting to refuel. I didn't wish to wake him as I couldn't talk about this right now. I just wanted to get back home. With no other cars on the road I pressed onto Malaga, full of frustration.

I'd set out on this trip with high hopes we might talk like father and son, but it hadn't happened and probably never would. I'd learnt nothing about him and his past, except that he had no interest in discussing it. I had been reminded that he had little interest in matters outside his own business. We could talk about his deals, his plans and his goals concerning the drug business but little else. The only gain from the entire trip, and it was by accident really, was I'd learned of his plans to import cocaine.

I hated the idea and wondered how I had got him so wrong? If so, when?

Combing through the years, I recalled Leyhill Prison.

It was at Leyhill, where, as a young boy, I had first seen the glint of idealism in his eyes. It was there I first saw the passion and the drive of some heroic proportions. Then, in all the years that followed, it had been consolidated by watching him build his companies. Every day, he'd had that same glint in his eye. He was always out to make a million, to take on the world, to do the impossible. Given my notions of the Old Man had been formed as a kid, had it made me blind to his true character? Had I failed to see that he had a dark side? A ruthless side? Is that why he had gone from the fine businessman of back then to the immoral criminal of now?

Is that what had happened?

His upbringing, his distant parents, his corrupting brother could never explain enough. They could never explain how whenever he was in a tight situation, he would simply do what he had to do.

It certainly explained the bank robbery.

And for me, it had really begun with the bank robbery. I remembered it well for I was eleven years old at the time and after the robbery, nothing would ever be the same again.

CHAPTER 13:
BANK ROBBER

MONDAY 13TH SEPTEMBER 1982

SECONDS BEFORE the bank closed, two bikers strolled in. They removed their helmets and pulled out guns.

"Get down! This is a raid!" the first yelled.

The second aimed a revolver at the cashier's head, "Keys to the safe – now!!"

The young woman's hand trembled as she passed them over.

The first biker headed through to the safe and proceeded to shovel what little money there was into a bag. The reserves were low – a clue that something was amiss – but it didn't register. He grabbed the bag, cleared out the tills, retreated to the exit.

Outside, the packed street was still. Shops and pubs had emptied; a sea of eyes fell upon the two raiders as they stepped out. A loudspeaker shrieked:

"PUT YOUR WEAPONS DOWN AND YOUR HANDS UP. I REPEAT –"

Both men froze.

Hordes of shoppers watched on in silence as uniformed officers filed out from the crowds and formed a cordon to confront the raiders. The voice repeated:

"PUT DOWN YOUR WEAPONS. YOU ARE SURROUNDED! ARMED OFFICERS HAVE YOU IN THEIR SIGHTS."

Both men exchanged glances, nodded to one another, lay their guns on the floor and placed hands behind heads. Officers moved in, forcing them to the ground. As the cuffs went on, the Old Man's masked face gazed out at the crowd.

How had it come to this?

* * *

THIRTY YEARS LATER, I stood outside that same bank. A fine and grand building in its day, it was now a derelict shell of peeling paint and smashed windows. The stone steps where the Old Man met the sights of the police marksman remained, though the bustling street he looked out on was no more. Much had changed. The area had been redeveloped and most of the pubs, cafes, pool halls and bookies had gone, as had the vast green that lay facing the bank.

There, on the day of the robbery, a dozen men had been playing football since midday. They were a lacklustre and distracted bunch – undercover CID. Their attentions were focused upon the bank opposite, on its comings and goings, on vehicles parking up, perhaps with the engine left running. They'd had a reliable tip-off.

At five minutes to five, the two bikers entered; police units were alerted. Within seconds, uniformed officers emerged from neighbouring shopfronts and several police cars moved into position. Some forty officers surrounded the bank, with a half-dozen police marksmen for good measure.

The robbers stood no chance.

I turned and strolled down a neat, clean street passing three phone shops, two hairdressers, a health food centre, and a nail bar. It had changed so much over the years. Back in the day, it was considered a wild and lively place. Most of the city's villains had a presence here via a second-hand shop, pawnbroker, pool hall or bookies. Rogues and villains would spend their days on this street, moving from one overflowing pub to another, buying and selling, boasting and boozing into the late evening when for many, it would only just be getting started. The neon lights of the clubs would appear followed by the wafting beats of ska music, the sweet aroma of herb, strolling youths black and white, reggae and two-tone. An urban jungle of villainy and creativity, Gosford Street had been where the Specials and The Selecter played, where a teenage Hazel O'Connor hung out, where villains and artists socialised into the cool twilight hours. It had once been the happening place, but now it was dull, gentrified and soulless.

Midway down, I halted at the driveway to a gymnasium.

Above hung a large sign proclaiming, 'Future Fitness Gym'. The name had changed several times over the years. I stood there a minute or so, picturing how it once was. To my left the main building had been the women's gym, and beyond it, across a mini picturesque roundabout, the men's gymnasium. To its right ran a whitewashed wall where the Old Man would park his damson red Jag. For a moment, I imagined him strolling between the buildings, handsome and tall, hurried and energised, so dynamic and still so young.

A man with the world at his feet.

* * *

I WAS ELEVEN YEARS OLD back in '82. For the last few years, I had accompanied the Old Man to work on Saturdays. Now the original warehouse had burnt down, our days began at the new warehouse he'd built on the wasteland to the rear of Gosford Street. Each morning, as blue overalled workers lifted and shifted cookers, the Old Man and Paddy would organise the day's long-distance deliveries to London, Manchester and Glasgow. By the time they were on the road, several familiar faces would have dropped by for a quick word, on a problem or a deal, a proposal or favour, but the Old Man would no longer linger and chat. He would make promises, scrawl some notes, and march off to the gyms.

"Jason. I'll be an hour and no more. Don't go far!"

I would nod. I understood the gyms were out of bounds but further understood that when he said one hour, he meant two or three. I would watch him march up the ginnel to the gyms and give him half hour before setting off.

To be sure our paths wouldn't cross, I'd take the long way around.

Down the gravel track, I would emerge out onto Lower Ford Street and glance right, wondering in which house Uncle Robert had suffered his fatal heart attack the previous summer. His death had been all but ignored in our house. Turning left, I would gaze across the road at the site of the burnt-out cooker warehouse, where there was still no activity as the insurance company was yet to pay out. It left the Old Man borrowing heavily, but he'd assured me this wasn't a problem. I would stroll on, round past the lines of cookers and fridges outside the Mainline Gas shop on the corner, and up a further sixty yards where I'd turn onto a wide clean drive, above which was hung a large straddling sign which read:

Welcome to Body Care.

The gyms had been realised just as the Old Man said they would. Those shattered buildings had been transformed into elegant structures. They were adjoined by a courtyard where cars came and went, leotards and tracksuits, keep-fit fanatics and bodybuilders, scores of people by the hour.

It was proving a great success.

Into a plush foyer with a long reception desk and pretty receptionists, I'd make a sugary coffee and settle down to the back of the seating area, watch the comings and goings, hoping not to be noticed. It was all as he said it would be. There were hairdressers out to the left, gymnasiums to the right, saunas, sunbeds and showers upstairs. Up ahead on the wall, under a spotlight, between red velvet curtains, was a gold plaque, announcing how Miss World Kimberly Santos had opened the venue. By open-top Rolls

Royce, the Old Man had driven her from the city centre flanked by brass bands and led by mini-skirted dancers. Arriving at the gym, she had cut the ribbon as the band played Specials' songs whilst the Coventry City squad and local beauty queens applauded for the cameras. I had missed the event, even though it had been a Saturday. Unlike the gas shops, it had been established that it looked unprofessional for my brother and me to hang around.

Nevertheless, whenever possible, I would sneak in and watch the buzzing new enterprise, until quite predictably, a staff member would approach me with a quid or two to move on.

I'd spend it on sweets and comics and head over to the men's gym. As the plan was to develop a franchise, it was also called Body Care. It had been launched by a Mr Universe and an assortment of Olympians and sportspeople. This had put the place on the map, yet it quickly became evident that it was losing money at an alarming rate. Customers came and went, but the pool of members was far smaller than the ladies' gym, with men spending far less. It was an increasing concern, but the Old Man was sure it would come good.

By the afternoon, he would more often appear at the gyms in a suit and tie, which meant a meeting with a visiting accountant, lawyer or bank manager. Their discussions would centre around his plans for continued expansion and the future franchise. Often, I'd eavesdrop and hear their cautioning tones. The Old Man had been pouring all the profits from the cooker businesses into the gyms. Furthermore, he had been borrowing heavily against the payout from the fire. However, the insurance company had refused to settle.

They cited his failure to declare his criminal record as well as two incidents of fires at previous premises. His lawyer argued these details were immaterial as no arson had been proven. Before long, they were locked in an expensive legal battle of attrition, with neither party backing down.

THE DAY WOULD END as it began — at the warehouse. The workers would be clocking off, a few cronies would drop by for a word or an update. It would take an hour or more to wrap things up. He'd lock up and we'd head off home, avoiding the A-road and driving across five miles of darkening countryside.

Down winding and twisting lanes, he would check his mirrors for the first few miles or so and then relax, though he spoke little. Once home, we'd settle to watch a film, except the Old Man would still be making phone calls, preparing tomorrow's lists. Later he'd head out once more on unfinished business, urgent matters that couldn't wait.

It was a sign that he had other things on his plate, and all was not well.

That summer we would move house. Except it wouldn't be to the luxury mansion on the Kenilworth Road we'd expected, but to a beaten-up semi in the north of the city. The Old Man had invested so much in the new businesses that he had something he called 'cashflow problems.' This was just a stop-gap, he told me. Things would come good.

Little did I know how serious things were.

* * *

THE INSURANCE COMPANY won the appeal.

Suddenly there was the potential for serious trouble. Once the news got out, the bank would rein in his borrowing whilst his creditors, of which there were many, would press hard for their money.

Top of the list were a raft of hard-nosed businessmen in need of their cash. Lawyer friendly, they would head straight to the courts. After them, were some of the villains he knew. Many could wait, a few could not. Some expected to be first in any queue for money owed. Nonetheless, before them, pushing to the head of the queue, was a Glasgow family he dealt with. They'd been sending down thousands of old cookers for months without payment, only to be fobbed off and messed about until their goodwill was exhausted. More deadlines were missed, final promises made, threats of violence promised if they weren't kept. It was under such pressures that he looked for other routes to fast money.

If the later rumours were to be believed, it had been a few years since he'd been involved in armed robberies. Since then, security had improved everywhere. Armoured cars, timed vaults and security cameras were increasingly common measures. Bank jobs were carried out by larger criminal gangs rather than two and three-man teams. Over the summer, the Old Man would join a seven-man team carrying out a series of robberies across the Midlands.

After one such job, a member of the gang offered to be a driver on a job the Old Man planned for the following week. The Old Man declined the offer as it was already taken care of; however, overhearing this exchange was another gang member, a Coventry bouncer, who would later be exposed as a police informant. Immediately, he informed his police handlers and they worked to identify the target, which didn't take long.

The Midlands Bank at the top of Far Gosford Street was the target and a bank the Old Man knew too well, for it was his own bank. How's that for daring? Or perhaps for sheer stupidity? He planned an old-fashioned two-man job, for which he had two revolvers: one real for himself and a fake for his accomplice, Norman Campbell.

The robbery was urgent as there were bailiffs visiting that afternoon. It was essential they were paid off and business carried on as normal. Even so, there was an even greater problem imposing itself. The Old Man had missed several 'final' cash deadlines with the Scots, and they'd issued death threats. Their people were said to be on the way down, armed with shotguns.

* * *

THE NIGHT before the robbery, hours after we'd gone to bed, the Old Man returned home. The next morning, he rose early and quietly. He looked in on my sister, kissed her on the forehead, and then on my brother and I, where he stood silent in the doorway.

I awoke as the door creaked, turned over and saw him standing there.

"Go back to sleep," he whispered.

I nodded sleepily and rolled over.

Too early, I thought.

* * *

IT WAS A DAY LIKE ANY OTHER: we took the bus home after school, went out and played until tea was ready. By five, we were back in the garden with some local kids, organising a makeshift obstacle course and taking turns to make times. After an hour or so, for no reason, I glanced down the side of the house to see a dark shiny car pull up. Two large men climbed out, wearing dark suits with grave faces. They marched up to the front door, knocked, waited and disappeared inside.

Instinctively, I knew there was something about them.

They were not like any of the Old Man's friends, or any of our relatives, or our teachers, or any council worker. I returned my attention to our game but kept an eye out for them leaving.

Ten minutes later they strolled out carrying several large plastic bags. One man was carrying the Old Man's briefcase. Our Mum watched them go, her back to me, but her head bowed and a tissue in hand.

Was something wrong?

We played until the neighbourhood kids went home, tried the back door, found it was locked. I banged away on its pane. Seconds later, Mum appeared and asked that we stay out for a while. I noticed her eyes were moist and caught the sound of a sniffle or two.

Something was certainly wrong.

Minutes later, our Aunt arrived. Serious-faced, eyes sharp and focused, I intercepted her at the door, but she cut me off. My sister was allowed inside, but my brother and me needed to stay outside. I looked across to David. He frowned; something was up.

We sat in silence for the next half hour waiting.

Finally, our Aunt reappeared, unlocked the door and asked that we come through to the living room. I walked cautiously along the kitchen, wondering what it could be. On the settee, Mum was huddled up with my sister, arms around one another, eyes red and tearful, my sister blubbing away.

Aunt asked us both to sit down.

We sat down without a word. She took a seat, leant forward and with her voice steady, looked down solemnly and spoke.

"Something happened today," she began.

My brother and I exchanged worried glances.

"Your dad…" she paused. "Your dad did something silly today…" she paused again, looked at our faces and came out with it:

"He robbed a bank."

Neither of us spoke and my mouth dropped open.

"The police have arrested him and he's in custody."

I looked over to Mum. She nodded as tears rolled down her cheeks. I looked over to Aunt who nodded slowly, and I looked down and away, my throat tight, tears rolling down my cheeks. I wiped them away as quick as I could and wondered what might happen next.

* * *

IT WAS LATE evening, and the sun was low. I looked over from the one gym that still stands, to the place where the other is no more. Across it runs a highway named *Sky Blue Way*, which also runs through where the cooker warehouses once stood. The alley that led down and out onto Lower Ford Street remained. I walked down it and at the bottom gazed across to where the burnt-out warehouse once stood. It was now a car park. I strolled along to the corner art deco building where the gas shop and office once were. It was now a whitewashed building in the early steps of a renovation planned for more students.

Like most of that old world, it has all gone like it never mattered.

At the local archives, it had proved easy to locate the news clippings of the robbery. They'd made the front page and the later sentencing a full-page rich in detail, though short on truth. The headline pronounced:

4th December, 1982
'ETERNAL OPTIMIST WHO TOOK PATH TO DISASTER'
Debt-ridden businessman Tony Spencer turned to serious crime to provide cash for his ailing companies. He robbed a Coventry bank on the same day that bailiffs moved into his health centre just a few hundred yards away. Today the 33-year-old father-of-three started a 10-year jail term for the robbery which ended as he and his accomplice were surrounded by armed police.

It narrated a tale of a self-made man who had overcome setback after setback – near fatal bike crash, earlier insolvency, prison sentence – to educate himself and go straight. It outlined how he changed his name to Spencer, became a successful entrepreneur with Mainline Gas and the Body Care gyms, but when faced with serious business problems brought on by a freak warehouse fire, returned to type when the insurance company failed to pay out.

It was a tale that would leave me with a lifelong dislike of insurance companies. For me, they were the villains of the piece. Them and the bank had given the Old Man no time and turned him over. In desperation, in order to save his beloved businesses and the jobs which relied upon them, he had robbed a bank.

This was the tale I would tell myself for the following few years. I would be a teenager by the time I could accept that this wasn't entirely true. And then I wouldn't know what to think or how to make sense of it all. The consequences of the robbery would stretch far into the future and leave scars that would never heal. Us as a family would not last. The prison sentence would change everything.

CHAPTER 14:
BACK INSIDE

VALDEMORO PRISON, 2003-05

I CAN NOW SEE how I'd reached the end of the road with the Old Man. The meeting with the Chinaman had tipped me over the edge, killed my appetite. After the trip to Madrid, I no longer drove for the Old Man. I offered the excuse that there was too much happening at home to be taking these trips. He was fine with this and no longer asked. Even so, I still received occasional messages, and he would check in every couple of days. But then, without warning, I heard nothing for a while.

No phone calls for ten days straight, and then one morning a small blue airmail envelope arrived, my address written in his familiar cursive writing. I tore it open and braced myself for bad news.

In an upbeat fashion, for the benefit of the prison censor, he explained how he'd got himself in a 'skirmish', how he was 'innocent', and that *RJ* was organising bail. In the meantime, could I send him money, phone numbers and addresses of family. He asked that I keep things to myself and have a clear out. In closing, he expressed great certainty that he'd be out in a matter of weeks and signed off:

With best wishes

Graham Penney

The name explained the optimistic tone. Whilst he was Graham Penney, bail was likely once Ryan James put up the money. I glanced at the bottom of the letter.

P.S: The attached article explains all. Remember though, I am INNOCENT.

Attached was a tightly folded A4 piece of paper, a copy of the front page of *El Sun*, the Spanish tabloid:

19th April, 2003

WELL OILED DRUG RING CAPTURED

A well-organised drug running operation has been rounded up after months of police investigation.

Three British men – Graham Penney 55, Christopher Pollock 30, and Clifford Preston have all been remanded in custody along with Irishman Geoffrey Dentzer. The gang had been running a slick operation bringing thousands of kilos of hashish from the coast of Morocco to Spain and the transporting it to Ireland and the United Kingdom.

The police operation code name 'Beato' the Spanish word for blessed, started at the beginning of the year...

My response was one of resignation. Prison again. The only silver lining was that he was arrested with hashish, not cocaine.

Maybe his plans with the Chinaman hadn't worked out.

* * *

THREE MONTHS LATER, from Alhaurin Prison, Malaga, the Old Man and his three co-accused were bailed. Except at the final gates, he was ordered back. A guard waved some papers: he was listed for extradition to the Netherlands. Not as Graham Penney, but by another name – Anthony Spencer.

The charge was murder.

In total, he was now facing drugs charges in Spain (seven years?), wanted for extradition to the Netherlands on a murder charge (twenty-five years?) and also wanted in the UK on drugs conspiracy charges (fifteen years?).

I had long accepted that he would end up back inside, but that he might spend the remainder of his life inside had never really occurred. Now it was a possibility, I decided I would do all that I could to help.

However, for the moment, the Spanish charges took precedent.

Some months later, he stood alone in the dock. His three accomplices had all jumped bail, and in their absence pleaded guilty. They received four years apiece. The Old Man pleaded 'Not Guilty!', hired Oscar – the so-called 'best lawyer in Madrid' – and submitted defence papers which were all but ignored. What would be a trial of several weeks in the UK was heard within just a few hours.

He received seven years.

As he was scheduled for extradition, he was transported to the high-security prison of Valdemoro III, near Madrid. The charges were for the "Homicide" of David Royle – *The Soldier* as he was known. He would fight it all the way but by now, he had other problems.

In the months leading up to trial, the shooting pains in his chest and back had increased. The prison dispensed a miniscule number of painkillers. Naturally, without treatment, the pain escalated and intensified.

One morning, he refused to leave his cell.

Upon examination, he was transferred to the prison hospital. There, he languished for several weeks with no phone credits, pens, papers or books. Days dragged as he awaited an X-ray, more medication, or a doctor who might address the source of the problem. Each week, the latest promises come to nothing, and each morning he joined the long queue to receive his daily meds.

Back in England though, things were about to get worse.

* * *

I MADE A RIGHT at the business park and swung into the McDonald's. He'd said it was urgent: "We need to meet face to face. At the usual place. Twenty minutes."

"Right. I'll be there."

I bought a coffee, took a seat, and wondered what was up. The man I was about to meet wasn't a man to panic, but something had spooked him.

Acclaimed as 'Britain's first black prison governor', Jogendranath Rajcoomar, or Raj as he was called, once had it made. From an affluent family in Mauritius, he received the finest education money could buy, and would join the British prison service, where he was promoted to prison governor within just a few years. A poster boy for equal opportunities, he was caught fiddling expenses and promptly charged, found guilty and sentenced to two years.

Two years for expenses! Fiddling expenses was rife in the prison service, he claimed. Their real issue was he had been outspokenly critical of the prison service; they were intolerant of a non-white being impassive.

On release, for reasons only known to him, he quickly became involved in a lucrative heroin deal with some undercover officers and a police informant. He claimed he'd been set up, but in the end, pleaded guilty.

He received five years.

Whilst away, he struck up a correspondence with the Old Man concerning the identities of the bent undercover officers involved in both their cases. When released, he moved to the Midlands and entered the Old Man's circle in a similar legal capacity to my own. Consequently, since the Old Man had been on the run, Raj and I had liaised on several ongoing issues and I'd grown to like the man.

He was a distinctive character.

He pulled up in a beaten-up Vectra whose appearance he frequently claimed was intentional. He had resolved to always look broke and humble. He didn't want to give 'those bastards' any excuse to think he was doing well. *Those bastards,* of course, were the police. After several years inside, Raj hated the police with a passion.

With three days of stubble, clothes unironed and a slow stroll, he appeared a man fallen on hard times, except he was quite masterful at rising above it all. He had an air of education and an articulated confidence rarely found in criminal circles. He would greet a person with a warm smile and a loud, cheery, "How are you, dear boy!" Though not so that day. His unshaven face was serious, worried, and bursting to spill. He sat down, glanced left and right, before leaning in on his elbows and getting to the point.

"I have just been visited by Dutch Police!"

"What?"

"A Dutch detective and the Dutch Public Prosecutor. I met them an hour ago. They are investigating a murder in Groningen. A schoolteacher – Gerard Meesters?"

Gerard Meesters?

It was a name I had only recently become aware of. Gerard Meesters was the brother of Janette Meesters, one of the Dutch translators who had worked for the Old Man in Spain. The two Dutch women had stolen two loads of hashish from the Old Man and disappeared. It turned out that the brother of one of the women had been murdered. Only a few weeks earlier, the Old Man had mailed me some legal papers from the Netherlands which outlined his killing.

Gerard Meesters had been visited by five men demanding he contact his sister Janette. They gave him a Spanish number to call and he had done so. However, he had not been co-operative but indignant. A few days later, one of those men had returned. He knocked on the door, waited, and when Meesters answered the door, pulled a gun and began firing.

Meesters died within minutes.

These papers detailed how the chief suspect was a *Daniel Sowerby*. Sowerby was the worker who'd supported the Old Man after he was wounded in Amsterdam. It had been Sowerby who urged him to take the gun along, which had undoubtedly saved his life. Recently, he had been arrested and charged with Meesters' murder.

I took a deep breath and feigned surprise, "So what do they want to see you for?"

"They want to meet with your dad, of course!"

I winced and rubbed my chin in thought, "And what did you tell them?"

"I told them it was nothing to do with him. He was in Spain."

"And they believed you."

"Of course. Why wouldn't they?"

I could think of several reasons, and so could Raj.

"Oh, and they have phone taps," he added.

My eyes widened, "Taps?"

"Yes, taps! They have phone taps of your dad speaking with Red in Holland, referring to the girls as 'Thelma and Louise'."

Thelma and Louise.

This rang a bell. It was the name he used for the girls once they'd absconded. I shook my head and frowned hard on this piece of info. This was just what he wouldn't want to hear. I sat back and considered this a moment, "Did they play you the taps?"

"No, but they have them. They would not make that up."

I wasn't so sure and thought a little more. Took a sip of coffee.

"Let me explain from the beginning," he added. "It will make sense then."

He elaborated on how his meet with the Dutch prosecutor had been arranged at a nearby hotel via local police. There, three Dutch – a detective, a prosecutor and an interpreter – explained how Dutch surveillance had tapped a British drug smuggler named Red for several months. Amongst the thousands of taps, the Old Man appeared. He and Red, amongst all the coded drug talk, had made several cryptic references to a murder.

Since then, in parallel, the police investigation into Meesters' murder had stumbled across some forensic evidence – a fingerprint on a cigarette packet – which led them to Sowerby and a second man, Steven Barnes. One of them had certainly carried out the killing. However, the greater question for the prosecutor was on whose orders?

"They now want to speak to your dad. They will arrange to fly out specially to visit him."

My head was already spinning, "He's not going to speak to them."

"But they say they know he did not order it. They believe it was another man – Ryan James!"

I paused. Ryan James, the Old Man's ex-partner; he was certainly a ruthless man. He could have been responsible for the murder. It was possible.

I said nothing.

Raj frowned in irritation, "He has nothing to lose and everything to gain. Can't you see that?"

"It doesn't matter. He's not going to speak to the police."

He leant back, sighed a patronising sigh, as if I didn't understand and he needed to explain. I thought the same back at him. Nevertheless, we debated the issue and finally, we agreed a plan.

I would fly out, visit the Old Man, let him know about the taps and persuade him to talk. The first part was vital, the second a waste of time. He would never speak to the police.

I had no doubt.

* * *

THE FOLLOWING WEEK I flew into Madrid and for the first time met Oscar, the Old Man's Spanish lawyer. In his fifties, heavy set and bold with a bushy black moustache, Oscar's manner was blunt but practical. Though he was fighting the Dutch extradition for the Royle 'murder', I was to break it to him that there was another alleged murder, and again, my father was 'innocent'.

He was not impressed.

"Innocent again! What is it with your father?"

This was a difficult one, "He has a lot of bad luck –"

"Maybe he has a lot of bad friends."

I shrugged and held onto my annoyance. Oscar had a point. I wanted to explain and excuse him, but it would be impossible. I kept my thoughts to myself.

That Gerard Meesters had been killed had come as a shock.

My recall was of the Old Man pursuing the stolen loads of hashish some months back. He had pursued a few leads from the Costa del Sol, which took him all the way to the small Dutch city of Groningen and a schoolteacher named Gerard Meesters. He was the brother of the Dutch woman Janette, the Old Man's translator. Having located the brother, via Sowerby, the Old Man attempted to discuss contact with his sister so she could return the stolen hashish. He had no interest in reprisals. It was business.

And then what?

What had happened during those final weeks?

We drove swiftly south to the small town of Pinto, situated a few miles down from the prison. To Oscar's surprise, I took a modest hotel and sent him away. He may have been expecting to chaperone me for a few days, but I feared another bill. Oscar's recent legal bills had already wiped out what little money I held.

This dire financial situation spoke volumes about the Old Man's criminal world. Whilst in the movies, criminals looked after their own, in real life they rarely did. Instead, they evaluated their 'friends' like commodities. To them, the Old Man was serving six years, facing drug charges in the UK, and a murder charge in Holland.

His stock price was rock bottom.

With Oscar gone, I kicked my heels in Pinto for a few days, waiting for a visiting order to be cleared and the Old Man to be released from the prison hospital. Whilst I did so, I gave long thought to the recent problem that had emerged.

What had happened in Groningen? I speculated that Sowerby and the other men involved had lost patience with the Old Man's wish to negotiate the parcel's return.

Few criminals had patience with the Old Man's business-like approach to such problems; after all, it had not served him well recently. Such negotiation had resulted with his own shooting in Amsterdam. He had taken the same approach with the Boatman after the cargo ship was seized. Others wanted the Boatman kidnapped and tortured until he returned the money, but the Old Man had held out to negotiate. It had got him nowhere. Others had seen this as soft and exploited the perceived weakness. The Irish had been the first (refused payment), Brighton the second (stolen load), and the two Dutch women the third (two stolen loads).

In their case, it had ended in murder.

* * *

AT SUNRISE, with no bus service running, I walked up to the prison along three miles of steep sloping lanes. As the sky brightened, more visitors appeared at every junction to form a long, broken line trailing up into the hills. Walking solemnly, I totalled up the years he'd actually served: three months for a teenage burglary, eighteen months for the copper theft, two years for the bike fiasco, six and a half years for the bank robbery, seven years for the counterfeit, two years on remand for drugs. Total: 19 years three months.

A waste of a life?

It appeared so.

And what was next?

Another ten years? Twenty years? Thirty?

It was possible.

Eventually I approached the summit and Valdemoro III prison loomed into view. From a distance it was like something from the days of General Franco: high walls, lookout towers and razor wire. It sat proudly on a sandy plateau under a warming sky.

I paused to take it all in, before walking on.

I followed the numbers to the visiting centre, an old crumbling building, computerless and backward. For an hour I waited, observing the visitors, the grey-haired mothers, the several sad wives, a few middle-aged men here and there.

Finally, we were called.

After a brief body search, we were herded along to a small dingy windowless room lined with tables and glass screens on three sides. Assigned a number, I found my seat and several long minutes later, the prisoners trickled in one at a time, with the Old Man one of the first to arrive.

He looked thinner than I recalled but otherwise the same.

With a glass screen between and no microphone, it was near impossible to hear one another. Like other visitors, we resorted to talking loudly through the air vent at the foot of the screen, and within minutes the room was a cacophony of conversations.

I conveyed all that Raj had relayed whilst the Old Man leant in and listened. Once done, I waited for him to digest the news. This didn't take long. He crouched in and spoke loudly through the vent.

"Right, this is the way to play it. Tell Raj that I'll talk to them. Tell them they just need to come out here!"

"What?"

He leant in some more and raised his voice over the racket.

"Tell them they need to come and see me."

"Are you serious?" I yelled back. And looked up to show him my puzzled face. He leant down to speak.

"Once they're here, once I've seen their paperwork, then they can go. They can leave… with fuck all!"

He looked up – to check I was getting this – and added, "But you just tell him… whatever you have to. Just get them here!"

I nodded thoughtfully, "And what about the phone taps?"

"Inadmissible at best! At worst…" he paused, "I think there's little there. If they were that good, they would have played them and frightened the shit out of him. It'll be nothing to worry about!"

This made sense and was reassuring.

And so the visit continued. With every minute the room grew louder still, and though alternating between leaning in and yelling or leaning in and listening, somehow, we managed to explore several scenarios and the line I was to take. The important thing was that the Dutch arrive at Valdemoro confident he would speak to them. From that point he had it sorted.

A guard stubbed out a fag and bellowed; it was near time. The visit had been barely twenty minutes. I quickly raced down a list of messages. He asked about each family member. I gave one-word answers and asked about his health. He shrugged it off as nothing.

Within minutes, I fell back in line with the other visitors, traipsing down the lanes to Pinto. The sun was high, the sky an imposing blue and already my mind was back in England, telling Raj the 'good news' that the Old Man would talk.

He simply had to arrange it.

* * *

A MONTH LATER, the Dutch Prosecutor and his team landed in Madrid. As requested, they submitted an *Outline of Evidence*. It included, as requested, the list of the questions they proposed to ask. At the prison, a private room had been arranged.

They sat and waited.

Whilst they did so, the Old Man phoned Oscar to confirm he possessed the *Outline of Evidence*. Once he had confirmation, he cancelled the meeting.

The prosecutor and his team were bewildered. They made some calls, lodged a complaint, but there was nothing they could do. The next day they returned to Holland.

A few days later, their *Outline of Evidence* arrived through my door. I read it hungrily, wanting to know what had happened in Groningen. It ran twelve pages long and detailed the series of events leading up to the Meesters murder and the subsequent chain of evidence which led Groningen's police to suspects, Sowerby and Barnes. The final section cited the highlights of the critical phone taps. There were a few damaging statements but nothing more.

Most critically, to me at least, the report was clear that the Old Man had not ordered the shooting.

Now I had to relay the news to Raj.

We met at the usual place.

He greeted me with his usual, "Hello, dear boy!"

However, minutes later he was dumbfounded

"Why didn't he talk to them?" he glared. "You said he was going to."

"He changed his mind."

"But they know he was not behind it! Why not talk?"

"It's against his principles," I offered and sensed Raj's temper simmering and threatening to boil over. I raised my hands for calm. "Between you and me, I never thought he would."

He shook his head in disapproval, and the anger spilled.

"He still does not listen to me. Why does he not listen? Does he still believe in all that criminal code, that being 'Old School', keeping one's words and all that bullshit!"

In Raj's world, criminals were all out for themselves.

"Let me tell you. They all grass off each other, rob off each other and demonstrate no morals. No morals at all! That's all of them. Why do you think there just a few who never get arrested? Never go to prison. Isn't it obvious?"

I gazed down into my coffee. I knew to expect this.

"Only your dad clings to this criminal code. Only he still believes in it. That's why he's spent half his life inside!"

I looked up. He met my eyes, hesitated, and paused. "I'm... I'm just disappointed. I thought he'd agreed."

"No. You should have known he wouldn't."

We sat there for a while. I drank my coffee. Raj calmed down.

I heard him out one last time and then made tracks. By then all a weary Raj could offer was, "Okay, dear boy, just keep me posted."

And with that, I believed it was all done with.

BACK INSIDE

* * *

THREE AREAS OF concern were still to be addressed. Firstly, he needed to win the appeal against his Spanish sentence. Second, he needed to avoid extradition for the murder of David Royle. And thirdly, he needed some reassurance that the earlier UK drug conspiracy had been dropped.

Added to this were the health problems exacerbated by the gunshot fragments. He would be rushed to the prison hospital whenever the symptoms increased and returned after receiving a course of meds. Several times, so serious was his condition that he was rushed out to a civilian hospital under armed guard.

It was on such an occasion that he was treated by an ex-army doctor who had served in Serbia and had specialised in gunshot wounds. He warned the Old Man that if he did not get the fragments removed, *"They will kill you from the inside out."* His prognosis was the Old Man would be dead within ten years of the shooting otherwise.

It was as serious a warning as he would ever receive.

Meanwhile, up in the Netherlands at a brief and simple trial concerning the murder of Gerard Meesters, the prosecution demonstrated beyond reasonable doubt that Sowerby had been the gunman and Steven Barnes his driver. In July 2005, both men were found guilty. Sowerby received 25 years. His accomplice Barnes received ten. Neither protested their innocence.

A month later, the Old Man's appeal failed and a few days later, chained to two guards, he was escorted on a flight to Amsterdam. From his arrival, the Dutch held him incommunicado whilst they questioned him. Consequently, as expected, I heard nothing. This gave me plenty of time to mull matters over and questioned the wisdom of helping the Old Man given recent events.

I reflected on the Old Man's role in the death of Meesters, his plans to deal in cocaine and his entire life of crime. He had drifted some way off from the path he had intended as a young man. From the beginning, he'd undeniably had a talent for making money but also a fascination for crime which, over time, had displaced his appetite for business. In the end, he'd become a criminal, employing all those business skills he'd developed in the early years to become a drug dealer.

Maybe that was built into his character, and for me, the reasons why he became a criminal were all pointing towards his character.

Why he had such a character when it ran opposed to his own self-interests was a mystery. It made him appear seriously flawed and ultimately self-destructive. To many, he ought to have been a millionaire, but for some strange reason had nothing. Rather, he was always starting over, building and building, reaching greater and greater heights, only to come crashing down to earth once more. He was a confusing individual, an enigma who got bored easily, who was always onto his next idea, who would neglect what was working for riskier criminal matters when it seemed unnecessary.

Why did he need to do that?

It could only be his character, but it was a character that made little sense.

So ultimately, where was I at?

Despite recent disappointments, I factored in the pressures he had been under and the situations he found himself in. And from this period of consideration, I accepted him to be a flawed but nevertheless good man. Someone who didn't deserve to spend any more time in prison. I therefore resolved to continue doing all I could to help him. He was my father after all, and above all things, I considered it the right thing for any son to do.

In thinking this through, I could obviously recognise that I had my own agenda. Chief amongst them was that I simply couldn't bear seeing him serve any more time.

To watch the Old Man languishing in prison brought back unpleasant memories.

CHAPTER 15:
HMP LONG LARTIN

1983-88

I STILL LOATHE prison visits. If the earlier prison visits at Leyhill had provided me with fondly held memories of us as a family, the visits to Long Lartin would gift me with painful memories of how our family unit disintegrated within a few short years. As in those earlier times, we'd rise early, dress in our good clothes, take an hour-long drive to the prison. However, unlike cosy Leyhill in its woodland surroundings, HMP Long Lartin was a large intimidating institution, set in the bare farmlands of Worcestershire.

Sitting by the right passenger window, I would gaze at the rising hills in anticipation. Gradually the tall, spoked prison lights would appear high in the distance, multiplying and emerging from beyond hillsides. We'd slow and turn right to ascend a winding lane, watching the lights growing taller and emerging from beneath them, high prison walls creeping into view. My stomach would tumble in excitement and apprehension.

As before, we would arrive early, aiming to be first on the list to secure the longest visit. For two hours our visiting order would be processed as we sat around killing time, observing the other families arriving, reading the prison notices, the warning signs, and the threatening posters, until eventually the door to the visiting room was unlocked and a screw arrived with the register. Finally, we would hear those familiar words bawled out:

"VISITORS FOR SPENCER!"

We would bolt upright and rush over to the desk. The screw would glance at our Visiting Order (VO), look down the register, tick the right-hand column and on the back of the VO write something like: '*Row C. Table 6*'.

"You can go in," he would say without a smile.

We, my Mum, sister and me, would enter a large unfriendly hall of sixty or so tables with a stern looking inmate sat at each one. I would hurry ahead, scan the tables for our row number before spotting the Old Man stood facing our way. He'd greet our Mum with a kiss on the cheek, my sister a sharp cuddle, and for me a firm handshake.

As HMP Long Lartin was a maximum-security prison holding terrorists, murderers, and bank robbers, visits were strict and formal. Also, due to the influx of drugs, there had been changes introduced.

Visitors could no longer sit to the sides of inmates but opposite, so the screws had a clear view. Additionally, we could no longer bring in our own food. They had installed a canteen manned by volunteers under the watchful eye of a screw.

I would be dispatched early to secure a place at the front of the queue. There I would wait, observing the room, studying the inmates and speculating as to their crimes. Most looked quite ordinary, but there were a few clues. Undoubtedly, an Irish accent meant IRA; larger burly inmates who received respectable nods would be lifers or bank robbers; those who received no such nods and avoided all eye contact were the 'nonces' as the Old Man called them.

Initially, I'd been quite impressed with the place. It was modern and clean. Not what I expected a prison to be. The Old Man spoke highly of the prison and played down any negatives. Being locked up really wasn't that bad. Like at Leyhill a few years back, he dressed in T-shirt, jeans and trainers with his hair cut short, and I noticed he did make an effort to fit in. He spoke differently, swore a bit, 'fucking' this and 'fucking' that, using prison lingo – 'screws', 'lifers', 'nicks', 'grasses.' It seemed quite exciting and to be honest, these early visits were even quite cheery. Often there would be three adults and us kids, but then we'd had a few joint visits with his co-accused where the numbers were doubled, and it felt like a social event.

The consensus amongst the visiting adults was the Old Man's ten-year sentence had been excessive and his arrest a stitch up. People were convinced the police had been out to get him, that he'd grown too big for his boots on Gosford Street and made too many enemies. There was speculation as to who the grass had been, but it would be some time before this would be known. Throughout such discussions, though, only Mum would point out that he should never have been robbing a bank in the first place, that it was wrong etc.

He would simply explain it was a mistake, a one-off. He was trying to save the businesses and had been desperate. He pointed around the room; prisons were full of people who had made mistakes. He was one of many, but he would learn.

Sounded reasonable to me.

I would return with a tray of teas, crisps and chocolate and find the Old Man updating Mum on what had been happening that month.

I'd take a seat, lean in, all ears, wanting to know more.

He regarded himself fortunate to be at Long Lartin as it was considered one of the best in the country for education. Enrolling on several courses in business and law, he claimed they would prove priceless. On release, he would be starting up new companies which would make more money than before.

"There's no need to earn lots of money," Mum would caution. "It's not worth taking risks for."

"There'll be no risk," he corrected her. "These will be legal businesses."

My eyes would bounce between them and sense conflict.

"Your Mum worries too much. I've plenty of time here to get the right idea that'll make a fortune. Making a lot of money is easy once you've got the right idea, which I will have."

I would nod and smile, though noticeably our Mum said little, her mind elsewhere.

These visits, month by month, had undeniably become discouraging. News from his family? As usual, very little. Ex-workers? Friends? Associates? Week by week, we heard less and less. Their promises, their favours? They more often failed to materialise. Visit by visit, the circle of friends decreased. It was apparent that many of his old 'friends' whom he'd previously talked of in glowing terms weren't so great after all. There were a few good souls, but more often than not it was Mum's family who came through when the car needed fixing, or the phone was to be cut off, or a bailiff's letter arrived.

Throughout the visit, he would talk through these problems as he worked down a long list of notes written in blue biro on the inside of his forearm. Somewhere midway down would be written 'DAVID' – increasingly in large capitals.

"What's happening at school and why hasn't he come?"

Mum and I would exchange glances. The answer was one and the same: truancy, fighting, and swearing. He had been suspended twice and expected to be expelled by the end of the week. The Old Man shook his head in despair at my brother who didn't listen. At earlier visits David had agreed to be on best behaviour; the Old Man, serving ten years for armed robbery, had lectured him at length about steering clear of bad influences and obeying the rules whilst I watched on.

The irony was not lost on me.

Since the Old Man had been away, David's schooling had deteriorated. At sixteen, he would be expelled with no exams taken and the dole queue waiting. Seemed the worst news to me, but the Old Man would sweep my concerns to one side. "Exams aren't everything!" he'd announced. "He won't need any. He'll be working for me when I get out."

I raised an eyebrow. From my understanding, he wouldn't be out for another four or five years. In the meantime, what were we all supposed to do?

He continued down his list: "Jason's school. What's the latest?"

I had found my application to senior school refused as we lived three hundred metres outside the catchment area. Thanks to the Old Man's shortsightedness we'd been moved from school to school to school until I found myself living in Coventry (West Midlands) and being schooled three miles away in Bedworth (Warwickshire). The Old Man had gotten our local MP involved, explained our difficult family circumstances and achieved nothing. I would be starting another new school in September.

I shrugged, nodded and pretended it was fine.

Next, he turned his attention to my younger sister Kate, a sweet eight-year-old unable to accept why her dad was in prison nor could she understand why he couldn't come home after each visit. To maintain a semblance of normality, he'd done all he could to ensure she kept her Shetland pony, which for me was a moot point. We were struggling for money, and she had a horse! After a brief discussion of horse shows and gymkhanas, he'd make promises for a new saddle or a new stable, and she'd be happy.

Around this time, a screw would holler, "TEN MINUTES!" The room would pause a few seconds, then conversations would resume, now hurried, louder and more urgent.

The Old Man would recap his lists and by the time the screws were ushering the last visitors from the room, there was barely a minute for goodbyes. Even so, as we came away my sister would create a scene, sobbing loudly, clinging to the Old Man first and then to the table and then to a chair until a screw arrived, and she'd be dragged or carried from the room. I would remain calm, shaking hands as he would invariably close with words: "Be good and take care of your mother."

At the door, as per usual, I would turn and take one final look, get a brief glimpse of his normality as screws barked orders and organised inmates into lines at the far end of the room. He might see me looking and manage a nod before a screw closed the visiting room doors, and he would be gone.

Until next month.

* * *

A YEAR LATER, only Mum and I were attending visits. David and Kate couldn't make it. He couldn't hide his disappointment. Our visits only required two chairs now.

When he'd first been sentenced, our visits often needed up to seven. Back then, I had looked at inmates with one visitor and felt sorry for them. I had also noted inmates with no visitor, just an empty chair. These were the no shows, often a public show of a relationship breakdown. The inmate would sit there in silence, publicly humiliated, waiting to be returned to their cell.

Now we were down to just two chairs.

My Mum would explain my brother's and sister's reasons which to me, at least, were not up to scratch. I hoped in their absence, my presence would mean more, but I was wrong. He'd be distracted throughout the visit and suddenly the visits were long at some two hours and the conversation a strain. He no longer had long lists of writing up and down his arms to discuss. I'd take along some homework to fill the gaps, but he had little patience.

I would listen in silence as he and Mum trawled down the growing list of money problems and the few people who had come through and the many who had let him down. Whilst they talked, I would queue for the canteen and watch a visiting room that had become familiar and depressing.

I would return with basic drinks and a single bar of chocolate. Money was tight now, there was little to waste. Before long, to lift the spirits, he would talk about his courses, the new qualifi-cations, his importation certificates. He would explain how he could easily take a manager's job in the sector, but instead would be setting up a haulage company upon his release. One day I spoke up.

"Would it not be better just to get a job? "I suggested.

"What?" he said, glaring at me.

I wanted to point out that it was his ambitions that had landed him in here, but I backed down from this, and offered, "Well, why do you have to own a company? Why not work for a company first?"

He bit his lip, frowned and came back at me, "Why let someone else make all the money? You can earn a lot more money if you own the company!"

I couldn't argue with his logic and by the time I was about to, he'd changed the subject and left me flailing. The next time the conversation returned my way, it concerned school and *how well I was doing*. I nodded, well aware of how little he knew of our lives outside.

By the winter of '85, we – my Mum, sister and I – were still in the same mold-ridden house. We lived in an area where we knew no-one, had no phone, and a car that failed to drive most days. My brother had long moved out and was rarely seen. The mood had become dark and depressing. I spent most evenings watching TV or drawing at the table; the upstairs rooms were too cold to sit still in. We saw few people; old friends no longer called. Each morning I shuffled off to the new school, kept my head down, took sandwiches rather than the free school meals which might draw attention. The last thing I wanted to be was the new kid whose dad was inside.

One weekend, mum declared we wouldn't be visiting. Her excuse was the car, which was considered beyond repair. I was annoyed, *'How are we supposed to get through this if no-one turns up?'* I thought to myself. *'What is our future supposed to be if we cannot make these visits?'* I sulked. I didn't enjoy the visits, but that was not the point. I saw them as essential to us all. What possible future did we have without them?

Several months passed; the visits didn't resume, and we soldiered on.

By the Spring my Aunt, who'd been there to break the news of the Old Man's arrest a few years previous, visited to break some good news and bad news to my sister and me. The good news was that we were moving to a new house near old family and friends; the bad news was that Mum and Dad were divorcing.

It would be a fresh beginning.

* * *

FOR THE FOLLOWING three years I saw him rarely, wrote infrequently. Prison letters were difficult. What do you write to a father in prison? How are things going? Is all going well? Everything you could write sounded hollow, fake and worthless. Father's Days, Birthdays and Christmas more so. You had to send cards and wish *'Happy Birthday'* to a father stuck in prison or a Father's Day card to the *'Best Father in the World'*, though you rarely saw him. Most letters focused on the future, and the word hopefully would be used over and over. I began to loathe my use of the word.

It was around this time that I began to hear rumours.

Some were quite unpleasant, with no notion whether they were true or not. There were stories of stashed guns, revolvers in wardrobes, under garden steps, stored in safes. There were claims of lorry heists, bank robberies, kneecappings back in the day. It was impossible to distinguish the truth from the fiction.

I naturally began to wonder whether the dad I remembered was the good man I thought he was. If half of the things I heard were true, then how could he be?

I stopped writing for a while. And when eventually I did write, I repeated the rumours I'd heard. Asked whether they were true.

He replied, saying that he paid no heed to gossip and neither should I. He knew the truth from the fiction. Mistakes had been made, he was not perfect, but he had no regrets and had done everything he could to provide for his family. When I was older, I would understand.

It didn't answer my questions.

Impossible to reconcile the rumours with the father I had known, it was easier to ignore it, not mention it anymore. Like most teenagers, I kept my thoughts to myself, my feelings shut, our family business a tightly kept secret.

Having moved to a new house, this was an easy thing to do. My school was now five miles away on the north side of the city. It would have made sense to move schools, but with just a few years to go, there seemed little point. Besides, at school, no-one knew where I lived, that my Old Man was inside or that my parents had divorced. As we had no phone or car, it was easy to remain anonymous and distant.

This seclusion meant I became somewhat absorbed in hobbies. Long hours of drawing and reading replaced nights with mates. School became somewhere I merely had to go during the day for a few years, until I was done, until my sentence was complete, and I could leave to do something I wanted to do.

Art college would be the answer. It is where I would go at sixteen, just at the point where I'd stopped waiting for the Old Man. In college, I would be with like-minded artists, some of whom were aspiring filmmakers. On weekends, I would join them and make a series of animated films.

Twenty-four drawings a second, piles of paper and cells, I would recruit other students to help out, painting backgrounds, inking cells, recording sound effects, filming and videoing. I was unlike any criminal's son.

So obsessed was I with this work, the Old Man was largely forgotten for a while.

Then one evening there was a knock at the door of our new house. I was sat eating some egg on toast, a tray on my lap, an episode of *Blockbusters* on the TV. I sighed, placed my tray down and stomped around to the front door. Still chewing on some toast, I opened the door and saw standing there, in a loose fitting dark blue suit, the Old Man.

He was greyer than I remembered. Shorter too, or was that me.

I was by then a lanky seventeen-year-old, an art student with John Lennon glasses and scraggly hair. I didn't know what to say.

"Alright Jason. Is your Mum in?"

"No… she's out."

He walked straight in without being asked, which left me at a loss as to what to say or do. This was our new house. "Just need a glass of water," he stated and helped himself.

"She'll be back later," I added, watching him gulp down a glass. "When did you get out?"

"A few hours ago."

I watched him and sensed how he was buzzing with energy, like I remember.

"Is Kate about?"

"No, she's at Sue's."

"Okay. Everyone's alright though?"

I nodded, "Yeah. We're all fine."

"I've a driver waiting, so I best get going," he said. And with that, for the only time in my life, he patted me on the shoulder. "I'll call back later," he added.

"I'll tell them you called," I said, following him to the door. "Do you know what time you'll be back?"

"Later," he called. And with that he was off. I watched him walk down the street to a new looking car with a driver waiting. He climbed inside, chatted with the driver, and after a minute or two, pulled away.

It had been almost seven years.

And just like that, he was back.

CHAPTER 16:
DUTCH JUSTICE

FEBRUARY 2006

AFTER TWO WEEKS held incommunicado, the Old Man was transferred from Amsterdam to Nieuwegein Penitentiary in Utrecht. A formidable and modern complex, this prison was a holiday camp compared to Valdemoro. With his own cell, central heating, a TV and a library, prison time would be easy.

He faced up to twenty-five years if found guilty of murder. That he would spend the remainder of his life in prison was unthinkable. I prayed he would receive a second chance, but if he didn't. Well, that would be that.

For me, regardless of the outcome, my time helping the Old Man was drawing to a close.

The previous year had been tough going. He'd had no-one else to turn to, but I had my own problems, and I had come to recognise that his problems were never ending. There was always one more thing, one more favour, one more something. And they all meant dealing with people I had come to tire of and at times dislike.

The task of raising his Spanish legal fees had fallen to me. He provided a list of his contacts and I relayed them to the Old Man's request. Truth be told, most on the list were writing him off. Only a few would chip in, and then small amounts.

Desperation would see me visiting a scar-faced club owner and relaying some bad news.

"I've had an offer," I declared.

Comfortable behind a large busy desk, his eyes narrowed with suspicion, "An offer?"

"A contact of the Old Man has offered to buy your debt up."

He stared into me and said nothing for a moment.

Immediately I was regretting the words.

He shifted in his seat, shook his head slowly, "Who's this then?"

My throat was suddenly bone dry. I looked down, cleared my throat, "A well-known family in the city."

It went downhill for me from that point.

"You do know what you're saying? You do know you're threatening me?"

Now he mentioned it, that was what it sounded like. Except, I hoped he might have seen it differently. He owed the Old Man eighteen grand. The club had been struggling and so the Old Man had given him a loan for a few months. That was two years ago, and he hadn't repaid a penny.

"The Old Man doesn't want it this way. But it's been a while now. A few months ago, I made an offer that you pay half —"

"Does that still stand?"

I was taken back, "Well, yes. Of course."

"Be back here tomorrow at eleven. I'll have it."

I felt my chest beating away; hoping I appeared calm.

He stood up, "Now, if that's all. I've business to get on with."

He walked me through the club, by the unlit dance floors and into a small, tight lobby. At the doors, he searched for a key and changed his tone, "Your Old Man shouldn't be scratching around for money. With what he's made, he should have millions tucked away."

"I know that's what people think, but…"

He opened the door. "Yeah. Same time tomorrow."

I stepped out into the street, not knowing what to think. Not wanting to go back tomorrow. The club would be quiet at that time. And I'd be alone. With someone I'd pissed off.

Over the next twenty-four hours I played over our meeting, questioning what he said and what he meant, why he wanted me to return to the club rather than meet in a public place. His club hired some of the hardest bouncers in the city.

Would he try anything? Should I take someone along? Or would that look weak?

I didn't know. I had no protection. I just had the Old Man's name.

The following day I returned, but phoned my cousin beforehand, "If you don't hear from me within the hour, there's been a problem."

What he would then do, I don't know. He would just know. He could get a message to the Old Man, somehow.

As it was, the meet went well in terms of the money. He paid it, but with a curious speech that ended with pretty much the following words: "I've worked hard to build up this club. There's been a few people who've taken advantage here and there. But I bide my time. I have a long memory. I never forget."

He stared hard at me and held out an envelope. I took it.

The walk to the doors took longer than the day before. Barely a word was spoken. He slammed the door shut as I stepped out onto the street. Immediately, I felt high with relief, but angry at what I'd had to do.

It would be the last time.

I had his legal fees for what little good they'd do. His seven years was amended to six, and the extradition appeal would fail all the way to the Spanish High Court.

Extradition to Holland would follow.

Either way, my days of running around after him would be over. Guilty, and he'd have to serve his time. Not Guilty, then he would be able to start over one day, but without my support.

I could no longer do this.

* * *

THE TRIAL when it came was simple and short. As forewarned, there was no jury but three judges. They made it clear the Court was solely interested in the killing of David Royle and nothing more.

By this point the Old Man had read every paper on the case – forensic reports, witness statements, phone taps – and realised the prosecution's picture was so incomplete and riddled with false assumptions, it was merely a matter of adjusting his account to the evidence. Critically, though, he could provide X-rays of the bullet fragments spread throughout his chest and clustered around his lungs.

This would make the difference.

With such incontrovertible evidence, he had the credibility to provide an account that step-by-step mixed fact and fiction to convincing effect. The cross-examination as expected was long and rigorous, but his account was tight and all encompassing. He explained his circumstantial role, how he and Royle were attacked, how he had been shot and, in the confusion, disorientated and scared for his life, grabbed Royle's gun and blasted away, unintentionally killing Royle in the process.

By the Friday, the judges retired for the weekend. The trial had lasted just five days.

On the Monday, his Dutch lawyer relayed the good news.

NOT GUILTY.

* * *

THE FOLLOWING WEEK, he called me on the prison phone.

"Have you got it with you now," he asked.

"Right here. It's short and brief, but it does the job… You want me to read it out?"

"Sure. See no reason why not; we've nothing to hide."

I held up the article, and as it was so brief, read it out in full:

10th February 10, 2006, Evening Telegraph
COURT: Dutch court accepts plea of self defence

CITY MAN CLEARED OF MANSLAUGHTER

A man from Coventry has been acquitted by a Dutch court of manslaughter.

Anthony Cyril Spencer had been accused of killing 37-year-old David Royle who was shot dead on May 26 2001 in Amsterdam Holland. The Foreign Office said a Dutch court had acquitted him of the charge. It is understood Spencer's plea of self defence was accepted and he was cleared on Monday. Spencer was shot in the chest during the incident when Mr Royle was killed [...]... he is appealing against the drugs conviction and may soon be eligible for release.

The article was a result of my badgering the paper's editor. He had previously run large headlines when the Old Man was wanted, but when found not guilty, had printed nothing.

"So, what do you think?"

"Good, good. It does what it has to do. It sends out a message."

"Yeah, it'll get around," I agreed, and privately hoped.

Hoped, because my own reasons for word getting around might have been different to the Old Man's. I didn't want anyone knocking my door for monies owed or to hear from a nightclub owner with a grudge. I wanted to feel safe to get on with my own life, without looking over my shoulder.

I believed that people knowing the Old Man would be out soon would achieve just that.

Another consequence of the not guilty verdict was it had taken the wind out of the National Crime Squad's sails. They had pursued the Old Man for a murder and drugs conspiracy but now found not guilty for the so-called murder, it only left the conspiracy. Conspiracy to smuggle drugs was not a crime in either the Netherlands or Spain. Therefore, he could not be extradited.

And so, the months passed.

After the verdict, he continued to serve his Spanish sentence from Holland where he was in comfort and the chances for medical attention were more hopeful. The Dutch had run all the tests the Spanish had, reached the same conclusions, and promised to remove the bullet fragments.

Whilst he awaited a date, he filled his days studying languages and law. Anything regarding crime was put on ice as he expected his correspondence to be relayed onto the Crime Squad in the UK. Our agreement, until he was returned to Spain, was to speak of nothing that could be interpreted to be of a criminal nature.

This suited me. I had nothing to relay to those phoning in, and so gradually the phone went quiet. Consequently, with no running around, no requests for favours, I began to look beyond working for the Old Man.

I enrolled for courses in Art, French and Psychology.

What exactly I was going to do with these qualifications, I didn't yet know. All I did know was that I had to start doing something, and these were my core interests and therefore my starting points.

Over in Holland, as the Old Man had become similarly occupied, before long, our phone calls began to resemble quite ordinary conversations.

"How's the French going?" he'd ask. "I've sent you some papers through the post."

"Got them this morning. Did you get the law book."

"It's at reception now. It'll be cleared by the weekend."

He had discussed writing a legal book of his experiences with the court processes in the UK, Spain and the Netherlands – 'Third Time Lucky' was its working title. I wasn't too sure of what its appeal might be, but I liked the idea very much. He'd be doing something legal and worthwhile.

And so, as the year 2006 drew to a close, and I considered a new future, I began to wonder whether the Old Man might do the same.

In Spain, he'd frequently referred to 'getting away from all this shit'. The 'shit' he referred to was the criminal world where grasses were everywhere, where people stayed loyal to money and rarely did the right thing. In Spain, he'd written telling me that he would be turning his back on all the hassles and the scale of what he'd previously been involved in. He talked of working small, with few workers, fewer customers – 'just the good people'.

I came to think this might be the best way forward for him. To live out in Spain, engaged in just a few deals each year; work with Long Hair, Albert and a few others. The Old Man had bought a transport company before his Spanish arrest; he could make money running that between the UK and Spain.

It could become a legal living. He could retire from crime.

And then another thing promised to have some bearing on his decision-making. Months before the extradition, my grandfather had died. I had spoken to the Old Man shortly after he had received the news; he sounded shaken, upset maybe.

Before going on the run a few years earlier, he and I had visited his father at a nursing home. Approaching eighty, my Grandfather was experiencing some dementia. Pale and old, he no longer asked what the Old Man was up to; it didn't seem to matter anymore. There were some awkward silences as the Old Man deferred to his father, expecting him to steer the conversation.

Growing up, his father had been an ex-soldier, a paratrooper from the 1st Airborne, a war hero of sorts. He had been part of Operation Market Garden, of the infamous 'Bridge Too Far' where thousands were killed as they parachuted into the Dutch flatlands of Arnhem.

The Old Man sat patiently by him, not knowing what to say.

Grandad, when he did speak, just wanted reassurance the Old Man was good and safe, not in trouble anymore.

"You've spent enough time in those bloody places," he'd muttered.

The Old Man nodded dutifully.

Minutes later, they'd departed with a firm handshake. As we left, the Old Man commented, "At least he knows I'm not inside now. It's best he sees that."

Now his father had passed, it remained a crumb of comfort that he never learned his son was back in prison. This seemed to have meant a great deal to the Old Man. His father must have once had such high hopes for him, and maybe he still did to the end.

I had ruminated on this event and wondered whether the Old Man might be reaching the juncture where he would consider walking away from crime together. Surely, after all these years, he'd grown tired of it all. Tired of the pressure, the risks, the people, the prison time. He was no longer a young man, and due to his health problems, the last few years inside had been particularly hard.

Was there any point in going through all that again?

* * *

SIX MONTHS LATER, I was sat at my usual seat in the McDonald's restaurant. Across from me, with glasses high on his forehead, reading a large two-page article was Raj. After two minutes of silence, he leaned back, lowered his glasses and nodded thoughtfully. "Good those bastards are away. Be gone a long time." He placed the article down, returned his glasses and smiled, "Another one down, dear boy. That will do him some good."

I nodded in agreement. Several ex-contacts had fallen over the previous year, with the latest being the largest. The middle tiers of Ryan James's gang had all received high sentences, ranging between five and twenty years.

"So, what now? Any news on his return to Spain? How's his health?"

Raj always asked about the Old Man's health. Many times, he'd offered to accompany him to India to remove the bullet fragments, but the Old Man simply hadn't the time.

"He's less than a year to go. Says his health is his number one priority. He's mentioned no plans for the future – nothing at all."

Raj looked down unconcerned and the moment passed.

"So, Tiff's back?" I asked, to move on the conversation.

"I saw him a few days ago. He's working in a pub – with his girlfriend – but he's bored of it all. Wants to know when your father's back."

"And Monty?"

"Raring to go. Apologies for that previous misunderstanding and anything he can do, well, your father only has to ask?"

There was, amongst many, an underlying assumption that the Old Man would be returning to work. Raj, Tiff and Monty were all keen to be involved, though I wondered why. All three had been in and out of prison, and whilst Tiff and Monty might have few options available, not so Raj. He had a fine education, family connections, a way with people. I had grown envious of such advantages and couldn't fathom why he'd rather work for the Old Man than start over.

"What can I do, dear boy?" he'd responded. "I am 55 years old. Those bastards have ruined my life. I am fucked! Who will give me a job?"

"But you know people. You're educated. You can write."

"No, dear boy," he said, shaking his head. "I have a criminal record. No-one will hire me. Those bastards have ruined my life! Did I tell you about the first time they arrested me? Back in '98. I was the governor of a prison, the first black governor in Britain they said, you know what they're like…"

I no longer listened to his bitter recollections. He'd taken his privileges for granted, I thought, saw life as owing him a living. He also saw his future wrapped up in the criminal life. From my experience, the criminal life brought few benefits. Of the Old Man's circle, half were in prison, some were dead, and the remainder were a mixed bag of 'good people' and those rumoured to have grassed on their rivals. The only success was Albert, the reclusive millionaire out in Spain.

Nevertheless, this was ignored by people such as Raj. They considered the Old Man an exception to the rule, a businessman more than a criminal. When he returned, everything promised to be different. Why it would, I really didn't know. He was such a marked man that keeping a low profile would be impossible.

It would be the same old story.

We worked our way down the agenda which had changed little over the last few years – the same names – the 'good people': Paul (London), Linx (Boston), Albert (Spain), Long Hair (Ukraine), Kevin (San Diego) and several local villains. There was little new to discuss.

Finally, we wrapped it up.

"Any news, just give me a call, dear boy."

"No worries. But it ought to be quiet for a while."

I watched him stroll away out onto the car park and climb into his beaten-up old car and pull away. Once he was gone, I reflected. There was a cluster of people ready and eager for the Old Man to return to work, but they were low-level criminals who could make few demands. The real heavy criminals were disappearing one by one, trial by trial. By the time the Old Man was released, there would be no reason why he couldn't turn his back on it all.

No reason at all.

I sat and nursed a coffee for a while, looked around the restaurant, observed a few customers coming and going.

And then, for a moment, I looked over at the distant table by the counter in the corner. It was exactly where I had sat the first time I ever visited a McDonald's, many years back now. I was seventeen; it was at nighttime, a little after nine o'clock and getting dark. I was with the Old Man. He'd just been released from the bank robbery and was attempting to get to know me once more. He had asked what I wanted to do, where would I want to go.

"McDonald's," I'd answered.

"What's McDonald's?" he'd asked.

Chapter 17:
THE DOLLAR COUNTERFEIT

1988-91

OUR FIRST MCDONALD'S sat on the north edge of the city. A modern one-story building with an American style drive-thru. This was the future.

I gulped down a few fries, took a long suck on a chocolate thick shake and looked up and waited... waited for the moment when he took his first ever bite of a Big Mac. I was sure he'd be impressed. I watched eagerly as he clutched it between his hands, held it away for a moment to admire its many layers, before pulling it to his mouth, and taking a large bite. Several seconds passed.

"What do you think?"

He nodded his approval as he chewed.

A long silence passed between us. He'd been away for more than six years in total. I hadn't seen him at all during the last three years of his sentence. By the time of his release, I was a seventeen-year-old art student, and he appeared, looking older and less dominating than I recalled.

He moved onto the shake and I watched on and awaited the verdict. After a few seconds, he nodded his approval, though he was struggling to suck it up the straw. He kept trying and his eyes widened, and his face reddened, and he began to laugh. He pushed it away and finally cracked up laughing. I smiled and laughed to myself. For a few moments, the awkwardness was gone, but then he glanced at his watch.

It was the third time he's checked his watch and for a moment I was reminded of how he was coerced into bringing me here. "Do something with him," Mum had urged him," as if I wasn't there. "Ask him what he wants to do?"

Without hesitation, I'd opted for McDonald's.

It was late and the restaurant was quiet. We sat there for twenty minutes. Eating and drinking, though not talking much. He'd been out a week and I still didn't know what to say to him. He had no interest in football. Had never heard of Gazza! Had no interest in the news, or films or music.

What then should we talk about?

I considered asking him about what he'd been doing, but given he'd been in prison for six years, thought better of it. I imagined prison was the last thing he'd want to talk about. Then there was his new wife and family – he'd remarried when inside – but I had no interest in them. His new wife was an ex-mate of Mum's and truth be told, we pretended she didn't exist.

We carried on in silence. He switched to his fries and I tackled my thick shake. All things considered, I thought it was going well. McDonald's was a good choice, though not quite the welcome home I'd imagined all those years ago.

After the divorce, the Old Man had remarried. He had a prison wedding with a dozen guests, wedding cake, even a photographer. My brother attended and broke the news to us. Any hopes I'd harboured that my parents would reunite were snubbed out. It left me angry for a while and I'd ignored his letters for a year or so.

That was three years back. Now we sat eating Big Macs as if all were forgotten.

He glanced at his watch once more. I was keeping him and could see his mind was elsewhere. He retreated into silence and I rushed my shake. We wouldn't be long now. He grabbed some lists from his pocket, ignored his shake and began to make some notes. I watched on, aware that he had a great deal of work on but also aware, I wasn't quite sure what this work was.

Since his release, he visited us – Mum, my sister and me – several times a week. Whilst Mum cooked him dinner, he would disappear to the front room and make calls. Like in the old days, he'd settle in a chair, phone in one hand, pen and paper in the other, as he rattled off calls. After he'd produce a thick roll of notes, give Mum some phone money and housekeeping, as if they were still married. He'd then make promises on anything she needed, all of which he kept.

Whilst we ate, his pager beeped several times; he checked it, said we needed to get to a call box. I hurried my shake some more, gathered up the packaging, rammed it in a bin and caught up with him as he strode ahead to the car. He was driving a simple Ford; cheap and reliable, he said. I climbed in, belted up and we sped off. He immediately checked his rear mirror, glanced at his watch once more, "I've got some business to get to right now, but tomorrow, would you want to come and do some running around?"

"Yeah, sure." I said.

"Good. There's lots to do," he said, checking his side mirror. "It'll be a full day."

I sat there, already looking forward to it. It would be like old times. I glanced across to the Old Man, thinking he would share my nostalgia, but he was too busy checking his mirrors. Concerned that some car was following us.

* * *

HE'D BEEN OUT just a few weeks, but already he was being tailed. A surveillance team had been placed on him around the clock. Their intelligence had identified suspected activities in regard to counterfeiting.

The Old Man had spent his final year running a printing service for the inmates at HMP Sudbury. He had also taken a keen interest in watercolour painting. Both activities served as covers for accessing materials for counterfeiting. He had spent his final months plotting with other inmates under the guidance of a prominent criminal figure.

This crime figure had been arrested several months before. He'd headed a gang who'd been manufacturing dollars and were on the verge of flooding the UK with counterfeits. Fortunately, police were tipped off and made a series of arrests. However, they had failed to locate the printing plates.

They were still out there.

The Old Man bought the plates and believed the quality of the dollars could be greatly improved. Furthermore, by ramping up the scale he believed he could flood not only the UK, but Europe and North America with tens of millions of dollars. Over the years he'd accumulated a rich network of contacts, prominent criminals in all the major cities, plenty of Irish contacts, Italian, Dutch and Russian, too. The international scale of the distribution could be mind-blowing.

Unfortunately, as it concerned American dollars, the police surveillance operation would be equally mind-blowing. It would be running twenty-four-seven with more than forty full-time officers. No expense would be spared.

He picked me up early and there was something different from the beginning. He drove erratically, frequently checking mirrors before scooting twice round a series of islands, "Anyone come with us?"

"Erm, no."

He drove to a second island, took a right, a left, right – into a council estate and out the other side. "I think we're good," he commented after one further look.

"Who are we meant to be looking out for?"

"When you come out of prison, often they watch you for a while," he said casually whilst swinging around another island. "None of their business, really. I've done my time. It's up to me where I go and who I see."

I nodded naively. It was hard to disagree. And so with the 'bad guys' far behind we set about the morning meets which would be like the old days when I was a kid, though with a crucial difference. No longer did I sit in the car with a packet of crisps and a bottle of pop. Now he took me along and I felt trusted, a small part of whatever it was he was doing. All I understood was that whatever it was, it meant meetings in car parks, on wasteland, at people's houses where they'd talk in the 'safest room'. Frequently we'd pull over at some call boxes, where he'd spend half an hour going down his lists and, from what I could make out, organising a small group of ex-cons on a venture which he assured me would make millions.

Whatever that was, he was yet to confide. I could only guess.

As he drove, he talked of his plans, future businesses and how he'd have plenty of money by then. He just never explained how. What was this mystery source of money? Drugs? Gold? Diamonds? What could it be? Whilst he was engaged in a meeting at the end of someone's garden, I would be left inside supping tea, reading a paper, racking my brains as to why the secrecy.

At midday, we called by the cemetery to visit his brother's grave. I watched on from a distance as he stood solemnly, head bowed respectfully, thinking God only knows what. At that time, I knew little of Robert except that he was a scary man who'd made a lot of money and died from a heart attack. The Old Man didn't stay for long.

We dropped by a garage to have some work done on the car. He knew the garage owner, so we jumped the queue and he instructed the mechanic to sweep the car, check for trackers.

"No worries Tone," the mechanic replied with not a hint of surprise.

Whilst waiting, we dropped by a café, where the owners recognised the Old Man, as would several customers, who welcomed him like some long-lost hero. He gave the normal spiel about new businesses in the pipeline and we found a quiet spot to bide our time. After several minutes, I plucked up the courage to ask about what had happened all those years ago, regarding his businesses? There were still things I didn't understand.

I expected it to be a sore point and not something he wished to talk about, but he proved me wrong on this. He simply told me in detail of the bad luck, the bad moves and how that's business – 'you win some, you lose some.' He now planned to set up some new businesses, including one called 'Cooker Care'.

"It needs just £70,000."

"You have that much money?"

"Not now, but in a few weeks I will. My young brother will run the company. You remember Jim, don't you?"

I did vaguely. The Old Man had a brother some fourteen years his junior, whom I had rarely seen over the years.

"And he'll be your partner?"

"No. He'll be the owner. I'll give him the seventy."

"Just like that?"

"Yeah. It's only money. I'll make more."

I reflected for a moment. Jim was his brother, an adult. Couldn't he make it on his own money?

"It's not hard to make a lot of money," he reminded me.

I nodded, smiled in agreement, impressed by his confidence.

"You did receive those blue folders, didn't you?" he asked.

This referred to a business plan he'd sent me whilst in prison. I'd used it as a template for my own business plan whilst at college. I had proposed the setting up of an animation company.

"Yeah, it helped a lot. The bank manager passed it – gave it a distinction. Only one in class."

"Good. Good. But remember, if you go into business, you'll have to stop with all that drawing. Being in business is a 100 hour a week deal. You can't mess about doing drawings. You pay someone else to do that."

I nodded but said nothing, as I disagreed. I planned one day to work for myself making animated films but pictured doing things differently. Like any teenager, I had my own ideas. I switched subjects, and as he was answering anything I put his way, I asked about the informant that grassed on him, "What happened?"

"He's dead."

My mind made a few calculations, "Did you get him?"

He laughed, "No. He died in a house fire."

I smiled at my naïve question.

"Saved me a job," he then added and laughed.

I smiled. He had a dark sense of humour, which I shared.

With the car checked, we moved onto Far Gosford Street, the old home of Mainline Gas and Body Care, and a place which knew him well. There, we strolled by a few businesses of old mates and over the next hour met a score of people who were in awe of him and couldn't wait to tell people, *"Guess who I saw today? You'll never guess – Tony Spencer!"* I enjoyed the attention and regretted that we had to leave. We pressed on, obeying his lists. With inhibitions lowered, I fired further questions his way, and he answered, but with just one proviso: not when we're in the car. They bug the cars of ex-cons, which was entirely wrong, he insisted.

"Britain's like a police state," he declared.

I nodded. He'd often referred to Britain as a 'Police State' and planned to move overseas once his business was completed. "This country's too cold," he'd declared. "Spain and Italy are better places, and the States. Lots of opportunities there. Why stay here?"

I didn't agree. He'd only been back five minutes and was on about leaving already. I expected and hoped he'd drop the idea given time.

We dropped by some dog rough pubs to meet a few old mates, and then finally, a small backstreet garage where the owner appeared to be avoiding the Old Man. A few of the mechanics recognised him by face or by name and showed him around the place. Finally, we left.

"Shame he weren't in." I commented as we strolled back to the car.

"No worries. I've got what I need" he said.

"What's that?"

"A ground plan of his business."

"What do you need to know that for?"

"The owner grassed on a mate of mine. I'm going to have his place burnt out next week."

He said this matter-of-factly, and I did not doubt that he was serious. I tried to think of something else to say, but he climbed back in the car and the moment passed. I was sure his reasons were good, but it otherwise added an unpleasant edge to the day.

Prison had affected him, I thought.

Nonetheless, I put it to the back of my mind and focused on the here and now.

By late evening, I was accustomed to checking mirrors and looking behind for surveillance cars. I was no clearer as to what his new business was, but knew that whatever I saw, I was to keep it to myself.

I was learning.

I was learning so well, in fact, that it occurred to me one reason for him calling by our house so often was that it was unlikely to be under surveillance; that our phone was unlikely to be bugged. We were a 'safe place', or 'offside' as he might call it.

I didn't mind, though. I was just glad he was around once more.

* * *

AFTER A FEW MONTHS, American counterfeit dollars began appearing around the country. In London, Cardiff, Glasgow, Belfast, a trickle of hundreds was followed by thousands which increased to a cascade. Tens of thousands of near perfect counterfeit dollars were being exchanged every day. Reports flooded into the Regional Crime Squad and surveillance was stepped up. By this point they had been watching the Old Man for more than six months but knew little of the gang he led nor where they were; what they did have, amounted to little. Consequently, they broadened the surveillance and then made a breakthrough.

An associate, David Goodman was caught with $30,000 at Luton Airport. Within twenty-four hours, they arrested, interrogated and turned him. He led them to one of the Old Man's bases. There, they found stacks of hundred-dollar notes with a few items containing the Old Man's fingerprints.

Alerted to these findings, the Old Man shut the group down, pulled everything offside and disappeared. Arriving back from college one evening, I was told the news. He'd only been back a few months, and like that, he was gone.

I would later learn how he established a new life in Leicester as Pat, a chartered accountant. At his lodgings, he became the boyfriend of his landlady Crystal, an ex-glamour model with three children. Each night he returned home from 'work', settled in for the night, watching films with her family, writing no lists, making no calls, rarely venturing out in the evenings.

Until one day, when 'Pat the accountant' did not return.

He had been arrested on suspicion of stealing rental cars and remanded to Winston Green Prison, Birmingham. Later, the Regional Crime Squad would realise Pat the accountant was, in fact, Anthony Spencer. He was immediately questioned and charged with counterfeiting.

I was in Manchester when I received the news, phoning home from a call box.

"They got him last week," Mum said.

I said nothing, went silent.

"He says not to worry. He'll write if you send him your address."

A pause followed.

"Are you okay?"

"I'm fine… I'll write back," I said, and wrapped up the call, walked away too upset to talk, too sad to do much for a while.

By this time, I was off forging a career in the field of animation. Working up in Manchester, I would think of him often. He wrote expressing surprise at how well I was doing, said he had friends in Manchester should I ever have a problem, but I was fine. I would return to my lodgings each evening, switch on the TV, and for a while would follow the latest from the Strangeways riots down the road. It made me think of the prison conditions, the Old Man inside, and the hard years that lay ahead of him if he was found guilty.

I would write often, more so than before.

Updating me on the case, his letters boasted of his legal team's confidence for the benefit of the prison authorities; he was ever cheerful, and optimistic. Encouraging in my career, he would occasionally impart some fatherly wisdom: *"Don't think it, do it,"* he once wrote, a reminder not to be a talker but a doer. And *"Turnover is vanity, profit is sanity."* A reminder to focus on the bottom line.

Once I returned from Manchester, another letter awaited me, written in his familiar neat cursive handwriting. Inside was a Visiting Order.

* * *

"VISITORS FOR SPENCER!" the guard bellowed.

My sister and I stood up and strolled over to the table. On the back of our visiting order, the screw wrote our assigned row and table number. I was nineteen, my sister sixteen. It was our first prison visit for more than five years.

A large hall with rows of small tables and a man to each one. To the side there was the canteen with a queue already building, and on the side opposite, a platform, upon which warders sat along a series of tables. From up high they could watch the visits for drugs being exchanged.

I looked up ahead and on row D, seat 7, the Old Man stood up. "Jason. Over here!"

As always, he wore the usual trainers, jeans and a T-shirt, his hair cut short as he preferred it when inside. He smiled upon seeing Kate – his 'little girl'.

It had been a long time.

She rushed over, they embraced, and I could see one of the officers looking over. They were touchy about all physical contact, such was the drug problem. We took our seats and after half an hour we'd rattled through the small talk, and he was updating us on his case.

The case against him appeared paper thin. It concerned a series of partial fingerprints on assorted counterfeit dollars and the word of Goodman, their only informant. As the Old Man had not been caught with anything incriminating, the charges were those of conspiracy.

Essentially, this meant the prosecution proving that a series of perfectly legal acts were designed and intended to commit an illegal act of some magnitude. It is a difficult crime to prove.

Even so, the Old Man faced several problems. The first was the informant who 'claimed' to be part of his gang, though the Old Man was confident he would be discredited. The second problem was that a few witnesses had placed him at places he claimed not to have been. He faced an identity parade, for which he would stall until he had dropped a few stones. The third was the alleged fingerprints, which were partial and arguable. Experts would be called to analyse the papers and prints, and plant seeds of doubt. However, the fourth and most insurmountable problem was the corruption of the police unit he was up against. Evidence had been switched, backdated, re-dated and lost when required. The solution to this was to expose them and have the case thrown out.

"Can that be done?" I asked keenly.

"Certainly. The same group have fitted up several of the Irish here. It's thought this police unit will have to be broken up. You heard of the West Midlands Serious Crime Squad?"

We shook our heads.

"Well, it's them. And they're desperate. My case is one of the last they'll handle."

This was good to hear and I was glad of his confidence. He pressed on and explained how that morning they'd just served him with the most ridiculous legal papers he'd ever seen.

"Why are they so ridiculous?" I asked.

"Well," and he grabbed a pen he'd borrowed earlier from a screw. He covered his hand and on a small scrap of paper wrote '$250,000,000' and passed it to me.

"That's how much they say I was trying to print."

I stared on in shock as he failed to suppress a smile, "It's ridiculous," he added. "Don't they know I'd never go that far?"

'Do they?' I wondered, and for a moment my demeanour changed as it dawned on me that if he didn't get it thrown out, he may never get out again!

* * *

THE TRIAL LASTED FIVE MONTHS, went through three juries, neared collapse at several points, and cost close to a million pounds. The prosecution posited the lower figure of $125,000,000 as the Old Man's target figure but had trouble proving the fact. Every detail would be defended and argued, every note, every print, every sighting, every police statement.

Month by month the trial inched forward, each month he wrote saying he was confident of victory. However, in the final month, with some evidence being found to have been tampered with, the defence was forced to withdraw on ethical grounds. The Old Man, with law certificates coming out of his ears, stepped up.

For the final few weeks, he represented himself, carrying out cross examinations, outlining new evidence and delivering the closing argument. It was then he spent over three hours persuading the jury to recognise that the police lied, that the informant was dishonest, that if they wanted to, they could see through the 'web of dishonesty and corruption' and 'recognise the mixture of misleading and blatant untruths.'

The jury took just five hours to deliberate five months of evidence. By the day's end, he was found GUILTY.

Branded a 'criminal mastermind', the Judge Richard Gibbs QC complimented him on his intelligence and outstanding ability but gave him eleven- and-a-half years.

It made the front page of all the regions' papers:

31st May, 1991

FORGERY KING'S JAILHOUSE PLOT

Master forger Anthony Spencer plotted to filter a million dollars' worth of phony banknotes into Britain and Europe. The 42-year-old conman from Coventry hatched the scheme while serving a six year stretch in jail for armed robbery. He ended up in the dock in a trial that lasted five months and cost £800,000

Spencer used his time inside learning how to print forgeries. He recruited fellow convicts to help spread the counterfeit around. [...] Instead, he ended up in the dock. Spencer was found guilty of trying to pass $100 bills and also conspiring to steal cars and pervert the course of justice.

Judge Richard Quibbs QC jailed Spencer for eleven and a half years today at Wolverhampton Crown Court.

Spencer was a petty criminal who moved into the big time when he was convicted for an armed bank robbery in Coventry in 1982. When he was freed in 1988 via Lowbridge a team of Wolverhampton based crime squad officers tracked Spencer's movements. Intelligence reports poured in about forged dollars turning up around the country.

Christopher Hotton, prosecuting said, "Using a football analogy, Spencer was a club manager. He organised and directed but was never seen on the pitch playing the game."

I hadn't had to search the archives for this headline. I'd bought a copy of that day's city paper; read it with tears rolling down my cheeks. It was mentioned by each person in the family, but we didn't discuss it. Best put it away, pretend it didn't matter.

I had folded the article up, placed it inside a book. It was still in pristine condition. Now with several similar clippings, I had a thickening scrap book which told of a man battling two instincts – one legal, that aspired to start businesses and do the right thing, and one criminal which had little patience, discarded rules and laws, demanded to make a million overnight.

Back then, the criminal instincts were winning.

Consequently, he was finished; at least that was what most people at the time believed. The Old Man would be in his late forties by the time of release. Too old to start over. And the toll it would take?

He wouldn't be the same man again.

* * *

AT THE TIME OF the sentencing, I was working down London at a new Hollywood studio owned by the movie-mogul Steven Spielberg.

Amblimation was a large studio situated in West London. Its purpose was to produce animated feature films for cinema release. The studio employed almost 300 artists, half British, half international. Each day, hundreds of artists flocked to 207 The Vale where they spent their days in small wooden cubicles making pencil drawings, inking cells, painting backgrounds for the movie *American Tail: Fievel Goes West.*

I wrote to the Old Man, sharing my good news, hoping it might raise his spirits. I would later learn that he was proud of how I was getting on, but at the time, I can't recall him saying much. I assumed animation was something he didn't quite get, something childish, maybe. Something that grown men didn't do.

He wrote back, talking of an appeal, but I wasn't optimistic. For a while I brooded over his situation and my own. I ought to have been proud to work for Amblimation, this great Hollywood company, except after a year, I was still just a small cog in a big machine. The upper tiers of the company were Americans, with just a handful of British artists involved. I could see no way forward. I was a decent artist, but not a great one. Besides, I had the Old Man's impatience. And following his sentencing, I suddenly had an irrepressible urge to get out there and do something more important.

Produce a film, set up a studio, build a company.

I now recognise my decision was as much about compensating for the Old Man's existence, as it was my own ambitions. One afternoon, I knocked the door to the production office, handed in my notice.

I was done working for other people.

CHAPTER 18:
LIKE FATHER, LIKE SON

1992-95

IT'S OBVIOUS NOW that my decision to pursue a self-employed path was influenced by the Old Man's bankruptcy and subsequent prison time. I had long nurtured the romantic ideal that one day I would correct the past, redeem the Old Man, lavish family with all the money I made and carve a large important future for myself.

For a while all would go well.

A year after quitting London, a client flew me into Douglas, Isle of Man, to raise capital for a TV pilot entitled *Pablo and the Palette People*. Arriving at the hotel, a pile of newspapers being delivered caught my eye. I grabbed a copy and smiled wide in recognition. Splashed across the entire front page of the *Isle of Man Islander* ran the headline: ISLAND LAUNCH FOR CARTOON CHARACTERS. Stretched beneath, a large drawing of mine featuring Pablo and his magical palettes caught the eye; beneath that, a five-hundred-word article outlining the fund-raising promotion and how the pilot was to be produced by the company of 21year-old animator Jason Shipley.

At last, I was in business and doing something that mattered.

* * *

THE OLD MAN lost his appeal. He was upbeat and explained the maths: *"Sentenced to eleven and a half years, given my previous record, I will serve maybe six or seven. I will assure the lesser figure by ticking all the boxes for the benefit of the parole board. I will be a model prisoner."*

Early days: My brother, the Old Man and me

On holiday in Devon, 1976, when the Old Man is on the run

Headquarters: The Old Man's office
on the second floor

'It could put us out of business':
A newspaper cutting of the
warehouse fire

Getting married behind bars, 1995

Businessman: At the Body Care opening with Miss World in 1981

The Old Man as a young man. 1983, taken at HMP Long Lartin

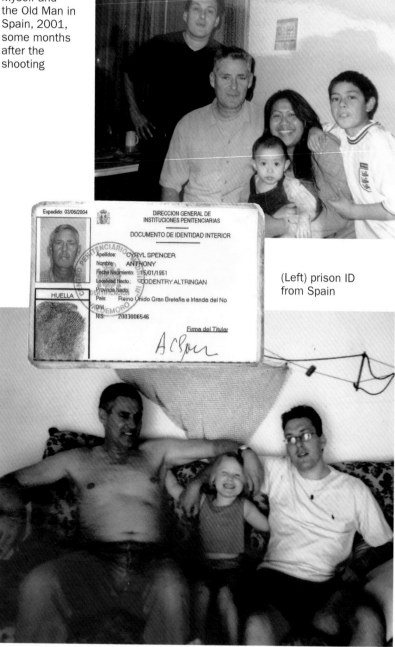

Myself and the Old Man in Spain, 2001, some months after the shooting

(Left) prison ID from Spain

The Old Man, my sister and myself – in Castelldefels in 2002

In 2007, on the Old Man's return from Spain – a quiet moment with granddaughter Kia

Pastille Jones, the crime boss modelled on the Old Man from one of my cartoon books

A surveillance photo of the Old Man in Amsterdam in 2009

A signing at former bookstore Borders for my Smuggling Vacation book, when me and the Old Man were observed by undercover officers

'Author's dad was Britain's most wanted': Newspaper story when I brought out my comic book in 2008 and (inset) the front cover of Smuggling Vacation

At work as per
usual, 2009

Front page news,
receiving a five-year
sentence a year later

nt **Deplored**

ie wreckage of the van in which
man was killed at Kirby Corner
yesterday.

ORGANIST'S LECTURE ON 'LOST ART'

THE meeting of the Coventry and
District Organists' Associa-
n on Saturday afternoon took
e form of a demonstration by
.anley Lambert of what is almost
lost art—that of improvisation.
At least the art is largely lost in
is country: I believe it still
ourishes in France.
The lecturer agreed that impro-
sation is a gift; it cannot be
ught, though there are books to
elp the organist, for every
rganist to have some little skill at
xtemporising.
He spoke of the need to prevent
nprovisation from becoming com-
letely formless but disliked the
dea of starting off with any
articular theme in mind.

ADEPT PERFORMER

He pointed out the opportunities
mprovisation offered to demonstrate the tonal qualities of an
organ, and warned organists
against the constant repetition of
he same tricks of modulation.
The lecturer then turned
organist and demonstrated the art

Coventry Man Dies as Van Overturns

DRIVER AND CHILD INJURED

A COVENTRY man was killed yesterday afternoon
when the van in which he was travelling skidded
overturned, and was wrecked, at Kirby Corner, Canley

The man, Stanley Gallimore (27),
of Caravan, the rear of 83, Westwood Heath Road, died from head
injuries.
William A. Shipley (30), of 68,
Kingston Road, Coventry, who was
driving the van also received head
injuries and was admitted to the
Coventry and Warwickshire Hospital. His condition was today stated
to be "fair."

Police Appeal

Mr. Shipley's two children,
Pauline (10), and Derek (11), were
also in the van. Pauline was
treated at the hospital for cuts
and bruises. The boy escaped
injury.
Police were today appealing for
witnesses of the accident. No other
vehicle was involved.

U.S. HONOUR FOR TRIUMPH CHIEF

THE American Triumph Corpor
ation, which markets Coven
try-made Triumph motor cycles i
the United States, has presente
of the British parent company
Mr. E. Turner, managing directo
with a silver salver "in recognitio
of 21 years of inspiring leadership,

Coventry Man Dies: A newspaper cutting of the
1958 car accident which killed 27-year-old 'Stanley
Gallimore' – how significant to the Old Man (inset)
would this event prove to be?

Even so, though he had served eighteen months on remand and six months at the Green, at best he had four or five to serve.

A release was many years off.

Sad as this was, I expected to write soon, telling him of my great success in landing a TV series. It was just a matter of time, I thought.

* * *

EIGHT MONTHS LATER, on an ice-cold morning, the bonnet was up on my beaten down Metro van as I whacked the starter motor with a broom handle. Parked up on the social club car park, it had no MOT or tax, with its insurance days from expiring.

But at least I'd finished that damned pilot.

In a makeshift studio, me and five young artists had spent six months animating day and night. After three months I had run out of money, took out a loan, bled myself dry. By the end, when the film was finally in the can, I was penniless with a pile of debts and no means to pay.

The van at last started up. I climbed in, dropped my portfolio on the passenger seat, placed a showreel in the dashboard. These were the two items I would rely on to dig myself out of the deep hole I'd created for myself.

To think, I'd considered writing to the Old Man to declare how I was on the precipice of a great success. I had posted a series budget of £60,000 per ten-minute episode of a 26-episode series. It would equate to a million-pound turnover and a thick profit to invest in the future. I lived for the day when I could write and tell him the good news.

Thankfully, I had held back. And in hindsight that would prove a good move for the TV pilot would come to nothing, the project would fizzle out; it would be just another good idea that would never see the light of day.

* * *

THE OLD MAN wrote to me with some boldness: *"I got married on Saturday to a girl called Crystal. She's a real nice girl, and I'm sure you will all like her. I hope you will meet her some time in the near future. I would appreciate it if you would break the news to Kate and encourage her to give Crystal a chance. She was very rude to Cretia (second wife) and I would like us all to get along."*

'Where did he meet her?', I thought.

Perhaps one of those women who wrote to inmates?

It would later transpire that Crystal had met him whilst he was on the run; this wouldn't endear her to my sister Kate. She had loathed Cretia, the Old Man's second wife, calling her 'Creature' at every opportunity.

I wrote back, offering surprised congratulations, said I'd speak to Kate.

* * *

BY THE SPRING, there had been a reversal of fortunes and after a run of good luck, I had relocated over to The Custard Factory, Birmingham.

The Custard Factory was a huge arts complex, a renovated five-storey factory building where scores of artists shared a creative synergy. My company – *Shipley Animation* – would be one of its brightest companies, producing local TV commercials with a dozen artists and myself as producer-director. The company received healthy media coverage with a string of high-profile projects. With money flowing in, I did the one thing I had learnt from the Old Man and invested everything I had in the future, saving nothing, speculating to accumulate like any entrepreneur should.

For the first year everything would go well. I dropped the Old Man a line, let him know his son was thriving, that the future looked good.

He wrote back and updated me on his situation.

* * *

HE HAD BEEN transferred to Ashwell, a Category C prison in Leicestershire. It placed him closer to Crystal, who could visit more often. We'd since learned that she had three kids, a lad and two girls. They were younger than my brother, sister and me. Nonetheless, it seemed we had been inadvertently replaced.

With Crystal, he had started a printing business for the inmates and was placing family photos on mugs, T-shirts and pens. He'd taken more than a hundred orders within just a few weeks. He was doing well.

Now four years served, just two or three to go.

I noticed he mentioned little of my progress. I thought maybe I'd understated matters, been modest, which wouldn't prove such a bad thing, as my so-called success wouldn't last.

* * *

OVER AT THE Custard Factory, my artists' utopia had come to an abrupt halt. No work for three months and thanks to my overspending, it was killing me financially. And then out of the blue, the bank called.

They wanted to discuss my overdraft.

Perhaps I had seen this coming, for I had already written to the Old Man and asked for a Visiting Order. He sent one by return of post, and the following morning I drove down to Wellingborough Prison in Northamptonshire.

The Old Man had been 'chucked' out of Ashwell over an incident. I never did learn the details. He fought the accusations like a lawyer and won. Nevertheless, the governor ordered him to be shipped out.

HMP Wellingborough was another Category C prison.

As it was a weekday, the visiting centre was quiet, and the canteen shut. I sat at a table, studying the largely empty visiting hall. A screw observed from a distant table, a few other visitors sat waiting. I was apprehensive.

It had been a few years since I had visited. I'd moved around, as had the Old Man. Last time, I would have been nineteen, a young artist just starting out. Now I was twenty-three, an artist and businessman to all intent and purposes, doing brilliantly well.

Underneath, though, I was sinking.

The visitors' hall had large windows running down its left side, like a school assembly hall might. Gazing out to wide lawns and low-level buildings, from one strode the Old Man, blue folder under his arm.

He entered the hall.

"Alright Tone," the screw said.

The Old Man greeted him the same, had a quiet word, explained something. The screw listened, nodded and walked off.

The Old Man came over, greeted me with our customary handshake. I took my seat facing him. It felt more formal than it ought to be, I was his son after all. Nonetheless, I had called this meeting with some urgency and due to this it did have a formal feel.

"What's the problem?" he asked.

I explained the issue with the bank, described the problems I'd run into, how the work was not there, how the exes were running, and the pressure was on to do something, whatever that was.

"That's the market, he said. "Sometimes, you've got to go where the water is."

I nodded, not sure what he meant by this.

From his file, he pulled out a pad of A4 lined paper and placed it down. He wrote _'Memo'_ as the heading and started firing questions and making notes, evaluating fixed assets, turnover, clients, investments. He underscored my clean credit history, never bouncing a cheque – the three Cs: capabilities, character and contribution.

A business meeting with us both on the same page; for a moment we were fellow businessmen – novice and mentor.

He drew up a page of assets and liabilities and began listing, searching for assets, minimising liabilities. Within minutes, he had concluded I should switch the overdraft to a loan and request an increase to £10,000. He listed the evidence and arguments for such a loan.

At this point, the screw arrived with two teas.

"No biscuits today, Tone."

"No problem," the Old Man said and continued writing.

He drew up another page: _Reasons for £10,000_.

He filled in the details himself, expanding on my points, exaggerating here and there, omitting where required. After ten minutes, he was finished and looked up with those frowning eyes.

"Go on the attack. Put him on the back foot. You have assets, but he isn't seeing them. All that artwork you have is worth money. Make him see it in financial terms."

I was already glad I called over, my confidence rising.

He continued, "Invite the manager over, let him see your studio for himself. Fill the studio with people that day, make sure the phone is ringing. Inspire him and let him know what you are about."

With twenty minutes of notes, he appeared to have solved my problem.

We spent the following ten minutes catching up on family, drinking tea, the Old Man checking his watch now and then. He spoke of his new wife Crystal and how he hoped me and my brother David would come over and meet her once he was on Home Leave.

"When would this be?"

He explained the maths, "Four years served. In a year, I'll be transferred to a Cat D/open prison. Soon after, I will be eligible for weekend leaves to our new place over in Nuneaton. Then after a year or less, I will be released on tag."

"And do you know what you'll be doing once out?"

"I have a few ideas I'm working on," he said. "I'll explain next time we meet."

He glanced at his watch. I had noticed the lists written up his arms. They weren't for me.

"Look," he said. "I am going to have to get moving. I've a few people to see and there's only a few hours a day when we're in the same section of the prison."

He stood up, tore the sheets from his pad and passed them to me. The screw looked up and nodded to affirm this was okay. The Old Man didn't seem concerned.

We shook hands and he wished me luck. The screw opened the door for him and he left the hall, walked back in the direction he came, folder under his arm, mind elsewhere.

We'd used up half an hour of our forty-five-minute visit.

*　*　*

THREE MONTHS LATER, *I'd gone where the water is,* which was central London. I'd rented two rooms of cheap office space out in the East End. I would spend most days on the phone, securing meetings with production companies and the odd agency when I could get past the secretary. At these meetings I would reel off a sales spiel, play them my company showreel, explain that we, my company of artists, could deliver any project that comes their way.

Most were unimpressed by a small provincial animation studio with a bright little showreel. It was hard going by any measure. However, as the Old Man had long drummed into me, *'you must speculate to accumulate'.*

Eventually I landed a lucrative TV commercial.

A few of my artists migrated down from the Midlands and we animated around the clock for three months. Once done, I squared things with the bank, paid the wages, and dropped the Old Man a line. I hadn't got the loan I'd requested, but his advice had bought me some time. I wrote, telling him that, *'I have gone to where the water is and am doing just fine.'*

This time, he didn't write back. I guessed he was either busy or had been shipped out.

* * *

HE HAD BEEN transferred to a Category D prison and, soon after, cleared for a Home Leave. This news he would keep quiet as he had some unfinished business.

Five years earlier, when on the run for the counterfeit dollars, he had buried a suitcase of dollars, a bag of passports, and the dollar printing plates.

On release, he would dig up these items and see how they had weathered.

He had initially buried the items in the belief he would be returning within a few months. Unsurprisingly, the dollars were unsalvageable. However, the passports were good, as were the plates. On this first home leave, Crystal would arrive home to discover passports being dried on the radiators of every room, as well as some suspicious looking plates being stored in her garden shed. The Old Man had fervently claimed he would be going on straight on his release.

Now she would start to have doubts.

* * *

WHILST HE COUNTED down the months to his release, I remained in East London, living hand to mouth, scrambling to earn a living. With no good news to share, I stopped writing to the Old Man.

And then one evening, a phone call.

I had missed a few calls earlier that day. Guessing they were from a debt collector, I ignored them. By the third call, it had gone nine; I was hunkered over a game of chess with Big Al, the security guard at the complex I rented from.

I picked up and said nothing.

"Hello," a quiet yet familiar voice said.

I answered slowly, "Yeah... who's this?"

"It's me. Why aren't you answering your phone? I've been calling you all day."

"This is…"

"It's your dad, of course."

I was taken back.

"Why are you speaking so quietly?"

"I've got to keep it down, I'm on a mobile."

Al looked up, awaiting my next move. I advanced a pawn two spaces and signalled I needed to take this. I headed outside, listened to the Old Man explaining his plans. He was due out on Home Leave.

"If you're up for the weekend, David's coming over. How about you call over with him?"

Had it really been seven years? "I'll see what I can do," I answered.

"Good. Be over around six. You can meet Crystal, have a meal, catch up." The call ended, I returned to my chess game and quickly lost. My mind was elsewhere.

* * *

IT WOULD BE another hard week of evading the landlord, chasing quotes, avoiding phone messages, awaiting a final cheque long overdue. On the Friday, once the post had come and gone, I re-directed the phone and slipped out of the building. Outside my car was parked up, tank on empty, not driven for several weeks. My pockets contained a return train ticket to Coventry and a few quid in small change. I spent it on a baguette and walked the three miles to Euston Station.

As I walked, my thoughts pondered the Old Man. Glad he would be out, curious as to his plans, but shy that he might discover how my own fortunes had declined, how I was far from shaking up the world with my small struggling studio. I had spent almost seven years applying all the business nous I'd learned from the Old Man as a kid, and despite a few high points, it wasn't working out.

That weekend, I would visit him, see what was going on.

CHAPTER 19:
RISE OF A DRUG IMPORTER

1996

IF THERE IS A SURPRISE to my own story, it is that one year I was a small-time animation producer hustling for work in central London, the following year I was part of the Old Man's drugs ring navigating the nation's motorways, dropping off drugs and collecting paperwork.

It was quite a transformation.

Taking a left at the brow of the hill, I slowed to a steady twenty by the new offices and checked the mirrors for a tail. Nothing appeared, so I parked up, pulled out a bag from beneath the seat and cloaked a jacket over it. Strolling up to the office, the bag was invisible to any surveillance camera.

The offices occupied the second floor of a small business complex on a Coventry side street. The front was a party planning business. All appeared bona fide with all the computers, faxes and phones you'd expect; it even had a secretary who worked part-time and turned a blind eye to the lack of business conducted.

Three months we'd been there without a single problem.

I entered the front office, where behind a grand cherry oak desk sat the Old Man, mobile at his ear, coordinating a drop-off. Before him, lay his daily lists, phone number sheets, and mobiles labelled with white stickers: *UK IN* and *SPAIN OUT*. Behind him along a counter ran a series of chargers containing the mobiles: *HOLLAND IN*, *HOLLAND OUT* and *SPAIN IN*. Next to them were stacked a dozen Nokia pay-as-you-go boxes and further along, two large money counting machines at which my 'little' sister Kate stood, feeding in piles of twenties.

Now 22, she was a tall, good-looking blonde with a sharp mind and a fast attitude. She had been working with the Old Man for more than six months and was perhaps the most seasoned driver on the firm.

The Old Man nodded at my return, continued his call, answered *UK IN,* and listened to a driver having problems with a pick-up. I walked across to my sister and emptied out a dozen brick bundles of cash.

"There should be fifty-four there – the four's in a roll."

"I can't do all of them!" she snapped. "They're all fuckin' tens and fivers there!"

She had a point. The tall stacks were packed with them, and the machines disliked tenners and refused fivers. Counting machines, so neat in movies, were a pain in real life.

"I'll do those if you just do the twenties," I offered and began separating the small notes off from the bundles. She nodded and continued preparing them for the machines. I knelt down, cleared some floor space and began checking and separating small notes from large. Suddenly, the Old Man raised his voice: "Tell that fucker I said Tuesday, not Wednesday or Thursday. We've got numbers to get out."

I looked his way, as did my sister.

"No. I said today…" He listened impatiently, shaking his head slowly, and then leant forward, bit his lip and angrily yelled, "YOU TELL THAT FUCKER I WILL SEND SOMEONE DOWN TO HIS FRONT DOOR AND COLLECT THE FUCKER RIGHT NOW…"

We exchanged smiles and raised brows at this familiar flash of temper.

Several seconds passed until there was resolution, "Okay… okay… so four o-clock it is. Make sure it is. If he fucks you about, call me."

He ended the call and we returned to counting.

The Old Man struck a few things off his list, "How much did you get from Ryan?"

"Fifty-four" I said without breaking my count. "Says he'll have the rest later".

"Good. Now, if you shoot up to Linx, he has fifty-eight waiting for you. Then cut back across to Ryan and grab that last twenty... that should give me two hundred and twenty." He flicked through some lists, "We've got flights going out at nine thirty. I need you back for six, no later."

"Who's going?"

He finished punching a number into *DUTCH OUT*, "It'll be David, maybe Neil. Nic'll be in soon and she'll get the flight details printed off."

"I'll finish this and shoot off then."

Waiting for the other end to answer, he added, "You haven't got time. Leave it to Kate".

My sister looked up and muttered. I smiled.

He covered the mouthpiece and asked, "You still got float?"

"I've got two fifty."

"He nodded and returned to his call, "Alright mate. We're almost there. Just rounding up the last few pieces..."

His voice trailed off as I bounded down the stairs and passed Ken (Front man) and Nic (Secretary), who were just arriving. I hopped in the car, located sunglasses and tapes, plugged the phone in, paused a moment to reflect. As a small kid, I'd dreamt of us working together in a family business one day, and now we were doing just that. Though admittedly, it wasn't the type of business I'd envisioned, it was nevertheless a business in every conceivable way. We were an organised firm supplying much-needed product lines to a large, insatiable market.

We dealt in just two lines: amphetamine and cannabis. The former was imported direct, considered 'our own line' and was highly profitable. The latter was simply a high demand product which was the bread and butter needed to promote the amphetamine sales. Importantly, both were classed as B and C drugs and weren't associated with addiction and misery. In fact, they brought a great deal of pleasure to many.

Over the next ten minutes, I crisscrossed my way across the city before shifting onto the motorway. There I relaxed, shoved in an *Oasis* tape, cranked up the volume and asked myself – *How has life gotten so good?*

The good thing was I knew how.

* * *

HE'D BEEN RELEASED eighteen months earlier on license after serving seven and a half years. During that sentence, he accepted drug dealing as a criminal enterprise and began treating it as any other business.

From what I could later piece together, he had begun dealing at a category A prison - HMP Whitemoor. He had secured a job as a cleaner of the visitors' room and toilets. Adapting the ladies' sanitary machines for storage, he would organise female visitors to deposit nine bars of cannabis in the machines. He would then gather up the bars whilst carrying out his cleaning duties. Over the following four years, at various prisons, he would practice dozens of similarly ingenious methods. By the time he reached an open prison, he was smuggling and wholesaling cannabis on such a large scale, his cell was nicknamed the 'off-licence' by other inmates as holdalls of cannabis and alcohol arrived throughout the twilight hours. He operated with a dozen SIM Cards, several phones, coordinating inmates in drop-offs and pick-ups from the safety of his cell.

And then he was cleared for home leave.

Home was now with his new wife Crystal and her three kids. They lived over in Nuneaton, a medium-sized town, north of Coventry. He invited my brother and me to visit on the Sunday evening.

I had mixed feelings.

In meeting up with him again, I hadn't known what to expect. He'd been away for thirteen of the last fifteen years. During that time, I had heard many things, some good, some bad, but throughout, he was still my dad. He was certainly not perfect, might not be the brilliant businessman he once was, but he could no longer be the notorious criminal some people alleged. He was too old, I thought.

Even so, if I had expected to meet a middle-aged man looking affectionately to the past, I was wrong. He looked fit and well from hours in the prison gym, and possessed the energy of a young man. He was all about the here and now: What's happening today? Where is there money to be made? What's important? Who's important? What do people want? What do you want? What do you need?

They lived in a decent house, a new build. Expensively furnished and modern. Already he seemed loaded, spending a grand or two on the weekend.

Both of us, my brother and me, were oblivious to his actual business, though it was obvious he was earning too well for any man still in prison. He explained this by confiding that he was dealing in cigarettes – Embassies mostly. Smuggling cigarettes was big business, and his contacts were bringing in container loads from the continent. Looking around the house, observing his generosity, the money was good. We'd spend what few hours we had catching up. He'd talk about setting up new businesses on release, but I noticed gave little detail. More than expected, he'd shown a greater interest in what we were doing and would make promises to help either of us once he was released. Neither of us needed the help, but the offer was welcomed. On occasions, we'd drive him back to the prison and as we approached, he'd dismantle his phone and conceal its elements in the hollow heels of his shoes. Even so, right up until that point, he would still be making calls, switching SIM cards, making promises for more and more cigarettes.

I didn't quite know what to make of him. He was younger than I thought he ought to be. I hadn't met anyone of his age who was so animated, so busy, so full of life.

Unknown to us, his release would initially be blocked by the prison governor. He accused the Old Man of drug dealing. Nothing could be proven. Even so, it would cause great dismay with the Old Man's new wife, Crystal. She'd married him inside and stuck by him through seven years of prison, believing he would be going straight once released. However, learning of his drug ambitions, she issued him an ultimatum: quit the drug dealing, or we are finished.

He didn't like ultimatums and agreed they were finished.

Following this, his release was delayed. He organised a new address: a damp, rundown terrace on the rough side of Coventry. From there he would build up from scratch with a mobile, some seed money, and the long lists of contacts he'd built up over the years.

He started small but thought big.

He would buy from suppliers in Liverpool and Manchester, buying five, ten and later twenty kilos a time. He'd sell them on and return for more, working his way up to larger and larger orders. The profits he invested in a network of rented rooms and cars with the idea of much grander things to come.

Meanwhile, I remained down in London, making few inroads and returning home once a fortnight. It was on these weekends that I would note the rapid jumps in his progress. As with the counterfeit, he was ever on the move, watching mirrors, increasingly with a driver so he was free to make calls, and then using one base and then another and then several. His drivers would change, usually an ex-con of some sort. But then my sister became a driver, and a few months later my brother joined them. I would arrive home on the weekend, broke and indebted, observe them making good money, driving new cars, travelling the country, organising passports for the trips abroad that lay ahead.

I didn't approve of the cigarette dealing, but then, what did I really expect him to do? With a long criminal record, he could hardly just get a job. Nevertheless, I decided to keep my distance, stick to the animation work. He appeared to me a criminal, albeit not a bad one.

After a year, though still on licence, he was able to travel without notifying his parole officer. From day one, he and a second man, Sean, a flash northerner, would drive the continent meeting up with the international contacts made inside. They covered thousands of miles, never catching a flight, avoiding any paper trail, working his contacts in Holland, Belgium and Spain as he moved up to become both wholesaler and importer.

It was around this time I relocated my wilting animation business back to Coventry. At the new place, where I both worked and slept, the Old Man began to drop by and as he could see I was struggling, he offered any help he could.

You've no phone? Take two, I've got plenty. *No passport?* Go get one, I'll pay for it. *Need a car?* Here's a spare one. *Short of money?* Take this and sort out your bills; pay me back later. *You need work?* I've plenty of work on. What am I doing? Selling cigarettes, of course – thousands of cartons by the week. It's where the money is.

"I still plan to do animation work," I reminded him.

"Well, do some driving for me in between. There's plenty to do. Been to Brighton before?"

"No".

"There's a guy down there – here's his number. He's got some paperwork. Go fetch it and get it back to me by the day's end."

I hesitated. My earlier disapproval was appearing self-righteous and foolish. It served no purpose and given my own struggles, I figured it was high time I grew up and accepted the world wasn't black and white.

He produced a roll and peeled off some notes, "You'll need some float. Here's £500 for exes. Tell me when you run out and I'll top it up when I settle your wages."

I took the money.

It was a chance to earn. Reluctantly, I was soon on the road and once done, allowed this one drive to lead to others. I subsequently spent three weeks driving the country collecting paperwork and meeting dozens of the Old Man's contacts and drivers, all dealing in cigarettes, all flush with money. It was all quite simple: phone someone, meet them, collect the money, return and count it, get paid. I quickly earned some much-needed wages.

Even so, once I'd earned enough, I stepped back and returned to the studio. However, it wasn't the same. I'd enjoyed the driving, the easy money, the sense of adventure, and seeing the Old Man each day. In just a few weeks, I'd accumulated a few rolls of money, several sleeves of cigs and a drawerful of alcohol, even though I neither smoked nor drank. Now there was a sudden comedown as I felt bored and detached

Then, out of the blue one Friday night, the Old Man called, "What are you doing?"

"Just watching TV."

"You comin' out?" he asked.

"What?"

"I'm out at a club. Perry's place. You know it?"

"Not really –"

"Kate's here, so's Ash and Sonny. You coming down?"

I didn't know what to say. My forty-eight-year-old dad asking if I'm coming out clubbing was something I had never anticipated.

"I suppose I could come down for one."

"Good. Your name's on the door. Just tell the owner you're Tony's son"

It would be the sign of things to come and soon enough, whenever work wrapped up at a decent hour on a Friday night, several of us would meet up and head out. And much as he had once done back in the day, we'd move from club to club, with Ash and a few others, meeting old businessmen and villains, never queueing, never waiting for anything, always being favoured. It seemed to be a nostalgia trip for him, meeting old friends, buying rounds, chatting up women, making plans. The attitude was strangely refreshing, and it soon began to rub off.

Within the month he had a couple of women on the go, but I'd still be going out, wanting to spend some of the driving money I'd earned, buying rounds and meeting people. Even so, this new world I was edging into wasn't all that it seemed. I did know that much.

There was more to this work than just cigarettes, but as I was only driving part-time, no-one was saying. Both my brother and sister had sidestepped any questions directed their way. "You need to ask Dad," my sister answered, repressing a smile.

Then one day I was allowed into the circle of trust. The Old Man, short of a driver, asked if I would be okay to drop off two sleeves of Embassies.

Embassies?

"It's actually cannabis bars," he whispered with a smirk crossing his face. "You drop them off to this number – he's in Dunstable – then pull offside, wait for him to return with the money. I wouldn't ask, but I'm short of drivers."

As before I hesitated, and as before I dared to press ahead. After all, I had only benefited so far from my dealings with the Old Man. He had been true to his word on all matters.

The bars came four to the kilo, wrapped in cloth bags to avoid prints. If a small delivery, you'd shove it under your seat. Something larger, it would be a bag in the boot amongst lots of clutter. You'd be driving a car registered to someone else, using a burner phone which you changed every few weeks, speaking in the code of cigarettes from which you never strayed.

For the first dozen drops, he'd guide me to the contact by phone. Coaching me to reduce any risk. On my return, he would discuss the drop, dispense further advice, and coach me on improvements.

"The more you know, the safer you are," he advised.

I nodded in appreciation.

It quickly became an established pattern. When there was no work at the studio, I would be collecting paperwork; when not collecting paperwork, I was delivering 'cigarettes'; when not collecting cigarettes, I was driving the Old Man around to meetings; when not driving the Old Man around, I was on standby, awaiting his call at the drawing board.

A call would come in, and I'd be off like a hound.

Most nights I would be on the road. No drop-offs were done after six, but paperwork would go on until nine or later. Usually, it would be dropped to the Old Man at his apartment. Modest and spacious, he gave us all keys, encouraged us to come and go as we please. There were spare beds upstairs, Sky TV, always food in the cupboards.

"Treat it as your own," he'd say. "But don't make a mess."

I'd learnt he was fastidious with order and meticulous with hygiene. I figured it was how prison life had shaped him. He could spot crumbs on a carpet from another room and quickly decided all his kids were messy.

"Your mother's spoiled you all," he'd frown. "Not taught you to tidy up after yourselves."

"Her Majesty's Prisons have spoiled you," my sister would call back. "Given you OCD."

He'd smile and laugh and finally repeat his point. "Just try and be tidy. It's not hard."

It was rare for him to sound like a parent.

And so, all this felt good – my brother, sister and me, all working for our dad. Like I'd hoped to as a kid when he had the cooker businesses. Adapting to the idea of a business selling drugs took some doing, but was eased by the belief that these drugs were quite harmless. Cannabis, used by those wanting to chill out on weekends; amphetamine used by those wanting a longer night out, or to lose weight, or work longer hours. My earlier disparaging view of drugs appeared snobbish, a self-righteous prejudice. These weren't addictive drugs forced on people but stimulants that people wanted but were denied by unjust laws: black market products, similar to alcohol in prohibition.

It was an analogy I appropriated.

And the money was good.

For product deliveries, on top of the basic £300 a week, all drivers were paid £25 per kilo of (cannabis), £50 per kilo of speed (amphetamine). It was easy to earn a grand a week. The Old Man coached each driver on the dos and do nots of drop-offs, so there appeared only a small risk of being caught. Any arrests could only come from the person you were dropping to or collecting from being under surveillance, or them setting you up. If this ever did occur, you were looking at five years for amphetamine, but only two or three for cannabis.

Even so, factored into this risk was the knowledge the Old Man was yet to lose a driver. Other firms had, but their people were often sloppy, unprofessional if you like. If your car was good, you blended in and followed the rules, there was little chance of being caught with anything.

Over the months, my brother, sister and I, alongside several other drivers, dropped off thousands of kilos to dozens of cities and towns and collected millions of pounds with no serious problems. Day in and day out we drove back and forth, up and down motorways, all around the country, meeting at hundreds of restaurants and car parks, dropping off kilos, picking up bags and bundles of cash until its counting had lost its enjoyment and become an unwanted chore.

* * *

I REACHED the long green A-roads of Lincolnshire, made a call to Linx, checked he was on time. Rounding up the last few pounds, he would be there as agreed. I pressed on.

Linx was a regional wholesaler. Typically, he might take fifty kilos of cannabis and five amphetamine. These he would distribute to the larger dealers of Lincolnshire's cities and towns. They in turn would deal downwards to local dealers across their cities and out into the suburbs and villages. All this was remote to my experience, though; I simply dropped product or collected money. It would never be both; product and money were never mixed. Always kept separate.

Half an hour later, I pulled into a Little Chef and parked alongside a white truck. Linx got out, hopped in, and from a black sports bag pulled out a bulky bag of cash. "There's £66,000 there, so I'm eight ahead. You know when the next load's in?"

"About three to five days, I reckon."

"Ay. Tell him I am waiting. Got people on the blower all day, every minute." And with that said, he hopped out and returned to his truck. Moments later, he sped off.

The bag of sixty-six was too large to slide under the seat, too large for the McDonald's bags in the footwell. A few miles on, I pulled over and stashed it away before the next pick-up.

I back tracked south and turned west towards Nottingham, where I planned to link up with Ryan James for his final twenty. It would be the last collection before the product arrived in at the weekend. The Old Man had returned from Holland a few days before and was expecting 400 kilos of cannabis and 50 kilos of amphetamine, which would become 100 or more after a mix. This was already pre-sold and would be gone within 48 hours. During that time, the Old Man and all us drivers would work offside, away from the office and the usual places surveillance might be on. Once all was delivered and done, we'd return to the offices and normal business could resume as we focused on the low-risk activity of collecting.

The first money in would be spent on wages, rents, small businesses the Old Man had committed himself to; the later money went out to Spain or Holland as payment for the next shipment.

Whilst this was organised, we swept all properties and vehicles for bugs and trackers before preparing, cleaning and reconfiguring everything for the next delivery.

* * *

I PULLED OFF THE motorway and drove into the Nottingham area, home of the Gunnies, the Dawes, Bulwell and several other gangs the Old Man supplied. For months, we had been delivering and collecting from the area, but that was about to change. Young Ryan James had been released from prison, and he was set to become the Old Man's sole customer for the lucrative Nottingham market.

I swung into a council estate and made my way around to Ryan's mid-terrace house where he lived with his girlfriend and kids. It was a street where everyone knew everyone, and no-one would mess with the James family. I walked up the path, nodded to one of his foot soldiers at the door, and went in.

"Alright mate. Got it all 'ere," Ryan was sat on the sofa pushing bundles of money into a Nike shoebox. "Tell your Old Man I'm going over at tha' weekend. I'll have my book (passport) Friday."

"Will do." I replied. Taking orders from someone my own age felt alien, but I had learned to make an exception in Ryan's case.

"If you see the Leicester man, tell 'im to give me a call. Ash innit. Yeah, I've left a message for that fucker," he shook his head, "I'm still waiting! I know your brother's passed on my messages"

I frowned in thought, not wanting to fob Ryan off.

"If he don't call I'll fuckin' go an' see 'im myself," he continued. "Fuckin' twat. I've a good deal for him but he needs to call. I've some of his line. Will give him the best price, but he needs to give me a bell."

It wasn't my job to run messages between customers – 'backdooring' they called it. Dealers and drivers bitten by ambition were ever looking to steal contacts.

"I'll let him know."

"Yeah, you do that," he said and changed the subject. "How's your brother? I saw him the other week. He's out all the time with that new girl of his. Geena, innit? She's not bad. Done alright there. Has he moved yet?"

Ryan James was always fishing and gossiping. Speaking to him for half an hour and you'd learn all that was going on in your backyard – who was shagging who, who was thieving, who had a smack coming their way, who the key players were and would be one day. He lived and breathed news, gossip and money, and it was easy to see why the Old Man was so impressed with that sharp encyclopedic mind of his.

I left the estate and headed back south, now carrying eighty-six, which Ryan helped to stash in the spare wheel. Otherwise, it only took a pull as I left the estate and it'd be gone. Either way, I would say nothing. The police would confiscate the money, and if I produced no legal paperwork to explain its origins, they would keep it.

"Better to lose money than a driver," the Old Man would remind me. "We can always make more money."

An hour later, I was back at the office. The secretary Nic was organising flights for my brother and a second man to deliver £70,000 to Albert in Spain. Albert, like many key players such as Ryan and Ash, preferred dealing with family members. They were considered loyal, accountable and dependable, not ones to gossip or turn; hence David was placed on the money trips to Albert in Spain. Within minutes, they had stashed the cash around their person and were off to the airport, leaving me, the Old Man, my sister and Ken on hand.

Ken, tall, clean and well-spoken, had the manner of a bank manager and was the Old Man's front man. His job was to keep the Old Man in the background and present an honest business face to the enterprise. He would make any legitimate enquiries when it came to premises, cars, flights, ferries and the like. In the event things came on top, we'd be relying on Ken to hold his nerve and front it out.

Few believed this would happen. All the drivers expected Ken to crumble.

For the last time that day, Kate de-banded the latest money and fed them through the counter whilst the Old Man wrapped up his calls. I would be driving him tonight, so I lingered as he finalised details with Ken regarding the new load due in. The Old Man was off to Holland the following morning, would be gone a few days but back for when the new load arrived in.

But first we needed to see Ash.

* * *

THAT EVENING, WE DROVE over to Ash's golf course. Positioned on Leicester's southern tip, Kingstead Golf Course was a sprawling land development spread over fifteen acres of countryside. At its core was the golfing range, a bar, Indian restaurant, and a recently added complex of apartments. It was owned by the Chenia brothers, Ash and Sonny. They were two of the Old Man's associates, to whom he supplied large volumes of amphetamine and cannabis.

Wildly ambitious, Ash was a short, dark-haired Asian man who affected the air of an affluent businessman whilst having few scruples. For him, everything was business, and he made no distinction between hippie hashish and hard heroin. "If a drug addict wishes to kill himself, that is his business. A prostitute wishes to sell herself, she should be allowed to do so. I am here to make money. It is that simple, Jason".

Given I had recently dropped my objections to all manner of things, I lacked the arguments to counter his reasoning.

"Drugs and prostitution are not crimes, they are business. Good business. Profitable business. One day the government will take them over, but until then, me and your dad will make money. Big money." He would smile and wait for me to agree, or something.

I would force a smile but add nothing. I didn't agree, though I knew not why.

That evening, he sank deeply into his sofa chair, cradling a drink in his hand. The Old Man had gone over the fields to discuss some business with Sonny. I was wondering whether to go and check on them when Ash began to pontificate on the virtue of fine things. It was a conversation I would recall vividly in the years to come.

Though he had praised the Old Man's talents before, this time he felt the need to redress the balance. "Your father is very good with making the big money, but spending it?" He smiled to himself, "I think your father would rather own twenty normal cars than one beautiful, expensive car. Have you seen my Mercedes?"

I nodded and raised my brows, impressed.

"Cost sixty grand," he said and looked intently at me, waiting for a response.

All I could manage was a shrug, "It seems a good car."

"All men want it. The women love it," he snapped. "Cannot keep them away".

This I doubted. I'd been out with Ash before.

He smiled and took a sip of his drink. I wondered if it was alcohol, but I thought he didn't drink. He set it down and stretched out his right arm to display his watch, "*Rolex* – cost me fifteen grand."

For some reason, that day he was like a kid in the school yard. Would he stop if I just told him how great he was? I decided to go the other way, "I think the Old Man always thinks of work, that's why he has twenty cars dotted around. If they're on him, they won't know which ones to tracker up, which ones to bug or which one he's driving that day. It creates confusion."

This had the effect of baiting him further, and the game of *who's better* continued. He leant forward and smiled, "I don't need twenty cars. Look around you," he paused as if I might do this. "Have you been around the complex? I know it like the back of my hand. If they ever come – there is just one road in and I will see them coming. And I have dogs. Have you seen them? They will never get past my dogs. They are the best!"

I pictured armed police shooting his dogs with darts; a helicopter coming in from above as Ash panicked and searched for a way out. Did he not realise that if there was only one road in, there was only one road out? He'd have no chance on foot. I didn't raise this point but agreed he was right, but only because he believed he was. Then on that note, I got up and walked out to check if the Old Man was finished.

From the golf complex we drove our way down its quarter mile of drive, out onto the main road and headed south. After several minutes passed, I shared Ash's boastful words with the Old Man.

"That's what he said?"

"Exactly that. He's said similar things before. Maybe you should be careful with him."

He said nothing.

I told him of Ryan's message for Ash.

"What did he say?"

"He said, he will only work with you. He didn't want to know." He nodded to himself.

"They both have a mutual interest and Ryan wants to pull him in."

"And the interest is?" I added and glanced across to note his response.

"They both deal in the Class A. Ash wants safe suppliers and Ryan wants fresh customers."

"And what about us?" I took a second glance.

"We don't touch that shit," he said, pulling out a phone book from his bag. "That stuff ruins people – seen it inside."

This was good to hear.

He changed the subject, "Did you set up some fresh phones?"

"They're sorted. Both are in the glove compartment."

He found them, checked them, and punched in a number on the first marked OUT. They had been set up specifically for tonight. Over the next few hours, he would employ both phones for one specific job as I turned a blind eye to it all.

* * *

THE PUB LIGHTS were out, the last customers gone, as the crooked man staggered away, drunk and alone. He stumbled along with his head down along the familiar pavements of the estate he'd walked for many years. He failed to see the three figures that converged on him until it was too late. The first hammer struck him in the back, the second smashed his ribs. For the following minute, the three men attacked him in a frenzied hammer attack. He fell to the floor, curled up on the ground, arms protecting his head until he could move or scream no more. There was a brief pause for just a second. Then the hammers attacked his legs. Blow after blow after blow until they were convinced both legs were broken. Two of the attackers now backed off whilst the third insisted on several more strikes to the body. Finally, he stepped back and admired their work.

The man's head was untouched.

They hurried away to a dark Mondeo and drove away at speed. On route, they made a call, "All's gone well. Job done."

"Good. Catch you later," the Old Man stated and ended the call.

That night, he had coordinated an attack on a sexual predator, a boastful paedophile from Nuneaton's Camp Hill estate. The man had been discovered sexually abusing a friend of a friend's young child. Convinced by claims, the Old Man had brought down three ex-army guys down to hospitalise the man. It had gone well, and he'd kept his word. The people on the estate would be pleased, though my feelings were mixed.

I had accepted all manner of things over the previous year, but the idea of dishing out a beating to someone didn't sit well. All others would condone the Old Man's action.

"And what would you do then?" would be the refrain.

"Leave it to the police," I blurted out. "What if the guy was innocent? What if there had been a misunderstanding?"

"No. People are sure. Your Old Man was sure. He did a good thing."

I told myself this was an exceptional case and hoped it wasn't a sign of things to come.

Violence had been unheard of in my experience with the Old Man. He saw it as an admission of failure, that all his diplomacy had failed, and that it achieved nothing other than making enemies.

"In this business, a nobody can knife or shoot a somebody. You don't want to make enemies," he would say.

Usually, he would persuade rather than threaten. He knew the names to drop, the implications to be made. "They might not be scared of me personally," he would underline, "but they'll be scared of the people I know."

I had seen this a few times in action.

There had been a series of encounters with local loudmouths who, as the Old Man had been away a long time, had little clue as to who he was. Often, they'd boast the backing of a big city name, whom the Old Man would phone, who in turn would phone the loudmouth to put them in their place. Raised voices were rarely needed.

Additionally, over the previous year or so, there had been dozens of other incidents, big and small, to which the Old Man would intercede with a few phone calls. It's all it would take.

Neighbours making your life hell?

"I'll send someone around to have a word."

The so-and-so's from Nottingham have ripped us off?

"I'll give them a call. Find out what the score is."

I've done something stupid, and the Irish are threatening to do me.

"I'll have a word. Arrange for you to apologise, put it right."

He knew all the top people in our city from back in the day but also the top families in the other cities whether up in Glasgow, down in London, over Birmingham or up in Newcastle. All the years inside had connected him to the key people. Occasionally he'd be called in to resolve disputes between firms. What were often explosive situations with fiery characters were resolved with a series of calls. The attack on the paedophile had been an exception. Morally, once he had the details verified, he saw himself as having a duty to do the 'right thing'.

We pulled up outside his girlfriend's place. He passed me the two phones, "Get rid before you reach home," he reminded me. "See you here at eight," he added and walked up to the house where his second girlfriend Irish Ange lived.

Often the day would end with my dropping him at a girlfriend's place, though Ange was different. She had a boyfriend of sorts, the father of her two children. They were on and off, and now the Old Man was on the scene, off.

"What if her boyfriend turns up," I asked him one night as we pulled up. "He's meant to be the violent type."

"What can he say? It's her business who she sees."

I nodded, "I suppose so." And watched him hop out and walk around to her front door.

That was his response to most things. People made their choices. Whether women or drugs, everyone had a choice. It was like a basic human right – to do what you wanted to do and have no-one tell you otherwise.

I watched the light come on, and him go inside before heading home. On route, I snapped the SIM cards and broke up the phone handsets before dumping them across several wheelie bins left out for tomorrow's collection. At home, I managed a short night's sleep.

Tomorrow we were expected in Amsterdam.

CHAPTER 20:
THE DAM AND THE SUPPLY

1997

FOR TRIPS ABROAD, the Old Man preferred the Channel Tunnel. They were less concerned with tobacco smuggling and booze cruisers, more so with potential terrorist attempts. Even so, a recent fire had closed the tunnel, forcing us to begin using the ferry where Customs and Excise were more stringent, or vindictive you could say.

He nodded to me as we cleared customs. Not a problem this time. The last occasion they'd hindered our departure with searches and checks. That time it was just the two of us; this time we'd taken a woman to drive at the ferry.

It meant the Old Man's name wasn't flagged, nor mine for that matter.

This day we were three. Myself, the Old Man, and his girlfriend Irish Ange. For a trip of business and pleasure, so she thought. Truth was, she deflected attention from the Old Man. It would be easier to blend in if accompanied by a woman.

The plan was for me to drop them off at a fresh car he had parked up in a large council estate inland. The Old Man and Ange would then head up to Amsterdam for a weekend of business and pleasure. I was to shoot up to Belgium and fill the boot with tobacco and on the return go by EastEnders for some alcohol. However, when after a good half hour, we couldn't locate the spare car, our plans changed.

I would be driving to Amsterdam.

First night, we stopped off at his apartment in a village on the Belgium-Dutch border. The Old Man spent most of his time making phone calls. Ange was unimpressed. Her romantic weekend away was proving to be what it really was: a business trip. Next morning, we drove into the Netherlands, where he was to meet a Dutch supplier.

"All meetings are on the Dutch side," the Old Man explained. "No conspiracy laws in the Netherlands."

"So…"

"You can talk and plot all you like. The police aren't interested unless you actually do something. No worries about bugs here if you're just talking."

"And back in France?"

"The French arrest you on mere suspicion. It's one place you don't want to be caught doing anything."

I nodded; all this was added to my education of recent months. I had no long-term interest in working for the Old Man, but while I was doing some driving, I wanted to learn all I could. The Old Man would answer anything I asked, and in the long hours of driving, I had questioned everything I could. Knowledge was power in his world.

"Nico will only meet with me alone. You'll have to take off and grab a coffee."

"Still think he's for real?"

"He came highly recommended. If he can't deliver, though, he'll have to return that £35,000. The Dutch people will order him to."

The 'Dutch people' were his contacts who ran Amsterdam. This top-tier of Dutch criminals owned much of the red-light district, controlled the biker gangs, and regulated criminal activity in the Dam. I hadn't appreciated that crime operated with such structure, with so many rules and principles. I began to appreciate why they called it 'organised crime'.

We took a table at a bar across a crowded square where we could view, at a distant café, the back of Nico's head in conversation with the Old Man. Despite the lack of conspiracy laws, these criminals still operated with great care. This was the Old Man's fourth meeting with Nico, and I was yet to see his face.

With an irritated Ange, I made small talk, our conversation limited.

Not talking was something I'd grown accustomed to. This world I had entered was one of few words, no emotions, all action. It had taken some getting used to. Emotions were for women and children; men controlled their emotions. They never betrayed their thoughts or revealed their feelings. If people thought you were solid and dependable, they'd trust you, talk with you, deal with you. If not, they wouldn't want you around.

Once done, Nico exited, his back to us. My suspicions of Nico were increasing with each meet. The Old Man rejoined us.

"So?" I asked.

"He's returning the money. He'll have it next time."

"You think he will?"

"Not sure."

I knew what he was now thinking.

"Do you think he's with the other lot?"

"Could be," he said. "I need to ask some questions when I get up to the Dam. Something's not right."

Immediately, we headed up to the Dam.

* * *

AMSTERDAM, ON PREVIOUS trips, had been a revelation. A city that was liberal and sophisticated, treating adults like adults, providing they did not impose their vices upon others. It opened my eyes and appeared to endorse our own drug activities. Here, was a capital city that had legalised 'our' product and prosecuted no-one.

Here the Old Man was not a criminal, but a businessman.

We parked up on a canalside, headed off to a series of meetings. Three hours on, we returned to find the car ransacked and our passports stolen. We spent the afternoon in the local police station arranging travel papers for our return home. They would be available to collect the following day.

Due to these papers, forty-eight hours later at three in the morning we were being frisked at Dover. A customs team explored the car with cameras and a sniffer dog. The car, as per usual, was clean. We related how we'd been down to Paris for a few days, which encouraged them to search desperately for evidence. Not a scrap of paper, not a stray receipt or a marking on a map betrayed our movements.

"And you've been up to Holland?" the senior officer asked.

"No. Paris," I replied.

"You have been gone a few days now."

"There's lots to see in Paris."

A dozen officers stood watching on as our travel papers were returned, and the senior officer held a stare on the Old Man.

"I'm sure we'll be seeing you again, Mr Spencer."

The Old Man said nothing.

"And you too, Mr Shipley."

I shrugged as if I didn't care.

From that day on, whenever I passed through Dover, I would be stopped on my return journey. I would grow familiar with the searches and the questions, the sarcasm and the frustration. Years after I finished driving for the Old Man, it would continue.

* * *

BACK TO THE Midlands, the Old Man had switched operations to a series of narrow boats positioned across the canals of Warwickshire and Leicestershire. Our locations changed daily as we navigated the region, burying stashes in the banks, look-outs on bridges, vigilante and offside.

I would spend this time driving the Old Man and occasionally feeling greatly endangered by the canal work. Amphetamine was the key product being handled. Some days I would drive the Old Man down, locate the boat, and spend an hour searching for the markers he'd planted last time. Once found, he would unearth the stash whilst I kept watch, at an uncomfortable distance.

It was about this time that I began to have second thoughts.

The bags of amphetamine would be driven to a safehouse ready for a mix, to be bulked up or stamped on. Whilst he donned his overall, gloves and goggles to 'do some work', he expected me to be his look-out. It was at this point I declared I was out.

"The cannabis, okay; but not this."

"What's the problem?" he asked.

"This…this is not for me."

He laughed, "It's no big deal. It's class B."

"I don't care. I'm not doing this. The Embassies and paperwork I'm fine with. But the Super Kings…"

He sighed, "Alright then." And lowered his eyes thoughtfully.

A silence passed between us, in which I think he wondered whom he might ask next. Most importantly, though, he didn't ask me anymore. At last, I'd held my ground. It had been a few months in coming, but finally…

Shortly after, some work finally arrived at the studio. I was glad to withdraw for a while.

I had landed a small contract for a series of animations for Channel 4. Low budget but hand drawn, it seemed as if they might be the final jobs I would complete for some time. As I sat at my table drawing, I contemplated closing down my struggling studio and what I might do next.

Working for the Old Man wasn't an option.

Whilst in a strange way I enjoyed working for the Old Man, it was based on a mixture of sentimentality and practicality. I liked him being around, getting to know him. The money was one justification, though part of me would have done it for nothing. The things I did for him – dropping money and collecting paperwork – I would have done for no-one else on earth.

It was a good thing I had other work to pull me away.

At the studio, I would work a few months on a Channel 4 series entitled *Natural Inventions*. I hit my targets, made some money, and enjoyed the craft of drawing once again. At half five each day, I wrapped up.

Often, by that time, the Old Man would have phoned. He'd be short of drivers and might I help him out? His drivers came and went. They would initially perform well, but as the weeks rolled on, few could handle the pressure. Whereas for me, aided by nostalgia and naivety, I was less easily affected.

At times, I had to remind myself of the business we were in, of the risks involved, and act accordingly. For the moment, I restricted myself to delivering kilos of cannabis and collecting paperwork. Each week I'd clock up the hours, and steadily my rolls of money became a pile.

What was I going to do with it?

I had no idea.

On weekends, I would head out. As an artist, I'd had little time or money for a social life, but that had changed. I'd fallen into going out on the weekends, doing what many young people evidently did with their time.

And then something quite predictable happened.

I met the finest young woman.

Out at a club, I had spotted two young Malaysian women, one dancing, one watching from the side lines. Both were attractive, but one was beautiful.

I stepped over, calmly and without thinking, and began to speak words that were totally forgettable but the most important words I would ever speak.

* * *

THE OLD MAN'S NEW place was a broad L-shaped house which filled the end of a mews off the main road. With enough space to keep all his cars off the road, he immediately organised security cameras, electric gates, and a fierce Rottweiler to watch over the cars at night. It was a difficult place to access for any surveillance team.

Everything was modern but not extravagant. I removed my shoes, strolled across thick cream carpets, followed him up the stairs as he outlined his plans for the place. He opened the door to the top bedroom.

"What do you think?"

A long triple length room with six single beds spaced evenly along one wall. It resembled a posh army barracks.

"For when we have visitors from across the water."

"For when you go to the mattresses?"

He laughed. "No, when some of the Dutch visit, they won't have to use hotels and draw attention. It'll be handy."

Like when I was a kid and he'd show me around a new cooker warehouse or gymnasium, he continued the tour. The numerous bedrooms, utility rooms, potential offices and a dog room for Bomber, the new guard dog. Downstairs we passed Blondie and Nellie, who lay watching cartoons on a super-sized TV whilst a few friends from the estate made themselves at home.

Blondie, he had met shortly after release. Almost immediately, she fell pregnant. This was a shock to me, but not the biggest shock. That she was my age was the greater shock. Regardless of this small detail, they were now making a go of it.

And I now had a half-sister whom the Old Man adored.

As the Old Man never talked business inside the house, we stepped out into the yard and he changed the subject.

"You still got that animation work in?"

"A few weeks more and I'm done."

"I'm short of drivers."

"I can do paperwork. Nothing else."

"That'll be fine," he said.

He let me out at the gates, and I strolled out onto the main road and down and along to where I had parked my car out of view. The mews was safe from invasive surveillance, but it was an easy place to watch. A camera on the entrance and they could collect reg plates all month long.

I reasoned he knew that. And knowing that, he must have known that he was attracting attention. The town of Bedworth was only a small place. It contained no big-league criminals. No doubt, the Old Man's presence here would bring a problem one day.

SIX MONTHS ON, and the exhilaration of working for the Old Man had certainly begun to fade. Not because the work had changed, but I had. A year earlier, when I had returned from London, I was hard-headed, with nothing but ambition and an optimism that things could only get better.

Since then, everything had changed.

I had dropped my stubborn loyalty to the past and my narrow view of the world had broadened. For the first time, I had worked at something other than animation. The outcome was that there had been significant changes.

Firstly, I'd met Tariana.

Smouldering and beautiful, modest and measured, I was bowled over. With her, my ambitions melted, and my stubbornness receded. We would disappear on weekends, drive up to the Lake District or Liverpool, spending afternoons walking the country-side, evenings in the pubs, out at nightclubs until the early hours.

I wanted this to continue and considered whether there was a legitimate future working for the Old Man.

Initially, I had figured that once he'd earned enough, he would go legit. There was an accumulating body of evidence to support this idea. He had been investing in various businesses and appeared to be building a small empire. I figured that once he moved out of the drugs game, he would need trusted people to run these businesses. Except as time passed, it was apparent he had no such plan.

As events unfolded, I began to realise that no matter how much he made, it was never enough. And to rub salt into the wound, what he did make, he seemed to waste. Each week brought new expenditure.

Another boat?

"We need it for the canals. A fresh one. It'll pay for itself."

A dog kennel business?

"It'll come in handy. You'll see."

A taxi firm? And it's losing money.

"Once it's modernised, it'll turn itself around."

Four new cars? We've got loads of cars already.

"They were a good deal. Couldn't say no."

A wine bar?

"It'll be a gold mine given time. I've an idea. I'm going to transform it. Make it into a gay bar."

Except he never paid any attention to these investments. He'd bought them as going concerns, but once their owners had received their big pay day, they had little motivation. If anything, they were experts at skimming the businesses they knew so well.

And so, one thought occurred. My brother, sister and me had each run small, underfinanced businesses. Why did he not invest his money in us? Were we not good people to invest in?

Instead, we were given the opportunity to earn money. "Want more money, earn it. It's what I've always done." I wondered what he expected us to do. Become dealers ourselves? It would be quite easy to become one of his customers, buy kilos at cost price, turn them around and make thick profits. But neither of us wanted such ambition.

Instead, whenever driving the Old Man around, I would observe how many favours he did out of sheer generosity. Rare was a week when he didn't give a car to someone, or a job because someone was down on their luck, or a caravan or trailer, money or a holiday. It seemed to me, my brother and sister, that if you were family, he'd give you the opportunity to earn, but if you were a stranger who might be of service one day, he would help you in any way he could.

Wherever he went, he would leave a trail of people beguiled by his generosity, all promising that if they could help him out one day, they would. Even so, most returned nothing. They would simply have a tale to tell of how generous that Tony Spencer was.

Naturally, I began to ask, what is the point in all this? It can't be the money. Otherwise, why didn't he accumulate some, and why did he waste so much? It became an ongoing source of frustration for us all.

I, meanwhile, continued to be cautious, driving only paperwork, except there had been a change in scale.

* * *

ORDINARILY, cash pick-ups rarely exceeded £60,000. More than that and it would be split into two drives. It was considered foolish to risk more on one trip. However, that would soon change.

"There's £400,000 to be collected from the Irish at Birmingham. You'll be driving. There'll be a car tailing you, should there be a problem." I glanced over, not able to believe what he was asking. I'd asked to do paperwork due to the low risk involved, but this was not low risk by any means. The thing was, could I say no to him?

"It's only thirty miles," he continued. "It won't be a problem."

I shook my head, "I know I said I would, but…"

"What's the problem? Don't you want to do it?"

"Well, of course not. If I was to get pulled, I can hardly say I've got four hundred grand in my boot and I'm buying a car."

"No, you simply say you're moving it for someone who you will identify later. Then I will organise mortgage papers for a villa in Spain or something."

I said nothing. He could see I wasn't keen.

"Okay. I'll get someone else."

I let out a silent sigh of relief, "It's too much money... I can't be..."

Perhaps he thought this new girlfriend was making me soft, but I cared less now. He grabbed a phone, gazed down his numbers, and gave David a call. If David didn't agree, there would be other options. The Old Man always had options.

I hung around for ten minutes, drank a coffee and quietly headed off, strange emotions bubbling away inside. What were they? I wasn't sure. In driving and doing this work, bottling things up and feeling little had proved an advantage. Not this time, though. This time I could feel the tension.

I was annoyed. What at, I didn't know. I couldn't articulate.

Arriving home early, I was greeted by the aroma of warm chicken and glittering spices, soul music playing in the background. Tariana's smile greeted me as I walked through the door.

Suddenly, my annoyance dissolved.

We settled down to eat and I explained the situation with the Old Man. She had long understood that he was a drug dealer, but in her country, it was no big thing. In Malaysia, every city contained a mafia of gangsters. It was commonplace. What she couldn't understand was how the Old Man did not take care of his family. She came from a collective rural culture where family was everything. If a person was rich, he helped his family.

It was difficult not to agree in principle. Family was indeed everything. But here amongst British criminals, it wasn't the done thing. You were meant to make your own way. At least, that's the way I understood it.

Putting this to one side, I focused my attention on us, the three of us.

Recently joining us at the flat was her six-year-old son, Troy. Like her, he had black hair, brown skin, but with large puppy dog eyes. A kind kid who liked to please his Mum. I would drive him to school each morning, pick him up from the child minder in the evening. Arriving home, the three of us would eat together, play cards together, and watch the football together. With him joining us at the flat, we had become a family.

Happy and joyful, my life had changed for the better.

Meanwhile, as the months passed, the studio sat empty, eating up rent, doing little really. I contemplated my future. I was still driving, less than before, but more aware of the risks, more fearful of the consequences.

When dropping off gear, it had always been a tense experience right up until you had handed over the product. It then lessened, increased when you collected the payment, and eased off once you were away. By the time you reached the motorway, the relief was good. In collecting paperwork, the pattern differed. Just a little tension whenever you collected. It was easy. Just check your mirrors, sweep your car now and then for trackers, be vigilant for anything out of place.

Often, these pick-ups would be at a McDonald's. You would sit in the car with your meal, wait for the driver, keep checking for signs. Anything unusual and you would delay or switch the meet, but this was rare.

I'd usually know the driver's face. He would stroll over, climb in and chat a moment, drop the bag of cash in the footwell. He might ask to be dropped off around the corner, out of sight from any chance observer or camera. Usually though, he'd drop the cash and stroll back to his own vehicle. It was quite blatant at times.

Unlike the first year of driving, I could sense I was less at ease. The previous year I'd had little to lose, this year that wasn't so.

Then a call.

"Don't return to base. There's been a problem."

It was the Old Man.

"Dump your phone and head over to where you dropped me last time. I'll explain when I see you."

I pulled over, removed the battery and broke its SIM card. Further on, I would bin the handset.

Later, I would learn there had been a major problem.

That afternoon, Ash, in the grounds of his golf course, was expecting 200 kilos of hash. The load was shared between two vehicles. My brother was one of the drivers. He was approaching the course when the Old Man, positioned nearby, spotted a police helicopter in the distance. He immediately phoned David to halt the delivery, which was less than half a mile away.

Ash wouldn't be so fortunate.

Police cars and vans poured up the drive to the golf course whilst the police helicopter swooped in low to monitor those fleeing. Ash was trapped and captured. His security measures had proved useless, his dogs tame.

Remanded, Ash was facing serious prison time. Police teams had searched the complex and discovered caches of class A and B drugs in the surrounding fields. Ash was looking at twenty years.

He was finished.

For the Old Man though, this would not serve as a deterrent. He would adapt, but not be deterred. Unknown to him though, the Regional Crime Squad who had so efficiently taken Ash down, were all too aware of the Old Man. They had placed surveillance operations on his group on two previous occasions, but they had come to nothing. Following the arrest of Ash, they would launch a greater more comprehensive operation.

CHAPTER 21:
THE NETWORK

1998

"IF THEY'RE NOT UNDERCOVER, then who the fuck are they?" I muttered.

"Tone seemed certain," BT added.

He and I were in Caravan Two, peering through the blinds, observing the vast grey container yard before us, watching people come and go, studying two apparent 'villains' moving some hooky gear. They were a scrawny pair, unshaven with long hair, wearing leathers, torn jeans and boots. The taller man was continuously on the phone, apparently making deals. He called himself Sam and claimed to be an ex-con. His partner was a short, stocky man called Mike. Both claimed Birmingham origins, but there were few traces of any Brummie accent.

They would prove to be undercover police officers.

The Old Man had thought as much the first time he'd met them. One night, his road suffered a power cut and within twenty minutes Sam and Mike were knocking the security gates of his home. They were his new neighbours in search of candles or a torch. As they waited for the electric to be restored, they got talking. Sam confided how they were new to the area, out on licence and doing some buying and selling. They offered the Old Man a few deals and told a few stories which, by coincidence, demonstrated they knew a few of the same people. Once they were gone, the Old Man poured himself a Bacardi, sat down and remarked, "Undercovers!"

Sam and Mike over the following weeks put a few shady deals forward. The Old Man explained he wasn't interested. He declared he was legit and busy running a container unit on the outskirts of nearby Nuneaton.

They backed off.

A month later they appeared at the yard wanting to rent a container. Their paperwork was passed, and they began appearing every other day with boxes of booze and cigarettes, as well as some greatly underpriced bankrupt stock. Week by week, they offered the Old Man the benefit of several more deals. Week by week, he refused, but they stuck around.

Meanwhile, we carried on as normal except whenever the undercovers visited, business would be halted for an hour. And continued once they were gone. This seemed insane, but no drugs ever came to the yard, only money. Regardless of this detail, Sam and Mike were appearing more and more, and BT and I waited for the Old Man to tell them to do one.

Except it hadn't happened. The Old Man spoke to them, tolerated them, and then even bought a few things from them. To my dismay, he seemed to be sparring and engaging in a game of wits with the pair.

On this particular day, the pair were again in the yard.

We watched on. Studying how they busied themselves unloading "dodgy gear" into their container, how they paraded around the yard making "deals" on their mobiles. Days before, they had appeared to be making inroads. The Old Man, for some insane reason as far as I could see, had accepted some leather jackets from the pair. The same day, they offered a pill machine for sale. The Old Man stonewalled the offer, but by the week's end, in their roundabout matey way, they asked if he could sort them out with a kilo of speed.

The Old Man asked for some references.

If he expected them to back off with this demand, he was wrong. They provided some names. The Old Man checked them out and considered the first too vague to be credible and the second to have gone AWOL.

Again, they backed off, but still they lingered.

I pursed my lips in frustration, "They're undercover alright. What else can they be? They're like a pair of actors out there. If you were pretending to be a villain, that is how you'd behave – you'd perform."

BT lowered his eyes and said nothing.

"You don't walk around making calls like that," I continued. "If you're from Brum and selling to Brummies, you don't set up all the way out here. They have to be undercover."

BT stepped back from the windows. "I've told Tone. Told him I ain't working whilst they're around."

I nodded. I was considering the same move. I had taken to parking my car away from the yard, making myself scarce whenever they visited. I'd made my feelings clear to the Old Man:

"What are we playing at? Why can't you let on you know who they are? They'll be off like a shot."

"They'll be gone soon. They're getting nowhere," he insisted.

I fumed with frustration. *What on earth was he doing?*

Years later, I could see what he might have been doing. He was playing with them. Getting a buzz. Playing chess with the opposition – engaged in a battle of wits. Every day he saw them getting more frustrated. More desperate. More obvious.

He was like a cat toying with a pair of mice.

* * *

I'D BEEN WORKING for the Old Man for about a year and a half. Collecting and delivering for a while, but after meeting Tariana, I had switched to paperwork. Consequently, I had become the main driver of paperwork and had seen more money in the previous year than I would in my entire life – millions and millions in cash, much of which I had personally collected and counted.

During the evenings, Tariana would come along on drives. With a woman accompanying me, I was less likely to receive a pull or close scrutiny. We drove all around the country –Brighton, London, Nottingham, Liverpool and Glasgow – meeting drivers in car parks, collecting and checking paperwork. I earned less money than those dropping the product, but now the money mattered less.

The raid at Ash's golf course had served as a reminder as to the seriousness of this business. It had been the result of a long-running surveillance operation. Ash was now in prison on remand, involved in a complex case of phone taps and surveillance logs. It didn't look good.

The Old Man, meanwhile, went from strength to strength.

By this time, he was the premiere importer of amphetamine for the Midlands region. Inevitably, he accumulated a series of cash businesses with prospects for laundering – the gay bar, a taxi firm, cafés, burger vans, an antique shop, some dog kennels, a party planning business. He then had the idea for what he saw as an ideal front – a container unit business.

It was inspired when he bought an acre of land at the Poole Road Industrial Estate. He had the ground levelled with a hundred ton of hardcore before erecting a ten-foot fence with razor wire along its parameter. At the road end, a series of caravans were to serve as offices and then, running down the yard, were scores of container units organised in lines. This would be a legitimate business, but still a front.

He advertised it by word of mouth.

Within weeks, scores of vehicles were coming and froing, dozens of customers loading and unloading, many were small-time villains, others, rogues and booze-cruisers. It proved to be the chaotic front the Old Man desired.

The Old Man based himself across three caravans and from morning to late evening was to be found running his drugs business, engaged in meetings and phone calls, workers driving back and forth, a thriving young business.

All the while, though, no drugs passed through the yard. That business occurred offside. What did pass through the yard was money – hundreds of thousands each week – but the police had little interest in money. Money could always be explained after the fact. It was drugs on the table they required, or at least evidence of a conspiracy.

The Crime Squad, we would later learn, had invested three months of surveillance on the yard – on cameras, bugs and trackers. However, the cameras were quickly spotted, the bugs proved difficult to plant, and car trackers proved useless as there were so many cars and the Old Man switched vehicles several times a day.

Undercover officers were considered the only way forward.

* * *

I WATCHED Sam and Mike lock up their container, stroll over to their grey Mazda, climb in and become immersed in conversation. Maybe they were wondering whether to wait on for the Old Man who was yet to appear that morning? Maybe they suspected he was avoiding them?

I stuck the kettle on and continued to observe whilst BT retired to the table and made some roll-ups – tobacco, that is. No drugs were allowed on the premises. BT, like me, had been coached on the importance of being professional, not drawing attention and blending in. For that reason, BT no longer wore branded clothing, baseball caps or jewellery.

It was important to be nondescript.

"So, what are these undercovers waiting for?" I asked in a raised voice, nodding to BT. "Deciding on their next move?"

This speaking aloud, of course, had a dual purpose. We'd recently moved from Caravan Three to Caravan Two due to the suspicion of bugging. However, Sam and Mike had dropped by the day before, and now it too needed sweeping. We both figured if there was a listening device nearby, we'd like them to know we were onto them. Then maybe they'd get lost and the Old Man's games would come to an end.

I fixed a coffee whilst awaiting their departure. In need of some background noise to cloak our conversation, I switched the radio on, lowered my voice and took a seat.

"We need to move off from here. Maybe go back to the canals. Even that was better than this."

BT looked up, "I'd be up for that again."

Suddenly, the canal work seemed safe in comparison. We had spent three months or more working on the canals, burying stashes in the banks, conducting mixes, planting spotters on bridges, switching operations day by day. All the time without a hint of surveillance.

I sugared my drink and returned to the window.

At last, they pulled off and turned out of the gates. I stepped away and took a seat at the table. BT continued to roll cigarettes.

"Your Old Man reckons he's getting rid of them."

"How?"

"Reckons he fixed it so their landlord will serve them notice. Says they haven't got long. A few weeks."

"Well, they need to get a move on," I said and took a sip of coffee.

We sat in silence for a minute or two. BT finished rolling, tucked his fags away. I brooded.

"Did he tell you about the camera?"

"Yeah," he said, "That's bad."

Across the road, an obscurely positioned camera had been spotted which, for no valid reason, took in the view across the Old Man's yard. To counter this, he had reordered that end of the yard by dropping in another caravan and piling up extra containers to block off the camera's view.

BT pulled out a lighter, got up to leave, "You can still see us when we move further into the yard. They'll have pictures of us all.

And there was a police helicopter flying overhead a few days back. Low it was."

I shook my head gravely, "Well I'm not doing any collecting whilst they're about. I'm out of here soon, I'm not fucking things up now"

"How long now?"

"We go next Wednesday – from Heathrow." I paused and took a swig of coffee, "Two months I'll be gone for. Assuming I make next Wednesday." I took a second swig of coffee, "Let's face it, they (the raids) could be here tomorrow or the next day."

BT nodded and stepped out for his fag. I remained seated and reflected on my own changing situation. When I had begun working for the Old Man, I had nothing to lose and everything to gain. That position had since reversed itself. I now had Tariana, a home and money with no wish to lose any. Also, I had booked us tickets for a two-month trip to Malaysia. For me, it would provide time to reconsider my future and exit the Old Man's business altogether. I was certain there was no long-term future here as it was all going to come crashing down at some point, it was just a matter of *when*, not *if*.

* * *

TEN MINUTES LATER, the Old Man with his new driver Polo pulled into the yard. He climbed out with a mobile to his ear and held back to complete the call. I watched on and gave thought to how to again raise the issue of Sam and Mike without sounding alarmist.

"Alright there. Everything good?" The Old Man asked, stepping inside.

"Okay." I murmured, "They've just left."

"Who's that?" he asked, as he pulled out the day's lists.

"Sam and Mike – the undercovers."

"I know. Dave called me to let me know."

A moment of silence passed as he organised his desk. I watched on. And then had to say without any subtlety, "The tall one's been parading about the yard making out he's doing deals for the last half hour. Christ knows to whom, as they're not from around here. They don't know anyone."

My words lingered in the air, ignored.

With his pen skating down his lists, he eventually stopped and made a mark, "Right." He leant across, turned up the volume on the radio a few notches to counter any potential bug, and added, "I've a late one for you – jot that down."

I scrawled the number onto my palm, "Who's that?"

"It's Ryan's new number – he needs five Super Kings."

"But we've nothing in."

"We have now," and with that, he beckoned me to follow him outside. I stepped out, stood with my back to the surveillance camera across the way. He kept his voice low with his back to the yard and leaned in, "I've bought twenty this morning." he announced quietly. "They'll be gone this evening."

My heart sank, was he serious? And why was he telling me? I hadn't driven Super Kings for more than a year now.

At this point, Sam and Mike's grey Mazda pulled onto the yard. They nodded to the Old Man as they passed and swung around to their container. I could feel my hackles rise. They opened up, busied themselves removing some boxes from the boot – as if they'd just made a deal. I looked sideways to the Old Man, brows raised, – *well?*

Without missing a beat, he switched to the business at hand, "Polo's putting it in a gas bottle. He's a mile down the road. Can you be with Ryan by four?"

I bowed my head and considered refusing the assignment.

He laughed, "Come on, you're off to Malaysia soon. You could do with the reddies, couldn't you?"

"Well yeah… Assuming I make it, that is. If you keep messing around with those two, it's not going to happen."

He dispensed some words of reassurance, "Look, if they (Regional Crime Squad) come, it'll be in the morning and when they believe we have a parcel. They won't charge in on a maybe, or on something small." He looked at me and awaited my agreement, "They're waiting for something big to land. Well, fuck 'em – by the next one we'll be out of here!"

I nodded as I could see his rationale – they weren't going to come storming in on a whim, they were playing a waiting game – waiting for a parcel to land. Accepting this as true, this could be one of the safest times to do a drop-off. To pull me or any of the other drivers would cause a panic, the Old Man would flee, their operation blown.

I was tempted.

"Okay, I'll get going."

I strolled out from the yard, down the hill and around to where my car was parked out of sight. Since the beginning, I'd appreciated the need to protect my car. It was imperative, especially now.

I took a roundabout route to meet Polo out on a country lane, where he gave me a gas bottle with five kilos of amphetamine concealed inside. I placed it in the boot with some further camping gear thrown over and made my way north to meet Ryan's people.

On route, I reflected on the games the Old Man was playing. He'd been engaged in a battle of wits with the police for many years. Going back to the robbery and then the counterfeit. He'd lost that one, but since then, I knew he'd handled scores of cases on behalf of inmates inside. Years of studying criminal law from both sides had left him an expert on criminal loopholes and corrupt police practices. He'd considered each case as a battle he simply had to win, no matter what. This latest battle with the undercovers was a similar battle. He had to win. He had to show them that he was so much smarter than them.

I drove north, extra cautious. In a matter of days, I was flying out with the beautiful Tariana and her son Troy to Malaysia. I'd meet her family, see a lifestyle unlike anything I'd ever imagined. It seemed too good to be true.

Something was bound to go wrong.

An hour later, down a dark wooded lane, I transferred the gas bottle over to one of Ryan's people. As he drove away, I felt the tension fall away. Just one more thing. I waited by the chippie to collect the paperwork and headed back, on route calling home to check on Tariana and Troy. With days to go, we were vacating our flat. All our belongings were going into storage. The following day, I would hand in the keys.

As well as this, I had closed my studio. My hopes and dreams to build an animation studio were over. I wasn't sure what I would do next, but I would contemplate my choices from Malaysia.

I told Tariana I had one last job to do and headed over to the yard.

The blackness of night covered the unit when I returned. Parked out of camera range, I shuffled along into Caravan Two where the Old Man was alone, sat at the table, making an odd call, writing tomorrow's lists. Bomber lay at his feet, snoozing away. In the background, the radio chattered away at a low volume. The room was peaceful.

I took a seat and began counting whilst the Old Man talked cigarettes and orders over the phone. Within minutes, another car pulled in and I dashed out to open the gate. It was my brother David and Ryan James, returning from northern France, where they'd been on a mission these last few days.

Several weeks previous, my brother had buried 60 kilos of amphetamine in a wood near Calais, and in the interim, a hurricane had galloped through the region and upended a thousand trees and all the burial markers. To locate the parcel, David and Ryan have taken along an "incredible" sniffer dog, who'd been specially trained in the intervening weeks to identify amphetamine.

Ryan entered the room, "Waste of fucking time!"

The Old Man threw his glasses down, "No good?"

"No. Every fucking tree's up-ended. It's gone."

"What about David? Surely he has an idea where?"

"No, he ain't got a fucking clue."

"And the dog?"

"Doesn't know what the fuck it's doing. It's just had the longest walk of its life."

David had little to say, "We looked everywhere – but it's just…"

The Old Man sighed lightly, "Fuck it then. Let's not waste any more time on it."

And with that, they moved on. David put the kettle on, Ryan sat and chatted with the Old Man about some deals he had on the go, and I counted the remaining paperwork. It would be a pleasant end to my final day working with the Old Man.

* * *

TWO MORNINGS LATER, I gazed down at a pale patchwork of fields passing below, growing larger and richer, sharper and more detailed, until I could make out the bamboo shacks and outhouses, oxen and tilling machines, farmers and field hands working the fields. As we went lower, the fields give way to large warm grey concrete buildings and a series of runways. Bathed in a soft blinding sunshine, this was Kuala Lumpar.

I'd made it.

Poole Road was more than three thousand miles away. In all probability the Old Man was already up, beginning another long day, armed with lists, fresh phones and his pages of numbers. The yard would soon be filled with cars and the chaos of the container unit. Sam and Mike would appear, and the Old Man would continue his mind games. Would he get out? Would he move offside?

For a while, I would forget about the Old Man and Poole Road.

Malaysia would be everything and more than I could ever imagine. The days and weeks were heat soaked as we bounced around the main cities and resorts, experiencing a country that never looked back. Optimistic, energised and playful, it was a new world. Yet throughout, I had something on my mind.

After three weeks, I phoned home.

I called Mum first, just to ask how everyone was doing and try and get a sense whether there had been a problem of some sort.

After several seconds, she picked up," Hello."

"Hello."

"It's me." I called over the faint line, "I'm just calling to see how –"

"They've been arrested."

"What?"

"They've all been arrested. Your dad. David. A whole load of them."

I took a deep breath. She continued.

"Your dad's inside. David and the others are out on bail. It's been on the front page of the papers."

I took another deep breath and gingerly asked, "What for?"

A long silence followed.

"You know what for," she bit back. "Drugs!"

I tried to think of something to say.

"And they've been here 'n all," she continued. "They had a warrant for your arrest. They want to know when you're back. They want to speak to you."

A brief silence followed.

Within that silence, I resolved not to return. I would wait it out. And for as long as it took.

CHAPTER 22:
BEATING THE ENEMY

1998-2000

I NOW APPRECIATE what a renaissance my life had undergone following the Old Man's release in 96. I had returned from London, burdened by a studio whose days were numbered, with a waning sense of humour, my optimism ground down. Due to this, I had trusted the Old Man, gotten to know him, opened myself up to an array of possibilities. Consequently, I had lived a radically different kind of life to what I'd known, an adventurous life filled with risk and reward. Through it all, though, I had watched and observed, accepting the Old Man to be complicated, both brilliant and frustrating, unlawful but principled. If I had spent some of my teen years wondering whether he was a good man or not, I now believed that question was answered. He was good and decent, albeit original. If anything, I now wondered why he was the way he was, but I wasn't yet troubled by such a question.

I was too busy being happy, and for this, indirectly, I credited the Old Man.

Without his influence, I would never have met Tariana. I would never have travelled Europe, I would never have looked to a future beyond the world of animation. Moreover, I would never have visited Malaysia.

Travelling the country changed my outlook. Out into the fields I would stroll, straw hat on my head, bagful of sketchpads on my shoulder, waving to the farmhands, making my way to the stilted bamboo shelter that bordered the local rice fields. I would read and draw for a while, and then, just occasionally, contemplate my next move.

That was until I'd received the news from back home.

Malaysia's beauty was diminished with the news of the arrests in the UK. For the next month I was distracted, phoning home every few days for the latest news. The Old Man had been remanded, a dozen workers released on bail, my brother David being one of them.

I would later learn that for him, this was the worst of times.

Returning to his car from a prison visit, he was accosted by five men and bundled into the back of a car. Taken for a drive, whilst one man rested a gun barrel across his knee, he was asked to explain what had happened to the money they were owed.

The nature of any such situation where any firm goes down, is that those who have had goods on credit stop paying, and those who are owed scream for their money.

"Nothing to worry about," the Old Man related to David on the next visit. "They were just trying to scare you."

"No kidding."

"We need to remain calm. I've sent them a message. Assured them we are good. They'll just have to wait."

David was not reassured.

* * *

THE ARRESTS HAD BEEN made by the Midlands Regional Crime Squad. They were all too aware that Central England had become the major supply hub for much of the UK regarding amphetamine. The Old Man they credited as the key figure of an alliance between several crime groups in the region.

With this in mind, security was ramped up for the Old Man's first court appearance.

The town of Nuneaton was placed in a vice-like grip as the surrounding streets of its courthouse were cordoned off by scores of armed police. On the surrounding vantage points, police marksmen positioned themselves. All braced themselves for the arrival of the police convoy guiding a prison van containing the Old Man and his co-accused, a man named Dave Brandish.

A conspiracy required a co-conspirator and Brandish, a fifty-five year-old ex-paramedic and property developer, was the most fitting candidate.

Security at the courts was meticulous. Metal detectors, police dogs and body searches were mandatory. Police anticipated an escape attempt. Arriving at an overflowing courtroom of reporters and detectives, David − my brother on bail − found a seat in the cramped public gallery.

Minutes later, DS Edmunds − the lead detective on the case − squeezed in beside him.

"Hello David. Good to see you," he quipped.

David smirked and frowned, "Bit over the top, isn't it?"

"Your father's an escape risk, David," Edmunds smiled. "We both know that."

David had been interviewed for several hours by Edmunds a few days earlier. He'd quickly grown to dislike the smarm and confidence of the detective and his gang of cronies. For the following hour they sat in silence until the judge arrived, the court rose, and the defendants were escorted into the court.

Cuffed and flanked by four guards apiece, the Old Man and Brandish took their seats in the dock behind a newly constructed bulletproof screen. Armed police stood either side.

It was pure theatre.

Both men were charged with conspiring to supply amphetamine and cannabis.

Both defendants entered pleas of 'Not Guilty'.

Both men were remanded to Blakenhurst − a Cat B prison − where they would remain for forty days. At that point, Brandish would make bail whilst the Old Man would be remanded to Woodhill, a high-security prison.

Learning this news, I considered remaining in Malaysia.

A warrant for my arrest awaited my return. Detectives had searched my belongings held in storage and seized computers and journals. A business card had been left requesting I get in touch. Slowly I was getting the full picture.

The police raids had occurred a month after my departure. The Old Man, despite his reassurances, hadn't moved off from Poole Road. Instead, he engaged in a battle of wits with the undercover officers. They attempted to sell him a pill machine: he stalled them. They wanted a bit of gear: he redirected them. Another offered to buy two kilos of amphetamine; he sidestepped the deal. In hindsight, this was clearly a strategy of complete madness.

These shenanigans culminated in disaster for both sides. Police, perceiving a large drugs deal in progress, burst in all singing and dancing with helicopters, vans and cars enveloping the container yard. Scores of armed officers surrounded Caravan Two. There, the Old Man was truncheoned to the ground and cuffed, at which point he turned to his driver, smiled and winked as if it was a joke, which in a way it was.

The so-called drugs deal that day was in fact all a bluff. He'd concocted the phony deal in the belief that Caravan Two was bugged, and within minutes was proven right. Nevertheless, with the police operation exposed, officers had little choice but to execute all warrants.

Across the region, they raided a score of properties and made more than a dozen arrests. Nevertheless, the searches unearthed little evidence, and the police interviews produced even less. All but the Old Man and Brandish were released on bail.

The resulting conspiracy would consist of the testimonies and tapes of five undercover officers, several months of surveillance footage, and three hundred hours of bugged recordings. They also recovered more than two hundred thousand Embassy cigarettes from a nearby container unit, but unfortunately, no drugs.

With a far from convincing case, they had work to do and set about building the case whilst the Old Man languished eighty miles away at Woodhill Prison. With him effectively held incommunicado, the head man on the case – Chief Superintendent Blair – directed detectives to work on turning drivers, appealing to witnesses and coercing their informants to give evidence.

As the weeks and months passed, they proved successful and beefed up the case as more witnesses gave statements. When the file was submitted to the Crown Prosecution Service, the Crime Squad were supremely confident of a conviction.

By this time, Tariana, Troy and me had returned. The police, noting the three-week distance between my trip to Malaysia and the raids, accepted I was not involved in the period of conspiracy they were investigating.

Quietly and without fuss, we found a new place to live, and I made arrangements to visit the Old Man.

* * *

HE WAS BEING held at Woodhill Prison in Milton Keynes, where he was awarded a double A Cat status and placed in the segregation unit. It assured no contact with other inmates, that all phone calls would be recorded, that all letters were copied and scrutinised. Furthermore, visits received intense attention with lip readers employed to study the surveillance cameras trained on the Double A Cat visits. We would spend much of the visit covering mouths and employing our familiar working codes as the Old Man discussed the case and any moves which might help the situation.

On the plus side, hundreds of hours of bugged conversation had been combed through and had not revealed a single reference to drugs. He had stuck to cigarette codes throughout. This played into what would be the cornerstone of his defence: that he was a cigarette smuggler, not a drug dealer.

Throughout all the premises, as was his habit, he had planted sleeves of cigarettes as potential evidence in any trial. It now substantiated his defence claim. Most critically, he could point to the hundreds of thousands of cigarettes police had recovered from the nearby unit, which stood yards from Caravan Two. Wisely, as a back-up, this delivery of cigs had been brought in to match the numbers on the phony cannabis deal.

By now, having been cleared for visits, I for once vented our annoyance.

"Why didn't you just tell them you knew they were police? They'd have been gone the same day" I'd argued, "we could have avoided all this!"

Blondie's mouth tightened, "You had to show them you were cleverer, didn't you Tone?"

He rolled with the punches and came back at us, "Don't you think I wish I had told them? I was in the process of getting them evicted from the area, but they played dirty in the end."

I nodded and backed off.

"It's done now," he insisted. "We just have to move on."

Looking back, it was an example of a deficit that undermined any criminal brilliance he had. Any normal person would have quit Poole Road and the advancing police operation. No-one in their right mind would have played games with them like he had.

Blondie was right, it was as if he had to show them; let them know he was cleverer than they were.

* * *

ONE YEAR LATER, Birmingham Crown Court at half six was almost empty, just a few lights on, cleaners at work. I sat outside waiting. It had been more than two hours since the verdict. He had punched the air and hollered a triumphant "Yes!"

He stepped down from the dock, smiling as you would expect, leaning across to shake hands with each jury member, slapping the backs of his barristers, congratulating and thanking them for their good work. He then marched across to the public gallery where, amongst the clusters of reporters and detectives, sat a stunned Chief Superintendent Blair.

The Old Man held out a hand, "No hard feelings?"

Blair rose, shook his head, turned his back and scrambled from the court muttering under his breath. A flurry of swearing detectives and toady reporters followed. The Old Man shook his head, unimpressed by Blair's lack of sportsmanship.

For the next hour or so, as the courts closed and the building emptied, Blair and his barristers attempted to halt the Old Man's release on minor charges regarding fake papers and possession of a stun gun. It was a farce; he had just spent twenty months on remand.

Finally, his silhouette emerged at the top of the court steps, carrying two large prison bags. I took a few steps his way; he paused.

"Turned out alright then?" I called over.

"Not a problem," he laughed.

"They're all gathered in the pub." I said, nodding to nearby Yates's.

"Let's get over there then," he said with an air of nonchalance. "Who's there?"

"The lawyers, some of the jury. Most of them, in fact. The women jurors are asking for you. 'Where's Tony?' they keep asking."

He laughed. Women had always been good to him, no matter where he went. We strode over.

"You have any money?" he asked.

"Less than fifty."

"Got a phone?"

"Yeah."

"Good. Need to make some calls."

And with that, we entered Yates's Wine Bar and began the celebrations.

* * *

TO THINK, FOR A LONG TIME it hadn't been going our way. The trial had started badly and gotten worse. He'd landed a mostly white and middle-aged jury who appeared to lap up the prosecution's case. Their barrister was Colman Treacy QC, a privileged Oxbridge toff who patronised the defence and spoke with a plum in his mouth. The jury appeared to like him, as did Judge Fisher who ruled with Treacy on almost every issue. So pessimistic was the defence team, the Old Man resorted to aggravating his angina in an effort to halt the trial.

Each morning, before stepping into the prison van, he would swallow a home-made salt concoction. An hour later, when the court was sitting, he would suffer an angina attack. The trial would be halted; a doctor would be called. Within the hour, the court would be adjourned, and the jury sent home. On visiting day, he explained the end game of this dangerous strategy.

"We're going to cut a deal," he told us.

After almost a year of planning, this was against all previous plans.

"We've little chance here," he declared. "At the moment I'm too ill for a trial. They know that. Court has sat for just two and a half days in three weeks."

"But I thought we were in a good position," I protested.

"We are," he insisted. "But if this goes against us, I'm looking at twelve to fourteen. If I do a deal now, I'm looking at six or seven – I'll be on home leave after three; I've already served a year and a half. I'll be out at the end of next year."

I glanced at my brother. He looked as disappointed as I did.

We drove back from that visit in total silence. Neither of us had known the Old Man throw the towel in before. However, we needn't have worried.

The prosecution agreed to a deal. They would accept twelve. Nothing less.

On the Monday, the trial was back on. The Old Man was healthy and positive, and annoyed. "If that's the way they want to play it," he'd threatened, "that's the way it's going to be."

What this meant, I didn't care; what mattered was that the fight was on.

* * *

A CHEER WENT UP IN THE BAR as the Old Man stepped through the doors. Hugs, handshakes and kisses followed as the Old Man again thanked the jury members. They had proven to be the most crucial element of the trial.

After the phony angina attacks, the trial had run for three weeks before being stopped after comments by the prosecution created a prejudice. Consequently, they had to start over with a fresh jury. The demographic of this second jury was what the defence had originally hoped for: two black, three Asian, two Irish, all mostly under forty. It was as good as it gets. Once the trial restarted, it was clear the new jury cared little for Colman Treacy. In contrast, their faces awakened whenever the junior defence barrister Charlie Benson made an appearance. Full of energy and a striking sense of humour, Benson was a young maverick with a low, booming voice that engaged the court.

As the trial was long, jury members would become accustomed to both sets of barristers.

They would also become familiar with the defendants as the dock was positioned adjacent to the jury box. Unaware the Old Man had been in cuffs moments before they were led in, the jurors would note the rapport he had with the 'court guards' and the consideration shown to his co-accused, who was clearly struggling with the stress of it all.

Dave Brandish was a middle-aged property developer with a heart condition. He had his fingers in many pies and was prone to talk. Unfortunately for him, he would be the wrong man in the wrong place at the wrong time. He rented properties to the Old Man and frequently appeared on the surveillance footage. According to undercover officers, on a long car journey Dave had boasted about his close business relationship with the Old Man, how they were like partners. According to the officers, Brandish all but admitted the nature of their true business. Unfortunately, they failed to provide the tape – apparently it failed on that critical journey, which was typical with Sam and Mike.

Both officers had taken their roles too far. More often than not, critical tapes and statements went missing or were misdated and 'corrected' at later dates. In the witness box, they were evasive and defensive as barristers Benson and Dermott Wright methodically picked them apart.

One particular police tape had been left running after Mike returned to his car and he was heard to quip to his colleague, "Shall we just fit him up? It'd be quicker."

The jurors' jaws dropped.

On the stand, Mike looked to the judge but received no support as Benson adopted a dodgy police persona to his questioning, which raised laughter from the jury and left Mike pleading it was just police humour.

The judge banged his gavel and called for silence, but the point had been made.

With the defence moving well, the prosecution slid the Old Man's previous criminal record into the trial. This automatically created a prejudice amongst the jury and offered the chance of a retrial. Even so, rather than demand this, the Old Man's team appraised the jury as being the best they were likely to get. That decided, they placed the Old Man's fate in their hands.

Consequently, they changed strategy. Whilst the prosecution attempted to portray the Old Man as a high-level drug dealer, the defence presented him as a charming rogue dealing in cigarettes. The second persona would ring true, but would be tested to the hilt when he gave evidence.

A day in the box saw the Old Man lock horns with Colman Treacy QC as both men clashed. Colman attempted to patronise and belittle, as the Old Man bit back and refused to be shoved around by a posh public schoolboy. The climax of his evidence came when the Old Man produced a news clipping featuring a vital prosecution witness – Kenny Parker – who unknown to the jury, had been an ex-mercenary who allegedly killed black people during the apartheid era. The Old Man held it aloft, stared across to the one black juror, and as Colman objected and the judge banged his gavel, asked her, "Do you see how low they will stoop?"

That juror would later confide that this was the turning point for her.

As the trial progressed, she and the jury saw a prosecution whose barrister grew more dislikeable by the week; Colman belittled the defence witnesses and failed to smile at any moments of court humour. In contrast, the defence team of Dermott Wright and Charlie Benson grew in stature as the trial progressed at a snail's pace.

Slow as possible was the strategy. The longer a conspiracy trial ran, the better for the defendants was the ensuing wisdom. Make the case so long and complicated that by the end, the jury had to have doubts.

After four months, the jury was sent out on the Monday morning.

I spent that day at the courts, reading and waiting, chatting with the defence team, with Brandish who was confined to the court building. Across the concourse, we could observe Crime Squad detectives and the news reporters as thick as thieves. They had no interest in the defence, no curiosity as to the accusations thrown at the undercover officers. There was us and there was them. A guilty verdict was desired and expected.

The jury would remain out for the rest of the day. No news at the day's end. Eyebrows were raised.

Tuesday dragged. I sat with Brandish. He ate from a sandwich box as I read and made drawings. Benson and Wright frequently wandered by; there was little they could do but kill time. The detectives looked less confident by the hour; the reporters less excited, their numbers dwindling to a loyal handful.

On the Wednesday morning, the judge announced he would accept a majority verdict: 11-1. Even so, it made little difference. By Thursday morning, they were still out. It appeared the jury were locked and there might be a retrial.

Friday morning, the judge announced he would accept a majority verdict of 10-2. By now most of the reporters were gone, the public gallery empty, the legal teams exhausted. Still we waited. The judge was expected to order a retrial at the day's end. It was inconceivable he would allow it to roll into a second week.

Finally, by Friday afternoon, there was some movement. The court reconvened and Brandish was declared 'Not Guilty.' He wished the Old Man good luck and stepped down from the dock. The jury retired to consider the Old Man's fate.

For two hours there was nothing. A retrial seemed certain.

Then at 3.30, the court reconvened once more following a request by the jury to listen to a section of *Undercover Tape* 34. The court listened intently to the Old Man referring to the numbers involved in a cigarette deal, to which several jury members responded with faces of recognition. The number of cigs cited by the Old Man matched the numbers of cigs found in the container nearby. It was clear to the jury that he was dealing in cigarettes rather than drugs.

Ten minutes later, they found the Old Man 'NOT GUILTY'.

* * *

IN THE BAR, there was a rowdy toast to 'British justice' from the tables where I sat with several jurors discussing the trial. I was listening to their analysis of their trial and how the issue of character had proved critical.

"Your father's a rogue, but he's not a bad man," offered Juror Three.

"We could see that," added Juror Twelve. "We saw him every day for months on end – never arrogant, never bad-tempered – always friendly and well-mannered."

I nodded in agreement. They had got him right. We carried on talking.

As the hours passed, the bar grew drunker and louder. Most of the jurors remained and relived the trial's highs and lows. It seemed a most conspicuous get together and as the lawyers had made themselves scarce, I began to wonder.

"Is this all above board?" I yelled to the Old Man above the din.

"Not a problem," he yelled back. "I'm a free man. They're no longer jurors."

I wasn't convinced.

"I mean, I noticed the lawyers shot off sharply. Are you really sure this is okay?"

"They've got professional ethics to consider," he explained.

"And what about the prosecutors? If the police were to learn of –"

"Fuck the lot of them," he said dismissively. "Sore losers. That fucker Blair wouldn't shake my hand. If I had lost, I wouldn't have complained. But him…" and with that he chucked a roll of money behind the bar and skipped out to make some calls.

I settled back amongst the jurors, who regaled me with their key moments of the trial that steered their thinking. They had frequently noticed me in the public gallery, recalled the testimony I had given – an alibi for the Old Man. They saw me as a dutiful son, well-mannered and loyal, an artist. Not a criminal type, and that really mattered to them. It certainly was an education in the collective mind of the jury and how character truly mattered. But then Juror Four asked:

"You *are* coming to the party, aren't you?"

"Party?"

"Your dad's hiring Juror Seven's Indian restaurant for a thank-you meal."

"It's next Friday night," Juror Nine added. "Everyone's invited."

"Can you ask Charlie?" Another voice called out.

"Benson?" I stammered.

"And Dermott!" Juror Four yelled. "Don't forget Dermott."

I could imagine the horrified faces of barristers Wright and Benson.

"I'll see what we can do," I promised, and resolved to find out whether this was such a good idea.

* * *

THE PARTY FOLLOWED as promised. All the jurors, their partners, and the Old Man's close family and friends attended. Even Ryan James and his people drove down. Of course, no lawyers or barristers could make it. Even so, the evening flowed drunkenly and happily with a series of toasts and speeches. The Old Man humbly thanked the jurors and explained how he owed them his life and would always help them in future if there was anything they needed.

Applause followed as the eleven jurors continued the evening in loud and happy spirits.

I say eleven, as one was absent. Juror Five had refused to come along. She had called 'Guilty' from day one, and only caved under pressure in the final minutes.

Her absence was an indicator that all was not well.

* * *

WORD OF THE jurors' party would reach Chief Superintendent Blair of the Midlands Regional Crime Squad. It merely confirmed his suspicions that the jury must have been nobbled.

In response, an investigation was launched, and several jurors arrested.

Placed in cells and interrogated at length, all were released, but the investigation would rumble on, eventually coming to nothing aside from a threatened lawsuit and a half page story in *Private Eye Magazine (Issue 1020).*

WEST MIDLANDS: TRIAL OF JURY

WEST Midlands police were so distressed at a not guilty verdict in a big and expensive drugs trial they proceeded to arrest several members of the jury.

One of them is a mother of three and a former nurse. She was called for jury service at Birmingham Crown in 1999 and served on one of the largest drugs trials ever seen in the city. In January last year the jury found the defendants Tony Spencer and David Brandish not guilty on all charges. The defendants were naturally delighted. After shaking hands with the jury members, they accompanied them to the pub for a celebration. [...] Approached by Private Eye, a spokesman for Midlands Police issued a statement: "The facts are correct. Several members of the jury were arrested but none were charged. It would therefore not be right for me to comment on the allegations against them."

It would be the final loss of face in a case which had been a bitter experience for the Crime Squad and particularly Chief Superintendent Blair. The legal costs alone had been estimated at £1 million plus. An eight-month operation and a four-month trial had come to nothing.

The defeat would stay long in the Crime Squad's memory. Despite their efforts and further defeats over the years that followed, they would have to wait more than ten years for a chance of retribution.

As for me, I had my own dilemma to face.

I had no wish to join the Old Man in returning to a criminal environment. I had seen enough. It wasn't for me. However, whilst the Old Man had been on remand I had earned little, just a handful of animation jobs. Now he was out, his phone calls returned, and my need to earn was more vital than before.

Tariana was expecting our first child.

That summer, I returned to driving. Paperwork only, but nevertheless, helping the Old Man build it all back up again.

CHAPTER 23:
BUILDING OF A QUESTION

2000

THE WEEK after the verdict, I was parked up in a narrow side street out in Walsall. It was a rough urban area, deprived and drug infested. This wasn't a place I'd usually be collecting, but I had little choice.

I had been sat waiting for almost an hour.

Whilst on remand, the Old Man had needed to raise some money and resorted to dealing with the yardies on his wing. From dealing with them inside, he considered them solid and trustworthy. Unfortunately, their drivers on the outside weren't the most efficient.

Usually, collecting money was a swift transaction. If they were running late, you received a call. It meant you weren't hanging around in the same spot, arousing suspicion. However, I had no number and there had been no call. Usually, I would drive offside for half an hour, but it risked missing the payment.

Neither could we afford.

I phoned the Old Man.

"He's still not here?"

"Fuck. He said he would be five minutes. Just sit tight, I'll –"

"I've been here a whole hour now. It's not the kind of place I can blend in."

"Okay. I'll phone him."

The call ended. I sighed, looked around. As I say, it wasn't the kind of place I could just blend in. Anyone lingering here drew attention. Already a few curtains were twitching away. Once the yardie turned up, they'd know I was okay, but until then...

I might be mistaken for undercover police.

Weeks earlier, I had read a book entitled *The Infiltrators*. The story of two undercover cops, they had been left sitting for half an hour in a Birmingham suburb before being attacked, shot and left for dead. An unlikely scenario, but one which made me nervous. In my door well, I kept a short bladed, kitchen knife for such an emergency.

To date it had never been touched and shouldn't be today.

This pickup was only for £6,500. Not a lot, but it was important as the Old Man needed capital. Since out, he had been dragging in paperwork from all directions.

For my part, I also needed money. Our savings were spent; Tariana was expecting, and my ex-landlord from the studio had served me with a writ for £4,000. He'd served it outside Mum's place. I turned and he was on me, shoving the papers against my chest and backing away before I could clump him one.

"See you in court!" he yelled before falling into a large grin.

I'd left the papers with the Old Man to look over. He'd assured me there was nothing to worry about. Counter-sue him for £5,000 was his advice.

I sat mulling it over, looking for angles, grounds for such a claim, and then was distracted. The road beneath pulsated to a beat, deep and dense, growing louder. I checked the mirror.

A large dark SUV approached slowly, taking up both lanes, its windows blacked out. Not the same car as last time, but the same rap music grinding and pounding away as it slowed and pulled up high alongside. The window lowered, releasing the aroma of weed and the lyrics of guns and bitches. Its driver turned his head, stoned eyes gazing down at me.

"Op in Man."

"Do you not have it on you?"

"It's at ma' place."

I looked down, no time to run this by the Old Man.

He nodded,"Op in. It's not fa'."

I stepped out, locked my door, and with grave doubts silenced by the thumping of rap music, climbed into the SUV, inhaled a chestful of weed, sat back and relaxed.

We headed off.

Normally for paperwork, they hopped in, dropped it in the footwell, and hopped out. Took a few minutes.

Not this time.

We cut through a maze of tower blocks and down the narrow roads of a series of sloping council estates. He picked up the speed, shifting up the gears, hitting sixty, checking his mirrors. I sat back, calm but concerned.

This was either his usual way of operating or he was putting on a show. Either way, nothing sinister ought to happen. I was carrying no money; I had nothing they wanted. The only possibility was they had no intention of paying.

Now that was a worry.

We sped across another estate, up to fifth on the straights, dropping to first on the corners, then back up to fifth, hitting sixty again. I resisted the urge to cling to the door handle. Being twitchy would do me no favours if there was a problem. I thought of my knife lying back in the door well. Should I have brought it?

We pulled out of another estate, and ascended a long scraggly hill into a small industrial estate. We must have driven three or four miles by now. All for six and a half grand! We swung by some derelict factory buildings and around to a small workshop, where the shutters were up high. We drove in and screeched to a halt.

Immediately the shutters lowered, the workshop darkened; I climbed out, adjusted my eyes to the light. Two men moved in the shadows; I squinted to see. My driver brushed by, "Here's your man" he called out.

The lights clicked on to illuminate a large sports car, primed for a respray, being worked on by two mechanics. Beyond them in the far corner sat Sim, hunched over *The Times* crossword. He looked over his glasses, lowered his pen, and smiled, "I've gotten your money. You want a cup of tea first?"

* * *

AN HOUR LATER, I pulled through the gates to the Old Man's place. In the yard, a worker was installing more security cameras, another was busy cleaning cars. The Old Man on the phone, wrapped up his call, looked my way.

"You get it?"

"Yeah. But I'm not doing that again. You know what they had me do?"

I relayed him the situation and he laughed.

"Nothing would have happened. They just have a different way of doing things. Besides, I'm done with Sim. He's too much hard work. Main thing is you got the money."

"It's a grand short, though."

"Doesn't matter. I'm just glad to get that. I'd almost written it off, so anything's a bonus."

He turned to one of his lists.

"Your landlord – Scully, isn't it? Have you got his number?"

"Yeah. Why? Are you going to phone him?"

"Can't have him bothering your mother again. You said he's been at her door again."

"To drop off papers. But he's unpleasant with it."

"He ought to just post letters through the letterbox like anyone else. No need to for all this banging at her door."

He dialled the number.

I stood back in silence, not sure if I wanted my ex-landlord to answer or not.

The Old Man waited and waited and then…

"Ron? Ron Scully?… This is Jason's Old Man… that's right…"

Scully talked, the Old Man listened, shook his head, "No, no you can't be doing that. There's no good rea –"

The Old Man went quiet, Scully's voice was raised. The Old Man listened, head nodding, mouth biting.

"No. You don't go banging anyone's door. You post it… No, you can't have his address. You have an address you can post any legal papers to."

He listened some more, temper simmering, until he'd heard enough.

"Look. You go to court. You play the game. If you win, you win; if you lose, you lose. BUT IF YOU GO TO MY EX'S ONE MORE TIME, IF YOU BOTHER JEAN AGAIN, I'LL GIVE YOU A PROBLEM. Do you understand?"

Scully's voice continued.

The Old Man awaited a pause. "Right. I've warned you, mate. Finding you won't be difficult."

And with that the call ended.

The Old Man shook his head with frustration, "Can see why you've had problems with him. Guy's a prick."

I nodded, "Do you think that'll do any good?"

"People like that don't listen. But I know him from years back, so he'll certainly know me. Let's just wait and see."

He glanced back to his list.

"Any thoughts for counter-suing?"

"Yeah, I've had a few. He was syphoning off his electric from my metre. Also, we had a flood which damaged a pile of artwork. He was meant to have building insurance. Plus, the lease, I paid for it and he's kept both copies. He knows he pulled a stroke on the rental figure."

"Good. Go after him on those points."

I nodded; my mouth tightened with satisfaction. It felt good the Old Man making the call. Odd really. All those years without him around, maybe this was how it would have felt, knowing I had someone in my corner.

I was about to thank him when he changed the subject.

"My book's arriving in the morning. They've put up a fight, but I've had Baz the solicitor on it. They're allowing me a five-year passport only."

"So..."

"Time to get over the water. Lots of people to see."

* * *

A FEW WEEKS LATER, at five in the morning, I was parked up in a silver Mondeo at the lighthouse lay-by in Calais. The Old Man was yet to arrive. With no French phone or numbers, I sat tight, pulled a blanket from the boot, and tried to look like a tired motorist getting some kip.

Within the driver's front tyre, I had £60,000 concealed. The Old Man was to collect it from me. I had little choice but to sit and wait, but as ever, felt a little uneasy.

I had caught the ferry, which meant Customs had noted me driving through. They'd taken to searching me on my return trips when I was carrying nothing illegal. Irritated, they'd questioned me as to why I was taking these trips alone to France and returning empty.

"I like the drive," I'd said.

This answer failed to satisfy.

It occurred that one day they would tracker up the car and tail me on the French side. It was easily done.

Dark when I arrived, the sky now brightened, and the sun peered over the horizon. I had been waiting more than two hours. A few cars had come and gone, staying less than half an hour at most. Concealed by trees and foliage, the lay-by was only a few miles in land, distinguished by a twenty-metre-high lighthouse. The Old Man had been using it for some years.

It was again a favourite meeting point.

Since the Old Man's passport had been returned, foreign trips were back on. He was able to import gear on credit, but inevitably the criminal landscape in the Dam had shifted. He'd been away twenty months on remand, and during that time some suppliers had disappeared, been arrested or fled elsewhere.

It was a similar situation in the UK where he'd discovered several customers had moved on, been remanded, sentenced, fled abroad, or gone missing. His circle of contacts lived unpredictable lives. Few stayed in the drugs game all that long. Some got in, made money and got out, but they were few. Most would fall to police operations at some stage. Few had the sense to quit whilst they were ahead.

The Old Man was one such figure.

From day one, he had been back on the phones. His reputation on release had soared in many people's eyes. Beating a conspiracy charge was no easy feat, especially one as tooled up as the one he'd faced: trackers, taps, bugs, undercovers. It had the lot.

Whilst this gave some confidence, it struck fear into others.

"Your Old Man needs to get abroad. If they didn't like him before, they'll hate him more than ever now. He'll be too hot for some to deal with."

I could see their point; the Old Man didn't.

A blue Volvo pulled in, circled each section of the car park and departed. *Customs officers?* Impossible to know. With English plates, I was easily spotted.

I considered driving off for an hour but thought best of it. The Old Man was due, and driving off ran the risk of problems with the tyre. I'd switched it a few miles outside Dover and from there kept to a 40mph speed limit. The Old Man planned to take the tyre as his spare. I sat tight and reflected on this recent madness.

If I'd just gone through all he had, I would have quit. But he hadn't even considered the idea. It was a reminder of what he was now: 'a professional criminal'. Not a businessman, but a criminal.

All his contemporaries viewed him this way.

Crime wasn't something he dabbled in but was his full-time job. I had been slow to accept this, but given the last eighteen months of prison visits, I could see that now. The Old Man entertained no ideas about returning to any legal business.

Why that was, I could only speculate.

In time, he would obviously be targeted by the Crime Squad again and end up back inside on remand. Why he would want to go through all this again, only Christ knew. From my own experience, I could see there was no long-term future in this.

At last!

He swerved onto the car park and screeched up alongside. I clambered out, stretched and yawned. The sun was over the horizon, the air chilly, the sounds of the highway louder. "Where have you been?"

"Up to Belgium. Couldn't be helped. A few problems to get sorted."

We spent the next fifteen minutes switching the wheel before he popped open his boot to reveal a boot full of tobacco, wine and some brown boxes.

"I need you to take these back. Just some wine and tobacco."

"And the boxes too?"

"Them as well."

"What are they?"

"Baby formula."

I paused, "You are joking?"

"No. They're perfectly legal."

"I can see them thinking that at Customs. Me driving through with bags of white powder."

"Nothing they can say."

"They're going to think they're for mixing."

He smiled wide, "They have such suspicious minds, those people."

"Seriously? You really think…"

"I can't take them all the way up to the Dam. If they ask, just say they're mine."

I dug my heels in, "No way am I taking them. You'll have to make other arrangements."

* * *

TWO HOURS LATER, I was sat on the kerb of the customs shed. Several customs officers were poking around the front of the car, shoving cameras down the air conditioning, pulling out the radio. To the rear, two others were emptying the boot. I sat, feigning indifference, waiting for a problem, answering a few questions from a tall, smug-mannered officer with hat and clipboard.

"So, the car's not yours, sir?"

"No. It belongs to a mate called Titch. I can provide his details later if required."

"Titch?" He smirked and wrote it down.

Earlier, neither me nor the Old Man could recall whose name the car might be registered to. A nickname could be credited to any name later.

He jotted it down, continued. "And the tobacco is all yours?"

"Yes. All mine."

"And the reams of Embassies, John Players, Super Kings, they're also all yours, sir?"

"Yes."

"You smoke all four brands, sir?"

I adapted my story.

"The tobacco's mine, the reams are gifts for friends and family."

"The tobacco, you're ten kilos over our guidelines?"

"It's for personal use," I reminded him.

He made notes, "Not all your own personal use though, is it sir?"

He returned to the car, where an officer was pulling out the brown boxes of baby formula. I looked away into the distance, waited, noticed out of the corner of my eye, him standing up, stepping back and approaching.

"You appear to be carrying quite a lot of baby formula, sir."

I looked over.

He smiled, "Can you explain why?"

"It's perfectly legal as I understand it. I've a baby due in a few months. I've been stocking up."

He held me in his gaze.

I added, "He or she is due on September 28th."

He smarted at this, returned his attention to the boxes; an officer began tearing them open, fishing out the tubs of formula. He peeled off the lid and protective foil from one, used its plastic spoon to scoop out some white powder, and examined it closely as if he had a clue.

He looked across and grinned, "I think we'll just run some samples, sir."

I shook my head and yawned, feigning tiredness and boredom, masking any irritation whilst, inside, it was only just occurring that I hadn't a clue where the Old Man had picked it up. Was it what he told me it was?

It would be a long half hour.

* * *

FORTY-FIVE MINUTES later, the same smug officer confirmed it was baby powder. I shrugged, what did he expect? He frowned, keen to reassert some authority, produced some papers and declared: "We're confiscating your vehicle, sir."

I argued several points, but it was futile.

"You've stated that not all the tobacco and cigarettes are for your own personal use, sir. We've written down a list of confiscated items. I'd like you to sign this please."

I scanned the list: sixteen kilos of tobacco, 1,200 cigarettes, two bottles of Malibu, one Bacardi."

"Where's the six bottles of whiskey?"

"You signing, sir?"

"You're keeping my whiskey. And the brandy? Where's the brandy?"

"We have all day, sir. I suggest you sign."

I signed the paper, relieved the baby formula wasn't listed or being confiscated. However, they were taking the car.

"And how am I meant to carry everything?"

He waved across to the corner of the shed where a large shopping trolley stood.

"Knock yourself out."

He turned and strolled away. Several other officers watched on. I called after him, "And I can take anything?"

"Anything that's not on the list, sir".

With that, I began to clear the car of every unfixed item with an air of indignance, not because I was annoyed, but because I needed to retrieve the baby formula without drawing attention. I was still shocked they hadn't confiscated it. They were fully aware it was a mixing agent for amphetamine.

I filled up the trolley – six boxes of baby formula, breakdown equipment, camping gear, maps and bags, blankets and pillows, any crap from the boot no matter how worthless, until the trolley was overflowing, Then, with a much as dignity as I could muster, I slowly pushed it the length of the customs shed and out onto a potholed drive, bumping and rattling along until I arrived out by the garage on Dover's main highway, where in the distance, up on the hill, I spotted a B & B.

* * *

BACK HOME, I chilled out that evening. I could do little else. Tariana was six months gone, in good health, but growing concerned that working for the Old Man wasn't the best idea.

I considered the money.

We had enough to get by, and the baby needed a father more than money. I had ridden my luck in the past, next time I might not be so lucky. Tariana would allow it to be my decision, but I knew she had little interest in the money. If I was driving for the Old Man, it wasn't due to her, or our baby, it was because I chose to.

Late evening, the phone went. Mum had received an envelope of legal papers from my old landlord, Ron Scully.

"I was just going out and he appeared at the door with an envelope."

"And what did he say?"

"Well, you'll never guess, but he was ever so nice. Asked if I might pass on some papers to you; said 'please' and 'thank you'. He said he was meaning to post them through the letterbox and that he wasn't going to knock. And then he asked if I was well."

I couldn't help but smile, "That sounds good."

"I'm guessing your father had a word?"

"They did speak."

I sat down with some satisfaction. Growing up, I'd missed out on having a dad around. And now I was twenty-nine years old, and he was there, sticking up for me like I was a kid.

Late night, he phoned in from the Dam. I told him of Scully's change of attitude, and thanked him for his intervention.

"No worries.," he said. "As long as he's not bothering your mother."

And then I broke to him the news of the confiscated car.

"Fuck. Good car that."

"They were chuffed to bits. Well smug."

"Mondeo wasn't it?"

"We've got ninety days to claim it back."

"We'll see. Might have lost that one. And what about —"

"I grabbed everything out of it. Everything."

"Good. Well done. You did the right thing."

"Anything else?"

"Yeah. They nicked all my whiskey and brandy."

"Cheeky sods" he laughed.

The call left me feeling good, just as he'd been a good father by helping with the landlord thing, I'd been a good son by helping with the baby powder thing. I smiled at the strange relationship we now had.

I returned to the living room, and as was our custom back then, laid out some quilts in front of the TV, arranged three layers of pillows at one end, a comfortable bed for us both. We settled down to a Chinese and a box set of *Friends*. I drank whiskey; Tariana drank orange juice.

Life was good.

These small things brought contentment. Not grand plans, money or status. It was the simple things, the little pleasures. I was probably happier than I'd ever been. Earnings from the driving work had certainly helped, but it wasn't essential. We could get by with less.

The following day, I rang the Old Man, let him know I had some animation work in. Just a few weeks but then, with the baby due, I'd be busy for a while.

"No worries," he said. "Just let me know when you want some work."

"Will do."

"And good luck at the hospital. Keep me updated."

I nodded and smiled, given how I'd barely known him just a few years back, now he occasionally sounded like how a father ought to sound.

Maybe how he could have been.

And whilst I had gotten to know him these last five years, I was left wondering why he was the way he was. He lived an exhilarating life, tons of excitement, mountains of money, but he had spent even more time inside, and day in, day out, experienced incredible stress. And did he ever really sit back and enjoy it?

I'd never known him to have a night in with Blondie, chilling out, watching the TV. He never seemed to switch off. Couldn't switch off, there was always something going on. Nothing was ever enough. And the 'other people' were always out there somewhere. Every day, every night, the Crime Squad were out there, planning and preparing.

And one day, they would be back.

CHAPTER 24:
THE ROAD TO AMSTERDAM

2001

OVER THE FOLLOWING MONTHS, he kept rebuilding. Most of the workers, the customers and the suppliers returned. As the parcels flew out and the money poured in, he reinvested intensely, rebuilding, making up for lost time, until a new infrastructure was in place.

Meanwhile, I stayed out of the way. Our daughter was born; we named her Kia. The Old Man called me shortly after, offering his congratulations, checking all had gone well and enquiring of her weight. Very normal father-son stuff. I promised to call up and see him, give it a week or two.

It had been three months already.

He was still in the Nuneaton area, too well-known, a familiar figure. I visited one of the new units and shook my head in disbelief as he elaborated on the new apartments, garages, boats, workers, and land he'd brought to create the ultimate drugs operation. It was as if this was all a legal business.

"I don't want to burst your bubble, but is this all so necessary?" I asked him that afternoon. "It's not like you'll be here for good, is it?"

He looked at me quizzically.

"You can't stay here for long," I added. "You know they'll be coming for you soon."

He frowned in thought, "Maybe. But once I'm gone, BT and the Mechanic can run things at this end. I'll be over the water (Amsterdam and Spain), directing and organising."

I couldn't argue with this logic. He always had an answer. Even so, he knew he couldn't carry on as before. The previous trial's publicity had marked everyone's cards as to his line of business and no-one took any business front seriously anymore. He was a 'drug dealer' to most people, plain and simple. Every criminal within twenty miles knew it, and so did local police informants.

Inevitably, trouble was not far ahead.

A few weeks later, on the canals where they were burying stashes, a worker spotted a miniscule surveillance camera positioned high up in a tree. Rather than ignore it and report to the Old Man, he took it upon himself to climb up and steal it. In doing so, he brought the police surveillance to a premature end.

The Old Man called me that evening.

"Have you heard?"

"Heard this afternoon."

"Had a clear out?"

"I've nothing to clear out. I'm expecting no-one."

"Just double check; you can't be sure. We're still having a tidy up and then I'll be off."

"That soon?"

"Could be here first thing."

I was later told he spent the last twenty-four hours having a clear out. Phones were ditched, places cleaned, cars stashed away, and all product put offside. Pre-dawn, heavily armed police carried out raids and arrested a dozen workers. Detectives searched eight addresses and discovered a large-scale "drugs factory" at a remote farmhouse. Earlier, the Old Man's address had been the first hit and despite expecting the raids, he was still there.

Again, he was refused bail and remanded to HMP Woodhill.

Even now, this is a difficult one to explain. Arrested by the same police unit, facing the same charges, remanded to the same prison. You couldn't make it up, but that's just how it happened. However, there was one difference this time around.

Remanded for sixty days, he studied the police case and was confident it wouldn't make it to court. With this in mind, he prepared a bail application and noticed how police lawyers in their haste had miscalculated the remand dates: they fell short by a single day. His lawyer requested bail on that day.

By lunchtime, the application was heard unopposed and the Old Man walked free.

The error recognised; National Crime Squad bosses scrambled to place covert 24/7 surveillance back on the Old Man. For several days, they shadowed his every move, watching intently and awaiting a breach of bail.

Then one afternoon, he vanished into thin air.

* * *

SOME MONTHS LATER, my newborn daughter of three months snuggled up to Tariana. I pulled the door to, gently. A glance at my watch showed 8.20. I needed to get a move on as heavy snow was forecast.

I retrieved from the cubby-hole a burner phone, the Old Man's new passport, and eighteen grand in cash. I took a long walk around to my car parked offside. With no-one around, I clicked on a hand torch, slid myself under the car's chassis, and carried out a quick search for anything resembling a police tracker. All was clean.

Climbing into the driver's seat, I switched on the burner, dialled its sole number. After a delay of several seconds, the line rang twice and a familiar voice answered.

"Sam?"

"Yeah, it's me. I'm just leaving. Be an hour or so."

"Okay. Where we said."

"Will do." I ended the call, switched off the phone and removed its battery. He'd warned me to be paranoid regarding surveillance.

Taking a round-about route, I checked my mirrors as thick flakes of snow began to fall. Ordinarily, such a drive would be postponed but not this one. This had to be tonight. Once satisfied no-one was with me, I hopped on the M1 north.

I'd be with him in just over an hour.

By the time I reached Nottingham, a blanket of snow covered the city and a blizzard raged. I parked up short and, through a blinding snowstorm, trudged across to the nearby McDonald's.

This would be our last meet for a while.

I grabbed a meal, took a seat deep inside the restaurant, away from the windows. As I unpacked my meal and attacked the fries, I scanned a bustling restaurant of diners who, due to the blizzard, appeared reluctant to move on. New customers continued to arrive, brushing and shaking snow from their clothes; the place was packed. It was impossible to spot any signs of surveillance. Several people drew my attention, but it was impossible to say if they were or weren't. I busied myself with a burger and fries and awaited his call.

I heard nothing for twenty minutes and wondered whether he had turned up, seen the masses of people, and backed off. I read a newspaper for a while, but my mind drifted; I found myself distracted by the single question that people had been needling me with in recent months.

Why?

Why had this happened again?

And why did they want him that much?

It would be easy to believe that the latest raids were solely in retaliation for the bloody nose meted out to the Crime Squad, except their hunger predated the Birmingham trial.

Shortly after release in '96, plain-clothed officers had been observed rooting through the Old Man's bins and removing bags of shredded paperwork. The Old Man's future co-defendant Dave Brandish alerted the Old Man to the fact. Dave would later spend forty odd days on remand for drugs conspiracy with the Old Man, and there, when sharing a cell, he would press him.

"Tony. Bottom line. Why are they so interested in you?"

The Old Man shrugged and considered an answer.

"Most likely, it's down to the dollar trial."

The 1992 dollar trial had brought him into the spotlight, not only of the West Midlands Serious Crime Squad but of the FBI, who followed all counterfeiting cases of American dollars. To begin with, the charges for the dollar counterfeit concerned $250,000,000, an incredibly wild amount. Unsurprisingly, the FBI sent representatives to liaise with the Serious Crime Squad with the explicit demand that the dollar plates were found and destroyed. By the end of a long and expensive trial, the plates had not been returned and would never be recovered.

This explanation made some sense, but it led me to recall something more.

On my visits to Winston Green Prison, the Old Man had explained how the West Midlands Serious Crime Squad might be disbanded before his case reached court. This would largely be thanks to them fitting up many Irish terrorist suspects held at the Green. I could recall him assisting the appeals of some of the Irishmen, and elaborating on how, like them, he had made complaints against bent detectives, which resulted in a few taking early retirement.

After discussing his own case, he would often move onto the Irish cases, and one in particular he was working long hours on. It was a defendant of the Hyde Park bombing, probably Danny McNamee, who had been fitted up on partial fingerprint evidence; an area the Old Man had specialised on during his dollars case.

This gave credence to the Old Man's rumoured dealings with the Irish over the years.

It also brought to mind the Old Man's encrypted contact list, which had been entrusted to me for safe keeping. This list was a crime directory with the first part ordered by British cities and the second part ordered by countries with South American, Russian and Irish sections being particularly dense. The Irish section was unusual as at the end it included the name of a Belfast bar – starred – which acted as the IRA hub, and for which the Old Man had a passphrase.

Maybe this association is what elevated his status with the National Crime Squad. I had heard rumours of the Old Man gun running for the Irish some years back during The Troubles. The dollars and Irish connections together might explain the disproportionate attention he received.

I was pondering this when the phone vibrated, and I picked up.

"I'm two minutes away," his voice informed me.

"Right. I'm here," I said and put the phone to one side.

No-one arrived for two minutes and then five, but then two tables away, a man nursing a coffee, dressed for the snowy weather, lowered the scarf from his face and nodded my way. The Old Man had been watching me a while. He strolled over, took the seat opposite.

"Everything okay? You've been careful?" he asked quietly.

"Doubly careful. Been here a good half hour. We're good."

He leant forward, hands around his cup, head dipped down, eyes scanning the figures behind me.

"That man's okay," I said. "His wife and daughter have just left."

"Right. I did wonder."

He leant back in his chair, made a brief glance to the restaurant's far side, and appeared to relax.

I emptied a sachet of sugar into my cup and looked up, "So what is the plan?"

"I'm off in the morning. It's all sorted."

"Where to?"

"Over to the Flat (Holland)."

"To do what?" I asked, though I knew the answer.

He paused to take a few further glances around the restaurant and decided he could afford me a few minutes.

"I'll start taking charge of the import side full-time," he said. "I can't do it from over here. I need to be seeing the people face to face." He shook his head, "Too risky for me to travel, too risky to even be here."

I lowered my cup and rolled my fingers around its sides, "You be okay?"

"Will be better there. Safer there." He nodded to affirm this point. "They can't extradite me on conspiracy from Holland."

"And what about here?"

"Ryan and his partners will run things."

"With your contacts, though," I reminded him. "They'll be taking more of your contacts."

"More, but not all," he said." I'm holding plenty back… Plus, most will stay loyal."

On this, I was not so sure. In the drugs game, stealing contacts was part and parcel of the business. Passing over contacts to the James group would make the Old Man surplus to requirements given time. Then what?

He changed the subject.

"You have a book (passport) for Red to collect soon. I'll let you know."

"Red? That's –"

He leant in and lowered his voice, "He'll be coming over to set up in Holland. I'll link him up with some suppliers, transport and seed money. Once he's working, he'll work the loan off, and we'll have another group onside."

Another arm to this thriving alliance of Midland crime groups.

"We're working on it now, plus there'll be one or two others coming over." For emphasis, he raised a pointed finger, "Just be careful with those books. Don't keep them at your house."

"No worries. They're offside," I lied.

"From now on," he continued, "they'll be looking for a link to me. They'll go to the addresses they've raided and to any known associates, but you've not been involved; you ought to be safe. Just keep your wits about you. I might need you to come over later."

I nodded once more, leant back and observed a man and woman in their thirties arrive at a nearby table. The Old Man had already clocked them and pushed his coffee to one side.

"I'm going to shoot off," he announced. "Got the paperwork?"

I slid across a McDonald's bag, "That's the last of the float."

He grabbed the bag, "Thanks." And with that, he stood up, strolled across the restaurant, through the lines at the counter and stepped out through the side doors into the snow where he disappeared into nothing.

I sat quietly, finished my coffee, and after a few minutes, got up and left.

* * *

HE'D BE up north six months in all. Once he'd jumped bail, he partnered up with Ryan James and his crew. The Old Man provided the contacts, James the organisational skills, and the other partners, the manpower.

Within six months, their turnover had jumped ten-fold.

The James group, with little fanfare, would quietly emerge as the largest wholesale supplier of amphetamine and cannabis outside London. Their ascension would take many by surprise. Overnight they had become national players to be taken seriously, but the Old Man was their Achilles heel. If he were to be arrested, they would lose their supply contacts. It made sense to move him to Amsterdam, where he could focus solely on expanding the drug supply.

* * *

ONCE RELOCATED to Amsterdam, our phone calls resumed. He needed me as a buffer between the James group and his Brighton and London contacts. Given my recent lack of work, I took up collecting their paperwork, and soon after, the paperwork on the Old Man's own solo deals. One such deal would be with his Irish contacts who, due to their history together, would only work with the Old Man alone.

It would be this deal that would lead to his shooting in Amsterdam.

For a hashish deal, the Irish agreed an advance cash payment of £230,000. This money was to be driven up to the Old Man in Amsterdam; however, there was distrust in respect of any non-Irish involved. Consequently, they demanded a driver they knew and trusted.

This was where I was to come in. I had previously carried paperwork between the Irish and the Old Man to the extent they would accept me to accompany the money to Amsterdam. I would receive a grand to sit with a quarter million in the back of a lorry for twelve hours.

I reluctantly agreed.

Even so, at the eleventh hour they got cold feet and insisted on one of their own people. Consequently, an Irish man displaced me in the role. He took the money and linked up with the lorry driver at Portsmouth.

Within half an hour, they were promptly robbed by three masked men waving shotguns.

Obviously, there was a leak. The Irish credited it to the Old Man, and he in turn suspected a leak with his partners in the James camp. Strident enquiries, partnered with a process of elimination, pointed towards a drug dealer nicknamed the 'Soldier', later to be known as Bradford man David Royle.

A northern drug dealer with a vicious reputation, Royle had been pursuing a vendetta with the James group. He had turned one of their drivers, who had tipped him off about the Irish hand-over. Even so, Royle believed he was robbing the James group rather than the Old Man and his Irish connection. When he realised the error, he was conflicted.

The Old Man spent weeks negotiating with Royle and then gave him an ultimatum: return the money or feel the full weight of the Irish. The implication was his whole firm would be wiped out.

It was then I arrived in Amsterdam.

* * *

AT THE APARTMENT, I let myself in and found the Old Man engrossed in calls. He glanced up, offered a brief nod and continued. I dumped my bag in one of the spare rooms and pulled out several wads of cash from my coat lining. Returning, he switched his attention my way.

"Any problems?"

"No. Straight forward. Took the ferry, checked the car at either end. Car's offside."

"How much did you bring?"

"Thirty-two. That's all he had."

"Meant to have been forty-six. He should know better."

He shoved thirty in a bag and pushed it to the side. The other four he pocketed. Referring to his list, he struck a line through one item. Then, pausing, he committed the remainder of his list to memory and fed it through the shredder. He checked his watch.

"Sowerby will be back soon, but we need to shoot off now. Got a meet at the Water in twenty minutes and then we need to get across to the Shed (caravan) and move a few things around."

I paid little attention to this and moved onto the one thing I understood was of the greatest urgency, "Any news on the Irish thing?"

He leant back in his chair.

"The Soldier got into Amsterdam last night. Says he has most of the paperwork, but he's spent thirty. I've told him to keep it. Take it off what Ryan owed him and we'll say no more."

I paused for a moment and moved onto my next question, "Do you trust him?"

He looked up, "As much as I can do. He knows I have the Irish behind me. He knows what will happen if he tries anything. He's not a stupid man."

With those final words, he got up, changed his jacket and grabbed a baseball cap, which he pulled over his greying hair.

Conscious of Amsterdam being awash with CCTV, he never left the apartment without his head covered.

We made our way to the meeting at the Water.

* * *

SEVERAL MONTHS in Amsterdam, and the Old Man had stepped up the imports and organised a network of bases across Holland. They assured a protective pattern of operating as well as a basis for expansion. Unfortunately, this meant supplying those lines he'd always been keen to avoid.

By teaming up with the James' group, he was obligated to connect them to suppliers of cocaine and heroin. The former he would go along with, whilst the latter he would postpone indefinitely.

These new lines meant new suppliers, and so that day's meet demanded greater caution. He had rented a new car, carried a fresh phone. He would call Sowerby before we entered the meet and again when we left to confirm there had been no problem.

With the Old Man checking mirrors, we crossed Amsterdam to its eastern outskirts. There, we arrived at a leisure complex of small island communities formed by scores of water channels feeding the nearby canals.

"Before we go in," he warned, "when we settle down to talk, I want you to move away. Go to another room or create a distance, so you're not a party to any discussions."

I nodded. I was familiar with this, though it had been a while.

"I haven't yet got a handle on these people. If there's anything amiss, I don't want you party to anything."

I was familiar with this also.

"These are new people with a heavier product. This will be the first deal and I'm still not sure of them."

I resolved to keep a clear distance.

We walked across several bridges to a tall Nordic summer home of dark glass with oak gables. Five men in dark suits greeted us. The two largest were clearly minders. The other three, all in their thirties, appeared to be brothers who welcomed us like old friends. The eldest, tall, polished and smooth, was the head figure. He offered some words about family and trust, which made me wonder if this was why I had been invited along. With the preliminaries over, we entered the house and found ourselves in a grand open-plan room with a forty-foot-high gabled ceiling, which echoed our every word.

Great for surveillance, I thought.

They settled down at a long glass conference table. Spread neatly along its centre were various refreshments for guests. This appeared to be a formal drug meeting, Dutch style. I browsed the walls for a side room to escape into, but there was nothing – this was it. I spotted a small table positioned in the furthest corner and took a seat.

The minders took positions either side of the main entrance. They greatly raised the conspicuous nature of the meet. I remained silent, observed casually, and resolved to question the Old Man as to the wisdom of such meetings in future. This looked just like what it was.

Voices travelled easily and despite being some ten metres away, I could hear every word. They discussed the problems and pitfalls of their business before arriving at the point of the meet. The Old Man took the lead and explained his terms, for which they were all too ready to comply. He stuck to his usual codes, but they were unfamiliar and actually used the word 'cocaine' which echoed around the room.

At this point, I wished to be elsewhere.

The minutes passed slowly and after fifteen long minutes they wrapped up; the Old Man promised to get back in touch within a few days once he had spoken to his people.

"We will see you and your father soon, Sam," remarked the older brother.

I smiled and nodded, hoping he would not.

Retracing our steps across various bridges and trails, my relief was palpable. The style of the meet flew in opposition to everything the Old Man had ever preached.

"No good," he declared. "Fuckin plastic gangsters. They'll bring trouble."

"You going to meet up again?"

"No. I'll let them cool off. Can't do business with people like that."

We arrived at the car; the Old Man retrieved his phone, switched it on and called Sowerby.

"Just came out. Back at base in twenty."

As we pulled away, one by one, he switched on his other phones. Within minutes, the Dutch phone rang. He listened at length and ended the call.

"That was the Soldier. He's back in the Dam. He has the money."

"So, when can you grab it?"

He pondered the answer for a moment. "Could be tonight."

We drove off in silence. I concentrated on the road but wanted to hear more. Eventually, I spoke up. "You are going to be extra careful, aren't you?" I glanced across to check he was paying attention and saw him browsing his address book.

"He's been saying he's got it for weeks now," I added.

The Old Man searched for a number, answered me slowly but without attention, "Sounds like this time he means it – wants it done and out of the way. For once, he's pushing for it." And with that he located his number and dialled.

"Seems odd he's now keen," I remarked.

* * *

I HAD RETURNED to Coventry by the time the Soldier got back in touch. Two more days had passed, and again he expressed his keenness to return the money. "Tonight," he said, and the Old Man agreed.

That evening at the apartment, he prepared.

He would dress casually as normal. His usual bag over the shoulder, carrying one phone rather than five. No notes, no lists, no address books. He threw in some blank note pads and some maps to give it some bulk. He looked across to Sowerby.

"Think we're ready?"

Sowerby nodded.

The Old Man paused.

"You going to take it?" Sowerby asked, "Best to be careful."

The Old Man frowned in consideration, "Yeah. I'm going to take it."

Sowerby smiled and headed into a neighbouring room.

The Old Man continued, "If that prick tries anything, then fuck it. He'll get what's coming."

Sowerby returned with a small but weighty blue cloth bag. He passed it to the Old Man, who pulled from it a .22 hand pistol. Holding it for a moment in his right hand, he felt its weight. Pointing it outstretched at the television, he stared along its short barrel.

"This'll do the job."

Approaching the table, he grabbed his coat and pulled it on, straightened the collar and stroked his hands down the lapels. Looking across to the mirror, he observed his reflection. He placed the gun in the left inside pocket of the jacket and checked once more. He turned slightly left and then right.

"Can you see it?"

"I'd put the darker jacket on," offered Sowerby. "It'll hide the bulge more."

The Old Man walked over to the coat stand in the corner, grabbed a thicker dark jacket, pulled it on, walked over to observe himself in the mirror once more.

"Better?"

"I think so."

"Right. Let's go and check the meeting place."

He grabbed his cap and made for the door. The meet was set for nine at the Deli on the north side. They would be there at eight, check the place out and move offside.

The meeting would take place but would not go as planned. Royle would be shot dead and the Old Man almost killed. He would emerge with a bullet having shattered into scores of fragments as it ripped through his body. Most would remain embedded in and around his lungs throughout the years that followed. During that time, I would begin to address the question: *why had he become a criminal?*

Whilst he operated out of Spain, smuggling hashish and hopping from one get rich scheme to another, I would learn all I could about him and his past. I would learn of his upbringing, of his parents and an older brother, critical to him moving into crime. Slowly but surely, I would come to understand his journey as a businessman who once ducked and dived and his evolution into a criminal who made drugs his business. Finally, I would come to realise that for him, it wasn't about the money.

There was something else going on.

What that was, I would not yet uncover, but I considered to be tied up in his character. It was riddled with contradictions, in many ways unsuited to crime. Lacking the ruthlessness required, he made big money and either gambled it, wasted it, or gave it away.

It appeared not to be about the money.

In the end, he would be captured and arrested in Spain, extradited to the Netherlands, still wanted in the UK. He appeared to be finished. Consequently, for the following four years I would help all I could and by the time he returned from Spain in 2007, our relationship would appear to have changed.

The question remaining was, though, had he changed?

Would he return to his life of crime, or would he turn his back on it all?

CHAPTER 25:
RETURN FROM SPAIN

2007

THROUGH THE BARS, he could see the first hint of sunrise, illuminating the razor wire of a nearby guard tower. At four thirty, the prison remained quiet and still, his cell dark and musty.

He eased his way out of the bunk, stepped over to the basin, took a cold wash whilst he considered the day. His small desk sat waiting, paper and pens at the ready. There was much to do, and the light in the cell was rising.

He took a seat and began looking over the lists he had drawn up the night before. Once he had reabsorbed their content, he began the day as he always did – by writing letters.

He warmed up by writing to his daughter Nellie. Over several minutes he composed an upbeat letter full of optimism and loaded with promises of how life would be once he was home: *It won't be long now, less than twelve months. How are things at school? Remember education is everything. Once you learn something, it can never be taken away from you. How was he? Fine. He was studying his languages, just Catalan now. He'd done enough German and besides, Catalan was the language to know. Spoken all over South America, it's where they would be working and living in future.* He wound the letter up at two sides, drew a smiley face and placed it in a pre-written envelope.

Onto his sister Margaret. He acknowledged the medical papers she'd sent, the money he'd received, and provided a list of new subjects to research. He repeated some lines from Nellie's letter regarding languages and then added a few lines concerning his health. *Yes, his legs still played up and the nights were cold, he had the thinnest blanket, and the mattress was hard. Still, he was used to it – smiley face! He asked her to keep pushing the embassy for another specialist – there was still time. Otherwise, he was busy studying languages and via a mate on the outside, studying for a sailing certificate which would be invaluable later.* Again, two pages were enough. He placed it in an envelope, referred to his list and then grabbed the recent letter of mine.

Several sheets of A4 paper and two large A3 sheets. The sheets were blown-up Xeroxes of some drawings. He examined them closely and considered where he would begin.

As he put pen to paper, sunlight peeked through the bars of his cell. He glanced up and could see the rising of a yellow sky. Within the hour the prison would stir, the heat would climb, voices rise, and jangling keys would be followed by the opening and slamming of cell doors. There was never enough time.

Beginning with simple matters, he acknowledged the receiving of the Spanish CDs, *there just the job*, and then the monies and medical research, *both essential*. He moved on to the cryptic notes within the letter. Riddled with nicknames, shorthand notes and metaphors, he studied the letter closely.

Since being acquitted in Holland, interest in his return had escalated and whilst the number of messages had increased, he appeared less interested than he had once been. It was as if he was contemplating another direction. And for my part, I had done all I could to encourage such thoughts.

One way had been to propose his support for a comic book about drug smuggling.

* * *

OUR NEW PLACE was a large, draughty house on the affluent side of town. By now, Tariana and me had been together ten years, Kia was at primary school, Troy away at Uni. I'd spent our early years driving paperwork for the Old Man, the middle years squeezing by on savings, the last few struggling to get by at all. Tariana would earn us a stable income as a chef whilst I cared for Kia and aided the Old Man in his legal battles. Even so, my creative yearnings were still strong.

After the Old Man was cleared in the Netherlands, I devoted my evenings to drawing once more. It had been some years since I'd put pencil to paper. The skills were rusty, but the will was strong.

My evenings at the board harvested designs and a storyline for a comic book based on my time working for the Old Man. It was entitled *Smuggling Vacation* with a plot lifted out of his world: a holidaying couple happen across some buried hashish, steal it and attempt to smuggle it home to the UK.

The plot resembled the many tales of thefts I had heard of in recent years. The characters were modelled on the Old Man's circle of associates, including Ryan James and his people. I wondered what the Old Man's response might be.

I had mentioned it in a letter; slid in a few drawings.

To my surprise, he liked the idea and offered to help in any way he could. For me, this marked an acceptance of who I was and the beginning of a more balanced relationship. Before long, I was sending him full pages for him to offer his thoughts. By the time he was returned to Spain, it had become the main feature of our correspondence.

He would write on the copies of the recent pages, offering pointers and corrections regarding the reality of smuggling: I *think this page (6) is about there now,* he wrote. *Would advise to alter panels 3 and 4. Police trackers are smaller than this, see my diagram. Otherwise pages 5 and 6 are both good. Suggest on panel 9 he says 'fast one' rather than 'coke', also adjustments on panel 12 are much improved.*

I had been amazed by his interest in the strip and his acceptance of basing characters on his criminal acquaintances. Furthermore, it was clear but never stated that the main antagonist, a crime boss named Pastille Jones, was based on himself.

Pastille Jones, the tall, fiery gang leader who was ever on the phone organising his workers was the Old Man to a tee. I'd dramatised his role, upped the temper, even given him a young girlfriend reminiscent of Blondie. In contrast, the main protagonist was based on myself, a naïve young man out of his depth, at odds with the modern world.

The Old Man would wrap up the letter asking for more money, more sailing mags, and that I make further calls to ascertain his legal position on returning to the UK. Were drug conspiracy charges awaiting him? Would the National Crime Squad, or Serious Organised Crime Agency (SOCA) as it had been rebranded, be planning to arrest him on his return?

He needed to know more.

During sunrise, the prison would stir, his cellmate would wake, and the prison would erupt with the rattling of keys and sliding of doors. He'd sign off *'Best Wishes – T'*, place it in the envelope, rub some soap on the face of the stamps; they would be used two or three times whenever possible.

His cellmate Cesar, a well-mannered Catalonian, would ease to the edge of the bunk, his feet dangling down, yawn loudly, *"Buenas Tardes señor Spencer."*

"Buenos Tardes Cesar. Com esta?"

"Esta Bien. Que vasa hacer hoy?"

"Mas estudio Cesar. Mas studio."

The Old Man's Spanish was improving.

Throughout the morning, if stuck in the cell, English would be off limits as they spoke Catalan until ten, English until twelve. In the event they were out in the yard for the day, the Old Man would trade English lessons for Spanish with the other inmates. By the time of release, he expected to be fluent.

* * *

BACK IN THE UK, I had developed an approach for handling the Old Man.

I believed his character couldn't change, but it could be managed. He had certainly mellowed with age, and if he didn't return to his previous criminal circles, I believed I could point him in a healthy direction where he might become a businessman once more.

The comic book, I hoped, marked the beginning of this process.

We worked away on the comic book as the months passed and as our correspondence continued, the book grew. As it did so, the Old Man continued to say nothing of his plans. I knew there was no imperative reason for him to return to the UK at all. In which case, he could remain in Spain and work. The only question was, what could he do to earn his living?

Without finance, what business could he set up?

I had no answers.

His remaining investments were with old-time criminals. Few would welcome a Tony Spencer intending to go straight.

And then events seemed to make the decision for him.

* * *

TWO MONTHS BEFORE the Old Man's release, an old mate of his – a city drug dealer with terminal cancer – died in his cell. The Old Man owed him a hundred grand. The debt was effectively wiped out.

A month later, another old mate – Leicester drug dealer Ash Chenia – was murdered. The Old Man had persuaded his legal team to take on Ash's case, which resulted in his 20-year drugs conviction being overturned. On release, he had returned to the drugs game with a vicious manner which saw worker Carl Fowler violently turn. Fowler stabbed Ash sixteen times to the body, killing him in the bloodiest fashion. Fowler then proceeded to pour petrol over Ash and his prized Mercedes and set them both alight.

The Old Man had owed Ash a hundred and sixty grand or more. It was also wiped.

In four years, many other players had fallen by the way, and these were two more. It was as if fate was easing the way for the Old Man's return. Furthermore, as his release date approached, old contacts and mates getting in touch quadrupled.

The clamour for his return was increasing by the month.

Any hopes I harboured that he would see this criminal world for what it was and retire began to crumble. And then, the Old Man's demeanour changed as he appeared to accept that returning to the UK was inevitable. He noticeably realigned himself to becoming part of that world once more, with perhaps the only exception being the book he and I were working on.

That was different, at least that's what I thought.

It later became clear that he was calculating how the book might be tied into his plans for a return to drug smuggling. To him, the answer was obvious. What could be a better front for a drug smuggling ring than a book about drug smuggling? It could provide cover for phone conversations, travel plans and criminal meetings. If he ever found himself in a courtroom, almost anything could be excused as the actions of a retired criminal undergoing research for his next drug smuggling book. The idea would prove irresistible.

* * *

LATE EVENING AT HEATHROW Terminal Four, forty-five minutes have passed and there was no sign of him. Had he been held up by customs? Or had SOCA officers been waiting? Or maybe he'd had another health scare?

I grabbed a paper, found a vantage point to the back of the crowds. Blended in.

Only a few weeks earlier, he had been rushed out to a civilian hospital. The after-effects of the gunshot wounds, inflammation and shooting pains, predictably erupted every six weeks. He sounded a mess. I dreaded to think what state he would be in. Would he be walking with a stick, or using a wheelchair?

Another stream of passengers emerged in the distance and as they approached and peeled off, they revealed a tall, familiar figure strolling casually with just the one case, carried effortlessly. It was not what I expected. Rather than looking like a sick old man, he had never looked better. Tall, handsome and suntanned, his hair was whiter than I recalled, but his manner was unfazed. We exchanged a firm handshake and he laughed, "It's been a while then?"

"Yeah. Just a bit."

"How's things? How's Tariana? And Kia? How's your Mum? She doing okay?"

I offered brief answers, struggling to comprehend how he appeared to be in such good health. We strolled through the airport; him cheery and upbeat.

"Did you get a rental?" he asked.

"Yeah, as you said."

"Cause they're watching. They pulled me as I came through."

"Customs?"

"Just welcoming me back. Letting me know."

I nodded and understood. We hurried away saying little, exiting the terminal, crossing the car park away from the hordes before talking further.

"What did they ask?"

"Usual routine. Asking questions they knew the answers to. Checking my bag for anything they could copy. There's nothing there, though."

We strolled around to the car, taking no notice of who might be behind.

"Did you get a phone?"

"It's in the car, all topped up."

"Good."

"You got my numbers?"

"Sure, they're here."

He smiled.

I reversed back, drove around to the barriers and out. By this time, my phone was buzzing away.

I glanced at the incoming number, "That'll be for you."

He grabbed it, "Alright mate?"

He paused, listened and laughed, "No, not at all." He laughed some more, "I'm like a bad penny. Always rolling back, mate."

Several seconds passed as he listened, checked his watch and smiled as he took in some news, "Well, we've a lot on already, but if you can get over our way about ten thirty, we can meet up at the usual place... I'll give you a fresh number then."

By the time we reached the M6, he had taken half a dozen such calls and was making lists. It was like he'd never been away.

* * *

THE NEXT MORNING, a warm blue sky emerged, sunshine sprayed the streets and pink tree blossoms sprinkled the pavements. I walked Kia to school. Seven years old, she'd been writing to her Grandad in Spain but had never actually met him. She peppered me with questions as we walked. "How long is he stopping for?" "Is he having Troy's room?" "Can I tell people?"

She was one of the reasons I wanted him to stay with us for a while. Being a Grandfather might slow him down, encourage him to take his time, to look around and smell the coffee.

When I returned, he was up, getting organised and mildly irritated. "Whilst you were out, someone knocked the door. Gave me this."

He handed me a flyer for a gardening service.

"I thought it would do no harm to answer the door," he continued. "A man was standing there, gave me the flyer and stepped to the side so the driver of a parked truck could get a clear view of me."

"You think…"

"They were taking my picture. I'm sure of it. Give it a call."

I dialled the number, waited…. A dead tone.

"I'll go and check the neighbours. See if they had the same flyer."

He winced, "Shouldn't have answered it. Meant to lie-in, but there's a lot to do. Didn't think."

Minutes later, I returned; we were the only house on the terrace to receive the flyer. That seemed to confirm it.

"It's a bit out of order, isn't it? You've only just –"

"It's to be expected."

Maybe so, but it seemed unjust. I hoped it wouldn't put him off staying with us. Our place, I thought, was his best option. We lived in leafy Earlsdon, the area of Coventry where he'd been raised. He knew the area, and had old mates from school still living here. None were criminals. It might, I thought, act as a good influence. He might even get a place nearby.

We headed up to the high street to work through a list of provisions he needed. As we worked our way up one side of the high street, we ticked off items on his list. But when we stepped out from one shop, he turned his back to the road and mumbled.

"Across the road. Man in white T-shirt."

I glanced over his shoulder. A slim, white-haired man in his forties stood with a newspaper on the pavement opposite, not doing much, just lingering.

I had known this high street all my life. It wasn't a place where you would just hang out. People here were shoppers; they were purposeful and ever moving.

"Further up," he murmured. "Woman in denim skirt and black shoulder bag."

Another glance. The woman turned sharply and walked away.

We turned and continued up the street and I looked across at the man in white T-shirt, and he smiled. He knew he'd been spotted. Didn't seem concerned. We crossed the road and spotted the woman with the black bag further up, peering out from a shop doorway.

"Let's just get back," the Old Man remarked. "We've got what we needed."

We crossed over and turned back towards base. The man in the white T-shirt suddenly crossed over and took a position under a shop awning to watch us. He was not subtle. Was this to be expected? Was this to be the future if he stayed here?

It was clear the Old Man wouldn't be stopping. Once back, he made some calls. He had a car and some money to collect, several offers of places to stay. Within the hour he was gone.

At half three, I collected Kia from school. She'd told a few people her Grandad was stopping with us, even had a drawing to show him. I broke the news gently.

"Grandad had to go."

"He's not stopping?"

"No. He can't sweetheart. He's got work to do."

THAT EVENING, I also returned to the work I had to do. I sat up late, ruefully thinking of an opportunity missed. If the Old Man had stayed with us for a while, he might have liked it here. He knew the area inside out. Mum lived just a few streets away, David and Kate weren't far; they also had children. And of course, I was here.

I stayed up, working on our book – *Smuggling Vacation*.

A website had been set up for its promotion. I was blogging our progress, posting up pages and drawing, building up a readership. Every Sunday, a few hundred people were logging on to read the latest page. He might have found this interesting, intriguing maybe. But then, perhaps I was just grasping at straws.

Nonetheless, over the following year, I would do my utmost to encourage the Old Man's interest in the book. It was a chance to do something legal and lasting. Something that might lead elsewhere, and who knows, surprise a few people.

CHAPTER 26:
OPERATION DOWNPOUR

2008

I CONSIDER the summer of 2008 to have offered a glimpse into what might have been. Unfortunately, it would not last, but I am just glad that it happened at all. Even now, it sounds remarkable how the Old Man and I had published a comic book about drug smugglers, whilst he was an active smuggler under surveillance of SOCA.

Their presence was evident within days of the book's publication.

Facing the entrance of Borders Bookstore, we sat at a large table with a pile of the newly published books. On impulse, the Old Man had joined me at the last minute – drawn by curiosity, maybe. In recent days, the book's publication had been cheekily covered by all the local newspapers and radio stations. The journalists loved the quirky nature of the book and it received more than your *usual local author writes book* story.

The book's title was '*His and Her's Smuggling Vacation*' with a front cover featuring the two lead comic characters arguing over two tons of hashish. Imposed around them were the threatening faces of the drug smuggling gang, who attempt to hunt them down. The book was prefaced by a title page which credited *Crime Consultancy by Tony Spencer*. On this page, the Old Man and I would sign our names.

It had been a busy hour, the numbers surprising, the store manager delighted. My wife and daughter sat to the side, drinking coffee and a cola. The week before, Kia and I had attended the Jon Gaunt signing and he must have signed fifty copies.

We were on course to do forty.

After an hour or so, the Old Man took a break, caught up on some calls. He had to be somewhere and made his excuses. However, before departing he agreed to a photo and we adopted a pose of signing a book each.

Then he held up a palm, "Hang on a minute."

He broke off and strolled across the store where he had spotted a police officer who had just finished dealing with a shoplifter. He chatted with the officer a moment and walked him back our way, "It's a crime book and it'll mean a lot."

"Not a problem, sir," the officer smiled.

The officer, docile and dutiful, stood behind us as we signed our books and grinned for the camera. The photo would be evidence of the Old Man's new job as *Crime Consultant* – for which he had business cards, letterheads and before long, a film contract. With the photo complete, he headed off to one of the many meetings that filled his days and left me to finish up.

I signed the remaining books, paused to grab a coffee, and then noticed at the far end of the store, two men. Both wore dark suits, without ties. They'd been hanging around the store for more than an hour now – since the Old Man arrived.

I was sure I'd seen them somewhere before.

* * *

THE SERIOUS ORGANISED Crime Squad (SOCA) had dropped all charges for the farmhouse conspiracy of eight years before due to lack of evidence. It was partly a tactical decision. They would go again, but this time the resources would be plenty.

After about a year, the Old Man had returned to importing drugs and rumours would reach the Crime Agency. There, senior officers gathered, reflected on their past failures and reconsidered their strategy. The Old Man had been subject to two UK drug operations; both had ended in costly failures. However, their capacity for more sophisticated operations had increased. This time they could liaise with their Dutch counterparts and employ all measures: surveillance, undercover officers, informants, phone taps, but specifically international taps.

Furthermore, rather than concentrating on the Old Man alone, their attention would broaden to target the dozen men with which he surrounded himself. Raj would be part of this picture, as would his son, Sunil, workers Tiff and Monty, and even the Old Man's new girlfriend, Katherine. Operation Downpour would sweep the Old Man's closest allies into a concerted operation featuring international phone taps like no criminal had ever known.

Even so, the Old Man declaring himself to be a Criminal Consultant would provide a further complication. This would be exacerbated as the book's promotion gathered strength. The Old Man would be intrinsic to all the news reports, the reviews and interviews; a visible presence provoking media controversy, inspiring phone-in debates, and an MP arguing for the book to be banned.

Such attention would be difficult for SOCA to ignore.

As for me, the Old Man had been true to his word. Advising and encouraging, he refused any compromise. Three thousand copies had been printed the old-fashioned way, like an old Asterix comic book. Published in two covers, the first in green was supplied to head shops and festivals, the second in red was supplied to comic and bookshops. The former was endorsed by an array of stoner celebrities and head publications (Howard Marks, Jim Stewart, *Weed World*); the latter by local celebrities and comic artists (Geoff Thompson, Bryan Talbot, Hunt Emerson). It made for an original graphic novel that stood out from the crowd. With a product we both believed in, the Old Man directed me to use his name in any way I wished to promote the book.

Consequently, I went all out, knowing he expected nothing less.

* * *

THE OLD MAN AT THIS TIME was living in the grounds of his wealthy girlfriend's cottage on the outskirts of Coventry. Surrounded by pastures and meadows, Katherine's cottage was luxurious, legal and honest.

An ideal stronghold.

Paranoid regarding surveillance, I parked up the lane behind some hedge rows. I then strolled down a steep lane, carrying the three boxes of books he'd asked for, wearing a baseball cap to hide my face, with an air of caution.

I held my head left as I arrived at the entrance to Rose Thorn Cottage; I'd been warned of a surveillance camera concealed in the thicket. At the gates to the cottage, I buzzed and waited for the Old Man to make his way around.

Sunday mornings were slow and the easiest time to catch the Old Man. In recent months, it had become our routine whereby we'd meet up at the compound for a weekly catch-up. Each week, I would aim to have some news. One week, I could report how the book was being serialised by *Weed World Magazine*; another, that *Comic International* had run four pages on the book; another, that I'd done some podcasts for American websites and was getting orders. I always felt I needed something to top the previous week's news.

The gates slid open, I stepped in and strolled around to the compound where he based himself. There, he had parked up some caravans and installed CCTV and a pair of Rottweilers. In the first caravan we could talk.

Once he'd brewed some coffee, I reached into my shoulder bag and pulled out a copy of that morning's *Sunday Mercury*, "All's good, but I've got something to show you."

He nodded with interest.

I placed the paper down and opened it to pages three and four, a large black headline ran across both pages:

IT'S THE COMIC BOOK GUIDE TO DRUG SMUGGLING
MP calls for ban on book that gives tips on how to escape the law.

"A COMIC book with top tips on drug smuggling from a Midland super criminal is being circulated at HMP Birmingham. Convicted drug smuggler Anthony Cyril Spencer, from Nuneaton, Warwickshire has helped his son Jason Wilson to write Him and Her's Smuggling Vacation..."

He nodded as he read, "This is good."

I smiled to see he was pleased.

He read on.

"Spencer was sentenced to six years in jail for importing cannabis in 2003 and has spent more than 20 years in prison. The book is based on a married Coventry couple who try to smuggle a large cannabis stash from Spain in the UK. It features crime tips, including the best way to transport cannabis...

"Jason said the book has proven a big hit at Winson Green where it is being widely read by inmates [...] But last night Birmingham Perry Barr Labour MP, Khalid Mahmood, said he was shocked that prisoners have been allowed to read the book.

"I'm absolutely appalled," he said. "I don't want to stop former criminals writing about their experiences. But to actually put information into a book like this which will only increase the criminal knowledge of inmates is highly dangerous. Prison authorities should have stopped this from getting into the wrong hands. We don't want our prisons turning into universities of crime."

I passed him a coffee, "What do you think then?"

He pulled back, removed his reading glasses and looked up with a smile, "That's a good bit of publicity. It steps it up a bit, which is what we wanted." He gazed at it once more, and I could see he was satisfied, which was unlike some other opinions I would hear later that day.

Others would not be happy.

* * *

AN HOUR LATER, Raj slammed the paper on the table. "This is good news for you, for your book, but not good news for your father!" He retreated back, shook his head, raised a pointed finger, "He needs to keep a low profile, and you have his picture all over the papers. This makes no sense!"

He continued shaking his head and muttering.

Tiff, the ex-boxer, sat slowly reading the article and nodding as he did so. Next to him sat Raj's son Sunil, a young, high-spirited lad with a mind unlike his father's.

"It's a good picture," he said, "that one with the policeman. How did you get that?"

Raj frowned at his son, and continued with the same angry tone, "It is not a good picture. It is a stupid picture! We need to proceed quietly. How can we, when his son is doing this?"

Sunil rolled his eyes and slumped back in the corner.

Silence followed. The Old Man was outside on the phone.

Raj sighed, "The article says they are blocking the book going into Birmingham Prison. Is that McGlinchey's doing?"

"Yeah," I said. "He's been sending them in for weeks, but now they've blocked all copies."

"Well, do you know what they will be doing at the prison on Monday morning?"

I didn't. None of us did, but he was about to tell us.

"The governor of Birmingham Prison shall be forced to call a meeting first thing in the morning. Senior officers will attend, and they shall be studying this article and taking it very, very seriously. You have a Member of Parliament asking questions, for Christ's sake. The governor will be most concerned."

I shrugged, so what?

Sunil spoke up, "You worry too much, Dad. Who gives a fuck about what they have to say?" Raj glared back, angry but speechless.

Tiff having finally read it through nodded in agreement, "Well I think you've done well pal," he said. "I told you, didn't I? You'll end up making a fortune with this."

Raj scowled and looked back at the article, "The SOCA people, they will read this!" He frowned hard, raised a hand to his forehead, "What was your father thinking? This is not good for him. It is not good for us all!"

At that moment, on cue, the Old Man stepped back in. "That's all sorted, then. I'm going to go speak to Long Hair shortly. Everyone know what they're doing?"

Sunil and Tiff confirmed they did. Raj said nothing.

The Old Man smiled Raj's way, then he and I headed off.

We were off to speak with Long Hair.

* * *

LONG HAIR WAS a Ukrainian criminal on the run down in Spain. The Old Man had met him prior to his arrest in 2003 and was so impressed, he viewed him as a future business partner. They planned to make a fortune together in the not so distant future.

This worried me.

Since the Old Man's return, I'd learned that Long Hair had good connections in South America. This implicitly meant cocaine would be the commodity they would be trading in.

We scooted up scores of narrow back lanes before circling around to a quiet country cottage tucked away behind a dense wood. From there, the Old Man and Long Hair, via Skype, would hold their twice-weekly meetings. Only the Old Man and I knew from where he was making these calls, and even I was wishing I didn't know.

Long Hair had mailed him an Apple computer, specially modified to be immune from hacking. However, the Old Man couldn't set it up, hence why he needed me along. I would set it up, connect the Old Man to Skype, and leave them to talk at their leisure.

From what I had overheard, they were discussing a new transport, a courier company handling parcels between South America and the UK. They had conducted a few test-runs before spotting a flaw in the system. Now they were considering their options.

I was relieved it hadn't gone well. Perhaps they would cool it a while, maybe drop the whole idea. Having heard enough, I would stroll the outskirts of the cottage, keeping a look out, just in case. These Skype calls were meant to be foolproof, but I was yet to be convinced. With all the technology available, SOCA was certainly capable of bugging any room or latching onto any software. Each week, as far as I was concerned, was a week nearer to the day when the doors came crashing in. I was by now forced to accept that despite my efforts to divert him into other lines of business, it had always been a losing battle.

When he returned from Spain, I had believed the book might become something to drag his interests away from crime. Early on, before the book was even published, I had engineered some interest for the Old Man to tell his story via a publisher and to appear on a few true- crime shows. Though he was flattered, he said no.

I could see the reasoning.

Once he moved to writing books or appearing on such programmes, he would lose his credibility. And there would be no going back. For me, this would be no bad thing, but for him − it would have been the worst.

Instead, he had spent twelve months hustling for money, organising a series of bank frauds, handling a few parcels. Once he had raised some capital, he pushed on with plans for importing with less patience and more confidence than ever before. Even when he learned of the police operation on his group, he was unconcerned. He planned to be off to Spain within three or four months, and so pressed on. He considered the surveillance as nothing more than an occupational hazard. Something to live with.

However, this time he'd underestimated what he was up against.

* * *

OPERATION DOWNPOUR was targeting the Old Man's entire set-up, which consisted of several crime groups across Kent, Lincolnshire and the West Midlands. Downpour had placed surveillance on each group before requesting phone taps on the key members of each group. For the Old Man, who was frequently hopping flights, they would employ international taps via Dutch police. It was unlike the old days; these taps followed him across borders, ignoring matters of jurisdiction. Critically, though, the major difference would prove to be the employment of a ground-breaking 'roving bug' technique employed by Dutch Police.

The roving bug technique was simply the remote activation of the criminal's mobile phone to behave as a bug on his private conversations. The technology was ordinarily employed by the secret services investigating terrorism. For reasons never explained, it had been passed onto Dutch surveillance teams in recent years, though due to its illegal nature – it contravened human rights – it could not be used as evidence in any European court.

Even so, the technology would provide the edge for Operation Downpour.

WHILST THE OLD MAN organised imports of amphetamine and hashish, I continued promoting and selling books around the country at festivals, fares and signings. Aware that my every movement might face later scrutiny, I was being careful to lay a paper trail that would place me outside any forthcoming drugs conspiracy.

The press, TV and radio coverage gave legitimacy to the book and my own involvement as writer and publisher. Dig a little deeper, the police would find books had been sold to credible companies such as Waterstones, Borders and Forbidden Planet. Additionally, hundreds of books had been sold in the United States and hundreds more across Europe through the book's website. If they had any doubt, they'd realise the book and I were not part of any conspiracy. Unfortunately, I was aware the Old Man saw matters differently.

The hyped-up storm surrounding the book's 'exposure' of criminal methods had resulted in his name featuring in a score of media articles. They gave legitimacy to his role as a 'Criminal Consultant'. Already, he saw the book as his ideal defence in any trial. Wherever he went – UK, Holland and Spain – he considered himself to be on research. He carried books, business cards and a copy of the film contract in a briefcase which accompanied him to every meeting. Compounding this was that wherever he travelled, he would leave a trail of books to give credence to his movements.

For me, this was an increasing worry, as were his new working habits.

Back in the old days, he would travel to Holland by road to avoid travel records. He drummed this into us – *flights leave records: drive whenever you can.* Now he ignored his own advice and simply caught a flight whenever required. More often, his right-hand man Raj would book the flight on his *own* credit card to his *real* address and leave me watching on in disbelief. Where was the restraint? The patience? Plus, why were so many people involved? At a guess, there were already twenty people involved in any conspiracy.

What happened to keeping things small?

After a few months, alarmed by the persistence of the surveillance, he overnight abandoned all premises and shifted operations. Relieved by this, I wrongly concluded that any surveillance had been shaken off for a while. Now writing a second book, I recommenced my Sunday morning visits. This new book was to be called *Day of the Deal* and, ironically, would document a police operation against a known drug gang.

Again, the Old Man would be credited as the *Crime Consultant*.

* * *

FOR HIS NEW BASE, he rented three houses neighbouring one another at the end of a new build cul-de-sac, which backed onto the countryside. Remote and secluded, few knew of its existence.

I parked a few streets away and proceeded on foot.

At the end house, Raj welcomed me in and led me through to the living room where the Old Man sat at a table laid out in the same old fashion with rows of phones, chargers, lists, and so on. Business had resumed as per normal, though I had noticed how they swept daily for bugs, such was the paranoia. With days to go before the new shipments, he was preparing for his relocation to Spain.

"Sounds good to me," I remarked. "They're never going to back off. Once they find this place, the surveillance will start afresh."

"They're already here," the Old Man said. "Corner house at the end of the close. We're sure they've placed a camera there behind some guttering".

"You're joking?"

He laughed, "No worries. I'll be gone soon."

I looked out at the corner house, couldn't spot the camera, but knowing they were already watching was making me feel very uneasy. This surveillance wasn't like previous operations, where they would stay for six weeks and move off. This was more like Class A surveillance, where they stayed on the targets relentlessly.

"No worries Jason. Your father will be off soon," Raj barked. "End of next week. I've booked his tickets. Then those bastards might leave us all alone."

I nodded in agreement, but my concern remained.

Returning home, over the following days I dismissed it from my mind and settled down to drawing the new book. It would aim to complement the first, but it would be more sombre in tone, a cautionary tale. It told a story of a criminal gang brought down by a comprehensive police operation. It reflected my desire to write something more sober, perhaps reflecting my belief as to what lay ahead.

Though the Old Man had acted as Crime Consultant once more, he had been less patient than before. He paid little attention to the plot, having other things on his mind. His move to Spain was essential. It had been delayed several times, but now they were on the verge of the breakthrough he'd long been working towards.

He was so close. But then...

* * *

A FEW NIGHTS LATER, at a secluded farmhouse on the outskirts of Amsterdam, the Old Man was overseeing the first of the new shipments: 100 kilos of amphetamine and 50 kilos of hashish. It had a purchase price of less than quarter of a million, but was the first of many, scheduled to run every ten days.

From the surrounding fields, Dutch police surrounded the perimeter and awaited the signal to go in. Armed police units, helicopters, and a pair of diggers to smash through the security gates were on hand. Closer in, officers posed as electrical engineers, fixing phone lines, monitoring the situation closely.

Nevertheless, inside the farmhouse, the engineers had aroused suspicions. When a worker dispatched down an escape route failed to return or answer his phone, they knew. With no way out, the Old Man directed the workers to destroy any forensic evidence in preparation for the raid.

The crashing of a bulldozer smashing through the main gates was seconds later followed by the doors caving in and armed police pouring in from all directions.

The Old Man and the workers were sat playing cards and drinking coffee. No-one resisted arrest.

Elsewhere, across Amsterdam there were further raids with eight arrested, a pill machine recovered, and various drug paraphernalia seized. In contrast, over in the UK, there was nothing. No raids, no arrests. Zero.

Alerted to a lack of contact from the Old Man, one by one, gang members began cutting off phones and having a clear out as they realised there might be a problem. For me, this meant shredding just a handful of notes and placing any of the Old Man's papers offside. I didn't expect a raid, but I was on tenterhooks.

* * *

THE FOLLOWING MORNING, I received a call from a man with a heavy and serious Dutch accent.

"This is Herr Lonterman. Are you Jason Wilson?"

Unsure if it was Dutch police, I answered cautiously, "Yes. Who is this?"

"I am your father's lawyer. Yesterday, he was arrested in Holland and charged with drug offences."

I paused a moment, "Is he okay"

"He is good but is in custody."

"What happened?"

"They found him in a farmhouse with a significant number of drugs." He paused a moment as if he expected I might be shocked. "Also, it is only fair to tell you… they have many phone taps. It does not look good. He asks that you notify his family."

"I'll get straight onto it." I answered, and with that I called Raj immediately.

The voice of a fatigued Raj answered the phone, "Any news?"

"It's not good. We need to meet. The pub on the bend where we met before. In one hour."

"I'll be there."

I headed out, watched for a tail, and on route bought two burner phones. Things were about to get immensely complicated.

CHAPTER 27:
UNDERGROUND SAFES AND ROVING BUGS

2010

IT WAS ALWAYS McDonald's. Always just Raj and me.

"I'm fucked. What can I do?" he said, his face resigned.

"We could dig it out."

He shook his head, "No. It can't be done, dear boy. It's too large, too heavy, too deep." With this, he sighed, looking down at his untouched coffee.

We were both stumped. The problem at hand was the underground safe buried in Raj's back garden. It had been planted there to store money and drugs. Now with the Old Man held in the Netherlands, with police raids expected any day, we struggled for an answer to Raj's problem.

"Are you sure they'll find it?"

"Course they will. Those bastards will bring dogs along. I have no doubt." He pushed his cup away, leaned back in his chair and shrugged, "What can I do?"

I had no answers.

He grimaced and frowned, "I knew they were on us. I told him and I told him. But as usual, your father would not listen!"

I sighed and attempted to steer the conversation forward.

"Maybe you're right, maybe he should have listened to you, but we have to focus on the here and now. Henley rang to tell me he's got rid of the van and the garage (where mixes had taken place) and has since cleaned and rented it out. So that's all good."

This didn't raise his spirits, "It's all too late and it doesn't matter, dear boy. They have phone taps – hundreds and hundreds of them."

"Which the old man says will be inadmissible."

"No, they'll get them in," he said, gazing across as two faces entered the restaurant. "You don't know these bastards... they'll stop at nothing." He looked again to the men sat nearby, and his eyes darted left to suggest we move tables.

Taking a table at the furthest corner, Raj leaned in, "They have your father in a farmhouse with 100 kilos of the amphetamine and 50 kilos of cannabis. There is forensic evidence everywhere. How is he going to explain that? You tell me!"

I leant forward and prepared to tell him, but could barely believe the answer myself, "He says..."

He watched and waited, "Yes..."

"He says that he was carrying out research for a book."

Raj leaned back, frowned and shook his head, "Who the fuck is going to believe that?"

* * *

A CALL TO THE OLD MAN'S lawyer shone some light on the situation but offered little reassurance. Barry Arnett had been the Old Man's legal confidant for more than twenty years and a man to be relied on in a crisis. I had told him everything.

"As I see it," he began. "Your dad is being held at a prison in north Amsterdam. They have, we are told, 168 phone conversations which record his movements in the lead-up to his arrest, and then the arrest itself. He's caught 'hands on' with 100 kilos of amphetamine and 50 kilos of cannabis. He appears to be banged to rights. But..."

I listened intently.

"But they have a problem."

"Which is?"

"The Dutch made the arrest. The taps are Dutch. And after his arrest, it was the Dutch who charged your dad with possession. This is in effect a Dutch case."

"So…" I wondered aloud.

"This gives SOCA a problem. They cannot charge him; they cannot extradite him. Your dad's lawyer is insisting he be tried in Holland on possession where if he pleads guilty, he faces no more than five years".

This was encouraging.

"He'll be out in less than three," he added. "Maybe even two."

"Good, good…" I murmured aloud.

"Remember, he was only found with Class B and C, which is not such a big deal in the Netherlands. As I understand it, there's been no class A drugs found anywhere."

I looked up in hope; all was not lost.

This was why I'd rung Barry. He could always see the positive and his thinking would be in line with the Old Man's. Even so, I needed to know the downside.

"What about the worst-case scenario," I asked reluctantly. "Say they did extradite him here?"

"Well…" he coughed and cleared his throat. "Here, he would be facing fourteen on conspiracy, and given your dad's previous record and his history with the crime squads, they would ask for fourteen, and they would certainly get fourteen!"

I quickly ran some maths, "So he'd be out in seven or eight?"

"But don't be getting ahead of yourself. At the moment, SOCA have to persuade the Dutch to drop their possession charges and allow the British conspiracy charges to take precedent; as these are class B and C charges, the Dutch won't be agreeable to at all. The British would have to trade them something – do a backroom deal."

"Would they do that?"

"The Dutch, as you know, are always practical. SOCA have had an operation running on your dad for the best part of a year. They desperately want him whilst, to the Dutch, he's just another smuggler."

"So he'll be extradited"

"It might take a while but once they have agreed something, I think he will be extradited, but…"

Good. Another 'But…'

"But once here, they have the problem in that your dad's crime of possession was committed in Holland, not here. They cannot charge him for possession. They can only charge him for conspiracy, and the onus will be on them to prove he was conspiring to supply those drugs to the UK. This means they desperately need to include phone taps."

Okay. I could see where he was going with this.

"Your dad's barrister will scrutinise and attack the Dutch phone taps and press for them to be excluded. If he finds the grounds, and they got ruled out, then the case would automatically collapse."

"And he would walk – again!"

"You got it."

* * *

A MONTH LATER, the Dutch agreed a deal. Within a single hour, the Dutch possession charges were displaced with an extradition request. That evening, I received another call from Herr Lonterman.

"Hello. Mr Spencer's son."

"I'm here. Have they taken him?"

"Yes. There was nothing I could do. They wanted your father very bad. I am sorry."

Lonterman had been convinced the Old Man would be tried in Amsterdam and receive a small sentence, but had been proven wrong. Immediately, I phoned Raj and several others in the Old Man's group. They all needed to be on their toes. There could be police raids within just a few hours.

I slept little that night. Was I considered to be part of the conspiracy? I was certainly on the police surveillance, on video footage, on phone taps. I'd even taken a trip out to Holland with the Old Man on one occasion. I'd gone to meet with some Dutch booksellers whilst the Old Man met with his suppliers. That was a mistake; there would certainly be a record, surveillance pictures maybe. Topping that, though, was the book coverage in the newspapers, on TV and radio. I had believed it would establish my legal credentials and create some distance, but it might have achieved the opposite effect.

I lay awake into the early hours, doubting certain choices.

The Old Man had been arrested carrying *Crime Consultant* cards with my trading name of Dealer Comics. He also was carrying a copy of my film contract, several *Smuggling Vacation* books and various notes of mine concerning crime research for future books. How could they not at least interview me?

I didn't sleep easy. The thought of police officers banging the doors at half five in the morning, them tearing through the house at the top of their voices, upsetting Tariana, frightening Kia, left me fearful with concern.

At sunrise, as long shadows stretched across our street, I heard something outside. Rolling quietly out of bed, I rushed downstairs and opened the front door. If there was a raid imminent, I thought it best I should let them in, avoid the noise, the drama, the attention from neighbours. But there was no-one. I dressed quickly and ventured out to comb the nearby streets for signs of a forthcoming raid, but there was nothing.

Arriving back home my phone rang, "Hello Jason."

It was the thick Mauritian accent of Gee, Raj's partner.

"They've taken him," she sniffled. "They just left."

I took a deep breath and spoke slow and clear, "Okay Gee. Just remember what he said. There's nothing to worry about. Absolutely nothing. He'll be back by this time tomorrow."

She sniffled some more and put the phone down. I looked again up and down our street − nothing! I was in the clear, it seemed.

Maybe this whole storm would pass me by. Still, there would be many arrested that day, with just a few spared.

* * *

THEY RAIDED NINE LOCATIONS – in Kent, Grantham, Manchester, Birmingham, Nuneaton and Coventry. Of the fifteen warrants, they were able to arrest ten. By late morning, the interview rooms were prepared, the suspects lawyered up. Across several rooms, the interviews commenced.

Incredible to believe, they considered Raj to be the Old Man's right-hand man. Accused of providing logistics support, it equated to everything from booking flights and transferring small amounts of monies to attending meetings and collecting paperwork.

Nevertheless, Raj was prepared.

He had robust explanations for everything, which he had rehearsed a thousand times in his head over previous weeks. His interviews began well, and during the earlier tapes he went on the attack. He hated "these bastards" and would show them. However, as Raj talked, detectives held back the phone taps until the very point when they would be most effective.

The Old Man's girlfriend Katherine Jones was two rooms down. A head-turning redhead in her forties, she was soon crumbling under the pressure. Pleading ignorance, she shed floods of tears as detectives went through her movements over recent months – playing phone taps of her talking with alleged drug dealers, showing surveillance photos of her and the Old Man striding the canals of Amsterdam whilst he met Dutch suppliers. She cried and stalled, pleaded and evaded, but detectives would be patient.

With old-time villain Mick McGlinchey, things were less clear. He could talk and talk, except not about what detectives wanted him to talk about. Playing his phone taps made little difference. McGlinchey meandered and circled, joked and confessed to things many years ago that were long gone and unverifiable. He talked about his drug addiction, his drink problems and what a wonderful man Tony Spencer was. And the book, that was a laugh. Would they like to know about how he was sending them into Winson Green Prison? Or the MP who tried to ban the books?

The detectives took a break and re-thought their strategy.

Not far away, interviews with the so-called hardmen of the group, Monty and Tiff, commenced. Both men had little to say until the detectives produced a video of the pair carrying shovels and walking onto some wasteland. The footage then rolled as they proceeded to bury an underground safe. Monty quickly retreated into a 'no comment' defence, whilst Tiff, the ex-middleweight boxer, flinched and began to unravel and break down.

"You can't stop him. He'll just keep going."

"That's Spencer you're talking about?"

"Yeah. He's unstoppable."

The detectives listened on and produced a receipt: for six safes. "Where are the other safes Tiff? Do you know where they are?"

Indeed, he did.

Over in Birmingham, the Old Man had sat through his interviews in silence. Occasionally he smiled, another time he smirked and then just the once, he shook his head and laughed aloud. By the afternoon he was back in his cell, interview over.

The other conspirators from London and Birmingham all acted as the professionals they were. When detectives played their taps, they either sat in silence or went 'no comment'. As the detectives had anticipated, though, it only took one to crack and they already had Tiff.

Within hours, they dispatched detectives to Raj's place armed with spades and directions to locate safe number two. Whilst this was underway, detectives examined the pickings from the morning raids. Alongside the scores of phones routinely seized were some cannabis bars from McGlinchey, amphetamine from Mitchell, and several other items to be sent for a forensic examination, one of which was a cement mixer displaying small traces of white powder.

Within 24 hours, they had enough. Of the ten arrested, eight were charged with conspiracy and remanded.

* * *

BIRMINGHAM PRISON, formerly HMP Winston Green, had become familiar to me over the years and would be again. I would visit the Old Man with his girlfriend and co-accused, Katherine Jones. Thanks to the near seven-figure value of her cottage, she had been granted bail. To her credit, she remained loyal and would visit most days. The visitors' room was still in the large hall, but the inmates now wore yellow bibs and there were vending machines at the far end of the room. Otherwise, there were few changes, with the same clanging gates, the same jangling keys, and the same sense of disappointment that engulfed me whenever I entered the main prison building.

Nine rows of twelve tables neatly filled the hall. On the far side I could see Monty and his girlfriend, Tiff in the row adjacent, further down our line were the two Londoners and down at the far end, Raj's son Sunil being visited by his girlfriend.

All eight accused had been placed within two wings of the prison. We suspected this was to encourage tensions to simmer, tempers to boil and splits to occur in the run-up to the trial. At times, it appeared to be working, most notably when each received copies of the interview transcripts and were able to see for themselves what each had said and who had caused all the damage.

However, despite the damage caused by Tiff's calamitous police interview, he was back on side and all nine would enter pleas of 'Not Guilty'. The group unity would be held and coordinated by the Old Man, who was insistent they would win the case due to the illegal phone taps. He was convinced they would be ruled out during the pre-trial arguments.

Of this he was supremely confident. Raj was less confident and with none of his co-accused listening to him, he was increasingly frustrated with the process. That he was an ex-prison governor inside meant he was reliant on the group for protection and on the Old Man to lead the way on the legal front. As always, Raj believed he knew best, but no one was heeding his words. For much of the time he would be the squeaky wheel of the group.

Whilst the Old Man would arrive to his visits, cheerful and upbeat, encouraging confidence and cooperation, Raj's approach differed as he argued and raised his voice with his one visitor – Gee – his girlfriend, twenty years his junior.

"He doesn't learn," the Old Man commented. "He should be grateful she visits instead of giving her a hard time. After all his years inside and he hasn't learned that."

The contrast between the two men couldn't be starker.

The Old Man had always given the appearance of prison being easy. He never complained, never self-pitied, never lost his temper on a visit. On occasion, he would laugh and remind us that we were there to cheer him up, rather than the other way around.

"Things will turn out fine," he reassured us both. "They're running scared. They're terrified the phone taps will be ruled out."

He would explain how the taps were illegal due to the employing of a 'roving bug' technique by Dutch Police. It was this error the Old Man contended was where they were set to be exposed. By the end of each visit, we would be filled with confidence.

As that afternoon's visit ended, we got up, filled with our usual optimism, turned for the exit and were intercepted. A wide-eyed Raj stood in my way, stepped closer, gripped my arm tightly, "Jason. You must talk to your father."

His face was desperate.

I looked left and right as visitors' heads turned our way.

"You have to get me out of here! Speak to your father – he has to listen."

He grabbed my shirt and came closer still, "He can get me out, but you must —"

"There's nothing I can do," I said, as two burly screws rushed over.

I raised my hands, "Everything's fine. We were just talking."

Raj agreed, "We are just talking!"

They grabbed his shoulders, pulled him back and dragged him away.

I watched on as he was escorted from the room, which had turned silent. Once he was gone, the pause ended; the noise returned. I took a deep breath and Katherine placed her hand on my shoulder, "He's losing it," she said.

I nodded but could understand why.

As we drove back, I thought of Raj and considered how difficult he must be finding this, how difficult his son must be finding it. His son Sunil was an intelligent young man, brought up with high aspirations, and for a while had great prospects. However, like me, as a boy his father had gone to prison, and his life had been transformed.

Like many who'd grown up watching their father inside, he was destined to follow his father into a world he wasn't made for. It could easily have been my fate also, or my brother David's or sister Kate's. We'd all been lucky enough to avoid such a misfortune.

Not so Sunil.

* * *

SOME WEEKS BEFORE TRIAL, I headed down to London for a rendezvous with *Guardian* journalist Nick Davies at the Grosvenor Hotel by Victoria Station. Davies at the time was the country's lead reporter regarding a series of phone tapping scandals that were making national headlines. Fleet Street reporters were hacking into the voicemails of the rich and famous, and Davies' concern was that this was also happening in other spheres such as politics and crime.

Here we had a common interest.

Part of the Old Man's legal strategy was to generate as much pressure on the prosecution regarding the phone taps. He considered this the weakest point in the case as they were essentially illegal, but more importantly, employing an illegal technology: the roving bug technique.

So, what was this *roving bug*?

For some time in Holland it had been standard practice for high level criminals to remove batteries from phones during meetings due to the police method of activating mobiles as recording devices. The Old Man believed he had concrete evidence of this being applied in this case and insisted their exposure would collapse the trial.

It was reasoned that if the 'roving bug' could be brought out in open court, SOCA would be forced to admit of its existence and confirm that it was a tool in their armoury. This confirmation would collapse the case but more importantly, it would give grounds to appeal for any UK case where phone taps had been employed. The implications were truly immense as most of SOCA's high-profile cases included phone taps.

Seemingly from nowhere, Davies appeared.

Expecting a studious grey reporter, I raised eyebrows at the youthful man who arrived. Wearing a black leather jacket and littering his language with smooth, articulate expletives, he was a maverick and just the man required.

We took a private booth, and immediately I outlined the case and presented him with a bag of phone taps in CD form with the accompanying transcripts.

The prosecution had encrypted the original recordings so none of the defence teams had been able to make copies. This fed into the notion of SOCA wanting to restrict their access to the defence teams, who would have little time to scrutinise the recording method. Nevertheless, I had hired an IT engineer to bypass the encryption. The result was the 'roving bug' tapes could be shared amongst the defendants, and with a reporter like Davies, who was developing an impeccable reputation for challenging such abuses of privacy.

Davies looked at the tapes hungrily. These might be the evidence he had long been searching for, the smoking gun which gave a greater explanation to the recent phone hacking stories he had broken and covered.

"And the trial starts when?" he asked.

"April 20 at Birmingham High Court."

He rolled his tongue and frowned thoughtfully.

"The roving bug tapes are marked," I added. "They clearly show Dutch 'phone taps' amongst the defendants in the UK who are not using their phones. It's most clear."

He cleared his throat, "To be truthful, I have already made enquiries amongst some contacts high up in the security services, and they confirm what you have told me. They say the 'roving bug' does exist, though officially, it does not."

I nodded and waited.

He smiled, "I shall make further enquiries. Though, if these are what you say… then the trial most certainly will not go ahead. The prosecution will not want the roving bug exposed in a British courtroom."

I nodded in agreement.

He frowned some more, grabbed the bag, "Leave it with me. I shall be in touch."

And with that, Davies left as swiftly as he arrived.

CHAPTER 28:
THE FINAL SHOWDOWN

APRIL 2010

THE NEW POLICE OPERATION had surpassed the normal measures employed against class B drug dealers. Operation Downpour had employed international phone taps across three countries, with three supporting police agencies.

Even the Dutch arrest was overboard for a class B drugs ring. A bulldozer had smashed its way into the farmhouse, followed by swarms of armed police under the cover of two police helicopters. When the Dutch police appraised the haul of just 100 amphetamine and 50 kilos of cannabis, it came as a surprise that it was considered of such importance to SOCA.

Whilst the Old Man appeared banged to rights, in the Netherlands he was looking at a mere five-year sentence. That SOCA went to such lengths to extradite him underlined that this was more than just another drugs case.

This was their moment when old scores would be settled.

However, despite appearing guilty, the Old Man was adamant he with his legal team would turn it around. And what's more, he had convinced his co-defendants, who had persuaded their partners and families that they could win this.

All eight instructed their lawyers to follow the Old Man's defence team.

I, too, was caught up in believing the impossible and backed the Old Man in any way I could. He was made for this situation. Over the years, he'd amassed a wealth of experience in conspiracy cases; it was reasonable to believe this was winnable if we all pulled together.

On visits, he had assigned me a role with two aims.

Firstly, I was to break the encryptions on the phone-tap recordings and provide them to Nick Davies as well as the defence teams, so the recordings could be scrutinised. This I had managed.

My second task was to complete and publish the second book that referred to the *roving bug* concept. This could then be used in evidence during the trial.

To date, the comic book had been ignored by the prosecution, as they considered it irrelevant at best and a distraction at worst. This suited the Old Man's defence. They would be holding back his defence statement until the eve of the trial. At that point, they would push the now two books centre stage and send the unprepared prosecution into panic. It would force them to change their strategy.

"The trial will be all about the comic books," the Old Man confided. "I'll bring everything in – the MP who wanted the book banned, the reviews, the news reports, any radio or TV coverage; we'll bring in the book's supporters – Howard Marks, Geoff Thompson, *Weed World Magazine* – they'll all be brought in to create confusion for the jury."

I listened on, aware that he had beaten two conspiracies before. Aware that if anyone could win this trial, he could. It was his character; he was as ruthless and as intelligent as the situation required. Even so, any success relied upon the phone taps being ruled out.

With them in, it would be a mission impossible.

For the prosecution, as they approached trial, they had their own concerns. They had expected a split amongst the defendants as firstly the Old Man had been caught hands on. Secondly, all defendants were included on the phone taps making damaging comments. And thirdly, one defendant – Tiff – had crumbled under interview and directed police to three underground safes. Even so, with weeks to go and no-one angling for a deal, the prosecution grew uneasy.

Their intelligence informed them that the lead defence was set to attack the phone taps on grounds of illegality. Moreover, if the taps were not dismissed, they would reveal in court the method of 'roving bug' they had authorised the Dutch to employ.

The alternative for the prosecution was to remove them from the case and pressure the Old Man to provide a good reason why he was travelling Europe meeting various criminals; to explain how he ended up in a farmhouse full of drugs on the edge of Amsterdam. In such a scenario, that he was carrying out research work for a new comic book would be more difficult to disprove, especially as early in the trial, a second book would be published and submitted as evidence.

What had seemed an insane defence some months ago would suddenly appear quite plausible.

* * *

AT HOME, all had turned in. The house was quiet but for the back room, where lamps burned away, a radio blared old tunes, where I sat completing artwork to the final page of *Day of the Deal*.

After 79 suspenseful pages following a cat and mouse game between undercover police and a group of importers, the final page was a half-page splash of a scrapyard surrounded by police cars, a police helicopter up above, on the ground several main characters being arrested. The Narrator stated: *'And so ends another adventure, full of naivety, stupidity, and on this occasion – such dire consequences.'*

A senior officer yells above the noise: *'Yes sir… we've got them all… Well, we always do in the end, don't we?'*

Bottom right, a title: *THE END.*

Art imitating life, the irony wasn't lost.

The front cover design depicted a doomed drugs shipment above a series of prison mugshots. The rear cover featured a dozen humorous quotes from inmates at Birmingham Prison. For example:

"The Highlight of spending 12 lovely months at Winson Green was reading 'Day of the Deal'. Loved it to bits!" – A6998A6; Peter Vijschaft (Dutch lorry driver turned criminal): Remanded for smuggling.

"Brought back so many fond memories, from just starting out in the game – to the day I got caught!" – A5800AG; Keven Hartley (AKA 'Billy the Kid'): five years armed robbery.

And so on.

The book was scheduled for printing the first week of the trial. Its late submission would take the prosecution by surprise. Given it would be receiving extensive coverage throughout the Midlands' media, it would be difficult to object to its late submission.

As I wrapped up the artwork, late night music switched to the news that a volcano in Iceland had erupted.

This would prove significant.

* * *

BY DAY ONE of the trial, the Icelandic volcano had been erupting for several days and released an ash cloud covering thousands of square miles that drifted south to fill the skies of Northern Europe. Air travel in a score of countries was in chaos, with thousands of flights grounded; UK and Dutch airlines were hard hit. Consequently, our Dutch telecommunications experts were travelling by road.

The defence had been hoping these experts would prove key to the phone taps being ruled out. Day one of the trial, the plan was to put the prosecution on the back foot. Without the experts in attendance, this seemed unlikely.

The omens were not good.

Birmingham Crown Court was the setting for the trial. Court One, the largest courtroom, had been reconfigured to accommodate nine defence teams. The trial was expected to run six months, but legal arguments would be heard first.

On the opening morning, all defendants arrived in great anticipation of the trial collapsing. However, there were no experts to be seen, and journalist Nick Davies' schedule, due to the Icelandic situation, had been thrown into turmoil.

This was not a good start.

From the canteen balcony, I gazed down at the long, grey concourse below. Lawyers, defendants and their supporters gathered in clusters around the courtrooms. A little before ten, a few barristers emerged marching on the concourse, heads high, gowns flowing, catching admiring glances.

The Old Man's team would be led by Charlie Benson, a junior barrister at the previous trial, he was now a QC. A smart, articulate performer overflowing with charm, juries loved Benson whilst prosecutors detested his smooth effectiveness. I had watched him, and Dermott Wright, run rings around the prosecution a decade previously. As ten neared, more barristers appeared. I headed down, weaved my way through the crowds to settle outside Court One, where nine groups – one for each of the accused – lingered. All on the same side but all keeping their distance from one another yet observing and noting who was who – defendant or lawyer, relative or friend, detective or reporter. As the Old Man was the lead conspirator and boss of the group, I could feel some eyes on me; the glares of a few lawyers who were less than happy with their subservient roles in the proceedings. I searched the crowds for the irrepressible Charlie Benson, due to arrive at any time.

Robed and wigged up, an older and greyer Benson appeared through the crowd and approached me with a smile, which switched to a concerned frown. He stopped close, leant in and lowered his baritone voice.

"How have they got your bank details?"

"My what?"

He peered over his spectacles, "We have just been served with a stack of papers, six inches high, concerning yourself and your book activities these last twelve months."

I was without words.

"They have evidently gotten wind of your father's defence and are attempting to trash you and the book first chance they get."

"The... fuckers!" I mumbled.

"Exactly – *the fuckers!*" he boomed loudly.

The comic book defence had been saved as a shock tactic, but evidently the Crown had been tipped off.

"So, what's the play?"

"The bundle they have served will wait until this evening. As for now, I am to argue for the dismissing of the phone tap evidence. They are most certainly illegal and have no place, but the Crown will argue venomously for its inclusion. Without them, they have a real fight on their hands."

"And with it?"

"I will do my absolute best, but..." he looked at me and having known me for more than a decade thought better to level. "Your father's made some foolish mistakes. I am most surprised."

I grimaced painfully to hear these words.

He continued, "It may be a thousand to one chance, but if your father asks me to give it my best shot then I will give him a hundred per cent. I will give the case everything."

"A thousand to one? Is it really that bad?"

"Caught with the drugs, phone taps, eight other conspirators, some smart, some bloody foolish. Then there's the safes; the surveillance, the countless flights made, money transfers and that *fucking* cement mixer covered in amphetamine. I am surprised at him."

Me too, I thought. "So, would you advise him to plead *Guilty*?"

"That would be for him to choose. He is his own man and will do what he thinks best."

A depression immediately engulfed me.

"It is not lost yet, though," he said with a smile. "There are the phone taps to argue, and if we are successful – well, anything can happen." He patted my shoulder, turned and marched back towards court, his gown trailing behind. I watched him join the crowds streaming into Court One and asked myself, *was the Old Man doomed? Were they all?*

* * *

BY THE END OF THE DAY, our experts hadn't arrived, and the taps were ruled in.

The defence teams flapped and some of the defendants buckled. The Old Man directed them to hold their ground, rein in the lawyers; as soon as one made a deal, the rest would be compromised. They had to move in unison.

Some of the defence teams fumed at this. Nevertheless, they continued to move and deal as one, with Benson leading from the front.

Meanwhile, I mulled something over that had been bothering me.

The Old Man had informed me that I would be needed as a witness, and my defence statement would soon go in, but I was yet to prepare one. On visits, when pressed on the matter, he had been evasive as to its content. All he would reveal was that my statement was to go in at the eleventh hour, so it could not be anticipated. The lack of discussion suggested there was more to it.

On the second morning, Benson entered negotiations with the prosecution and by afternoon announced he was striking a deal for the Old Man to plead Guilty, but with a twist. He argued the sentence for the Old Man must be in line with what he would have received in Holland, as that is where he was arrested, where the taps originated, and where the two other workers, arrested with him at the farmhouse, had already been tried and sentenced to just two and three years. He referred to the guidelines for such sentencing and reminded the judge that his hands were tied. He could sentence the Old Man to no more than six years.

All other conspirators would have to receive sentences beneath this benchmark, which took into account their relative roles in the conspiracy.

The notion of doing a deal, of pleading guilty, sent many family members and their lawyers reeling with disbelief, including myself. However, there was the flip side. The prosecution was also angered by the proposed low sentences.

Suddenly, a trial was appearing unlikely.

Whilst they thrashed out the details, supporters for the defence bided their time in the court's cafes and corridors, waiting for news, hoping for relief. It was whilst killing such time that a member of the Old Man's defence team pulled me to one side, "I think there's something you ought to see."

He led me upstairs to a small windowless room where, upon a desk, sat a laptop, switched on, its screen full.

"This is your father's defence statement he entered just a few days ago. I think you should read it." And with that he left the room.

I took a seat and slowly began to read. By paragraph three, my throat was dry.

The Old Man had placed me at the heart of his defence statement. More than this, he had exaggerated everything with the most grandiose Walter Mitty type lies he could concoct: 60,000 books published in several languages, my requirement for him to make all these trips to Holland and Spain on research, a movie already in production with more films to follow. He evidently expected me from the witness box to corroborate and commit obvious perjury.

This was why he hadn't allowed my statement to go in. He knew I wouldn't go along with this unless I felt there was no choice. I reread the statement and stared on in disbelief. Then the member of the defence team returned.

"Are you done?" he asked.

"Yeah," I responded, attempting to repress my sense of shock.

"You can see why he has to go guilty."

I turned, managed a fake smile and held back a tear, "He's an inventive soul, isn't he?"

He returned a tight smile, "We have to make this deal. He doesn't have a chance."

I nodded, my disappointment raw.

Minutes later, I stumbled from the courthouse, escaping the chaos for a while. Walking into the city centre, I found a bench to sit down for a while in a square of the business district. Edifices of commerce towered all around me, city workers dashed back and forth, fag ends littered the pavements.

I sat in silence, alone with my thoughts.

* * *

BY THE FOLLOWING AFTERNOON, the deals were done; it was just a matter of going through the formalities. To an overflowing courtroom, eight of the nine defendants took their positions. The Old Man rose first to hear the charges. He then, for the first time in his life, offered the plea of "Guilty."

The others followed.

Heads bowed to a packed court of family and friends, one by one, each pleaded guilty. Some were relieved to get it over with, others felt obligated, others humbled. In return for this collective plea bargain, they received lenient sentences.

The one person excused was the Old Man's girlfriend, Katherine Jones. A condition of the Old Man's deal was that all charges against her were dropped. It was a deal-breaker as far as the Old Man was concerned and the prosecution, realising this, agreed her omission.

Of the eight, Raj received four rather than the ten he had been facing, his son Sunil and the ex-boxer Tiff both received three, Monty two, and the remaining conspirators took fours, threes and twos, much to the chagrin of the prosecutors. From the outset they had hoped for twelves, tens and eights. Nevertheless, they would promote the case as if they had won an incredible victory.

On this occasion, the TV coverage was laudatory.

That night I sat at home, despondently flicking between channels: BBC, ITV, Sky News. All announced justice as Tony Spencer and his 'Cement Mixer Gang' received 44 years for their foiled multi-million drugs operation. They featured surveillance footage of the Dutch farmhouse; Tiff and Monty burying safes; boxes of *Smuggling Vacation* being employed to conceal kilos of amphetamine; the Old Man strolling through airports and the streets of Amsterdam. The footage was summed up by SOCA detectives pledging to strip Spencer of all his wealth with confiscation orders.

I managed a smile. *What wealth?*

They didn't know him at all.

Combing the morning papers, the story made all the Midlands" front pages and a few nationals. The detail was extensive, they even ran the photo of the Old Man and me with the police officer at the book signing the summer before: *'Ringleader was 'crime' expert for son's book'* the headline informed the reader.

It was a bittersweet memory now.

* * *

AT BIRMINGHAM PRISON, the Old Man lay on his bunk, relieved it was over. It had been hard work, but he had scored a result. This was no revenge. Out of his three drug conspiracy cases against the crime squad, they had won one – weakly.

With time served, he would have home leave by the autumn of next year, with his full release the following summer. Out of the six, he would serve three. It was a joke. Once out, he could start again. This time it would be different. He would keep it small but as always, think big.

Long Hair had already been in touch. He had sent money over to pay any bills. He was a patient man. Their plan to deal with South America was untouched and could wait eighteen months, two years if necessary. Then they would make the fortune of which they had dreamt.

As for me, I continued with a sense of emptiness. Reading the Old Man's defence statement had been a blow. I tried not to take it personally, but it was clear he planned to use me, to put me under pressure, so I would commit obvious perjury. I reasoned that he was desperate, under tremendous pressure, but it was difficult to entirely excuse.

I considered whether I would ask him about the statement.

What could he say? And did it matter.

It was brinkmanship, after all. He was fighting for his life and eight others, plus all their families. Besides, though I hadn't been part of the drugs ring in the legal sense, I was complicit ethically.

I had been all along. And maybe it was now time to stop.

Despite my best efforts, the Old Man was back in prison, history had repeated itself, nothing had changed. Nothing had changed because he never would.

This was, I think, his seventh spell in prison. He had to date served almost 24 years inside. Again, it seemed to be more about the adventure than the money, more the excitement than the profits. And why was that?

Everything pointed to that character of his. Suited to both business and crime, he'd chosen crime but not in the way others had. For his peers, it was clear they were in it to make money and nothing more. For the Old Man, though, it was like some sort of game which always ended the same way: him captured and facing a trial for his life.

Ever the same ending. Sometimes he would win; sometimes they would, but once released, the game would start over.

And why was that? Why did he like this game they played? Because that is just what it was. It was a game.

During the trial, I had stumbled across the social game known as 'Cops and Robbers'. It was coined by a transactional psychologist named Eric Berne. The term referred to the game that certain types of criminals play. He describes it as thus:

Because many criminals are cop-haters, they seem to get as much satisfaction from outwitting the police as from their own criminal gains, often more. Their crimes, at the Adult level, are games played for material rewards, the take: but at the Child level it is the thrill of the chase: the getaway and the cool off.

He goes on to outline how Cops and Robbers mirrors Hide and Seek, and that like any good game, the thrill comes from almost being caught, that any game without this risk is not a game at all. Berne describes how some habitual criminals play like adults, do it for the money, shun risk and are rarely caught. These are not considered good players. Whereas those who are good players, who are in it for the game, take the greatest risks, delight in their cleverness, but ultimately and eventually are caught. For them, it is essential for the pursuer to know how clever they have been. This second type of criminal, due to this tendency, is eventually captured and seldom does well financially.

He offers variations of the game: Auditors and Robbers, Customs and Smugglers, and 'courtroom' where criminals hire lawyers in an attempt to avoid punishment and restart the game.

It was an intriguing theory

Viewed this way, the Old Man's life had been a series of games.

Berne's theory didn't offer an explanation why someone would be drawn to such games. That I would continue to consider as the Old Man served his time. For a while I entertained sharing Berne's idea with the Old Man, seeing what he made of it, but then events would unfold, and we would never discuss the matter.

CHAPTER 29:
AT THE CROSSROADS

2012

EIGHTEEN MONTHS LATER, a frosty side-street on New Year's Day. We sat in the Transit, taking a break from a chimney up high that needed pointing. It had been a slow, bitterly cold morning.

My brother's chain-smoking filled the cab, but I kept the window up. It bothered me less than the biting chill outside. I folded the newspaper to one side, checked my phone for messages, and looked up to notice two figures ambling our way.

The taller figure was a gaunt pale man wearing a large black trench coach and hat; the second, a red-headed woman, donning a thick burgundy winter coat with white fur sleeves. The man walked steadily but unevenly, leaning to his right. As they neared us, I froze, recognising the figures as the Old Man and his girlfriend. Straight away my attention was drawn to his face and how his right cheek was sucked into the bone, pulling down his right eye, giving him the effect of having suffered a stroke. He looked seventy if a day.

My mouth fell open.

Two days ago, the Old Man had undergone a five-hour operation to remove a cancerous tumour. He was meant to be recuperating at home.

I swallowed hard, felt the coldness of a small tear breaking at the corner of an eye. I blinked it away. "He's… "

"He don't look good," said David, stubbing out his cig,

We both hopped out as he neared the van.

"Ah, here you are," he said in a strained voice, "Your mother said you were working down here."

"Just a pointing job; said I'd have it done by New Year," David explained, and from there outlined the job at hand. The Old Man took an interest, looking between us and the chimney up high.

"Must be a good customer to be here at New Year's," he said.

"Nah. We need the money," David answered. "January's the slowest month."

For the next few minutes, they talked of chimneys and building work whilst Katherine listened in silence, and I attempted to avert my eyes from his facial damage.

At close quarters, the damage was extensive, disfiguring and ugly. He appeared not the same person to look at, nor to listen to. His talk was usually about his plans, his work and what he was on with, but not today.

Eighteen months into his sentence, he had been diagnosed with terminal cancer. His oncologist had given him six weeks and warned he could be dead by Christmas. His final prison letter gave instructions for the funeral. He wanted a burial in a small private cemetery. No fuss.

After a few weeks he had been released on compassionate grounds and the oncologist advised an operation which might grant him an extra few months. The operation would be savage. He appeared unconcerned.

After a few minutes of small talk, his operation made its way into the conversation.

"Oh this? It's out of the way now. Give me a few weeks and I'll get going on a few things I've got in the pipeline."

"He's going to rest for a while," Katherine interjected. "He mustn't be doing too much."

A brief awkward silence followed.

"Yeah, Kath's right," he added. "Once I'm ready though…"

"But your health is all that matters," she added.

His eyes shifted and I could see he was irritated, though he knew she was right on this one.

She stepped back.

"Well…we must get going," he said. "I want to get over and see your sister, and then there's my mother."

We nodded our agreement, whilst both taken back by this sudden interest in family.

They walked back from the direction they came. We watched on in silence. Both wondering how long he might have.

* * *

FOLLOWING THE TRIAL, the defendants had gone their separate ways. One by one, they were transferred to lower category prisons near their respective families. Most departed on good terms, with Raj perhaps the one exception.

He had wanted to "show those bastards!" He absolutely believed he would have got his 'Not Guilty' verdict if the others hadn't accepted deals. Angry that none in the group would listen to him, he blamed the Old Man for denying him his opportunity.

Once away, he would never talk to the Old Man again.

Sunil, Raj's son, would think otherwise. He had followed the Old Man without hesitation and received two and a half years. It may have been more, except the judge expressed some sympathy with his plight. He had drawn the court's attention to Raj's negative influence on his son and implied he had failed in his duty as a father. I wondered what Sunil made of those comments. I had thought the judge correct in this view, though I had no doubt Raj would have thought him wrong. In all the time I had known Raj, he had never admitted being wrong on any matter.

Tiff, the ex-boxer who broke down under questioning, had been extradited to Spain to serve the four-year drugs sentence for hashish he had absconded from some years earlier. His reputation irreparably damaged, he wouldn't see the Old Man again.

Meanwhile, the Old Man had been transferred to HMP Onley, a Cat C prison in Rugby. There, Katherine continued to visit each week, counting down the months to his release. They planned to retire to Spain, open up some businesses and live happily ever after. The Old Man agreed that he was finished with crime and within earshot of her would declare that he'd had "enough of all that shit," – but then would quietly insist I remain in touch with Long Hair, Albert and just a few others.

I couldn't see him retiring just yet.

As for me, I had a book to sell and threw myself back into what this time was a lonely process. Nevertheless, the media coverage was healthy. I had changed the tone of the promotion. Instead of courting controversy, I went with a cautionary approach that highlighted the futility of the Old Man's world, the dangers involved and the penalties to be paid.

Regional papers carried it with an abundance of headlines: **'NEW BOOK'S TOUGH MESSAGE ON CRIME'; 'COMIC CAPERS KEEPS BRUM CROOKS QUIET'; 'NEW NOVEL REVEALS HARSH REALITIES OF DRUG CRIME'; 'COMIC CAPERS AND A CRIMINAL DAD'; FAMILY'S CRIME LEADS TO CARTOONS'; 'DAD WAS MY INSPIRATION FROM HIS JAIL CELL'**

Unfortunately, controversy sells, and the new angle didn't.

Before long, it was apparent the books had little future beyond being a hobby, so I adapted and changed course. The first thing I did was enrol with the Open University to study for a psychology degree; the second thing was I took a job working as a labourer for my brother. I was set to enter a long period of transition.

The Old Man had remained unfazed, though. He would still phone in from the prison. We'd talk in code; I would relay his messages, there were still a few in touch. He only had two years to serve and the time was going smoothly.

That was until there was a change.

The recurring pains, in and around the lungs, from the gunshot injury, had continued to flare up every few weeks in recent years, but he'd simply adapted to it. After the trial, the pains intensified until he was cell bound and demanding an outside doctor. Eventually he was taken out for routine scans.

The results were clear: his lungs were riddled with cancer.

It was terminal.

* * *

AS IT TURNED OUT, thanks to the operation and a round of chemotherapy, he entered into 2012 with some hope. Residing with his girlfriend at her exquisite cottage, he was surrounded by rolling hills and peaceful meadows. It was a retired life. Idyllic.

But he was bored, and there were soon signs he was improving.

We – my eleven-year-old daughter and I – arrived on one typical afternoon. The Old Man opened the gates and walked us around to the cottage. Since the operation, I noticed the physical improvement had been significant. The facial damage had evened out and he was looking and moving like his old self. If there was a difference, it was that he was no longer racing; he was patient, the tension reduced. We settled in the backroom, looking out to a paddock of grazing horses as the Old Man organised some drinks. With no phones ringing and no people dropping by, the room was eerie.

The dining table stood empty. There were no lines of phones sitting in their chargers awaiting calls from Holland and Spain. There was no stationary, phone cards, address books or his A4 lists of things to do. No bags of change sitting there for trips out to call boxes. The table was just a table.

The room was just a room.

It was silent.

He brought out our drinks and sat himself down. There were no mobiles anymore, Katherine had insisted. Therefore, he was unbothered by people and away from all temptations.

"So how are you, Kia?" he asked my daughter.

She opened her school bag and pulled out her Spanish homework. He smiled and was immediately engaged. He opened the textbook, browsed through and listened to her explaining what she was learning in class. They laughed and joked together as he doled out some grandfatherly wisdom.

"Learn everything you can, "he preached. "Whatever you learn, no-one can ever take off you. You have it for life. Be sure to remember that."

I smiled to hear this, hoping she'd remember these precious words. She had long written to him, since he was serving time in Spain, learning of the Grandad far away who studied languages. To see them together was a rare moment and the closest he would come to playing the part of grandfather.

Suddenly Katherine entered the room, with her twenty-something daughter, and his demeanour changed. They were welcoming and polite, and he moved across, out of the way as they settled down to talk about their family issues – things to do and buy, plans to go for a meal, shopping to do. I glanced over and immediately recognised his boredom.

He hated all this – everyday life. It bored him deeply.

He sat in silence as they talked, deferring to them, nodding occasionally as they threw an irrelevant question his way.

He glanced across to me and for a moment I caught his gaze, and recognised a sense of helplessness like a small boy lost. He didn't know what to do here. He was powerless and experiencing a state of nothingness.

If this was his life now, what was the point?

He might only have months to live, but he needed something to do that brought some meaning into his life. As far as I could tell, he was dying of boredom. This life of being normal, being legal, being conventional was not him.

After an hour, we left, and the Old Man operated the gates to allow us out. The yard was quiet. Not like before when he'd had cars coming and going, deals on the go, workers on the payroll. Now he was insignificant.

I thought back to Eric Berne and his 'Cops and Robbers' theory. Is this what life was like for the Old Man without the game?

Dull and lifeless.

And was there really any point anymore?

* * *

I RETURNED TO WORK, spending long hours barrowing breeze blocks and filling skips as we began work on a large extension. The monotony of the chore was welcome as it freed my mind to think and wander.

I contemplated the previous twelve months and how the Old Man, after forty years, found himself doomed to cancer whilst being forced to relax in the wealthy surroundings he hadn't earned. He was living in a home as fine as any he could have bought from crime, and yet he was bored. Ending his days with no purpose, with nothing to strive for.

Was this living or existing?

I, for my own peace of mind, was glad he was free and wouldn't suffer the fate of dying in prison. That would have been the worst. At least he was out and free, able to meet family and friends, to spend time with his grandchildren.

Nevertheless, this normality wasn't comfortable for anyone. We had to find other topics of conversation, but crime and the old days were difficult subjects to avoid. As I was studying psychology, it was an easy subject to raise. I reminded him how Margaret had given me his psychology papers from when he was at Leyhill more than thirty years ago.

He frowned thoughtfully and was able to recall some of the topics. We talked through them, me outlining how psychology was fusing the old ideas with the new to create fresh approaches.

It was a welcome distraction, but whether it was my psychology, Kia's homework or any manner of subjects prompted by the people around us, he wasn't his old self.

For him, this was no way to live.

* * *

A WEEK LATER, I received a call.

"He's left Katherine!"

"He's what?"

It was Margaret on the phone.

"He's left her. I've just heard."

I paused to think. Was this a good thing? "So, where is he?"

"At your sister's. He's living in a caravan on her drive."

I made my way straight over.

My sister Kate lived in a large weather-beaten cottage a few miles out from the city. I parked on the grass verge, strolled up the drive where a two-berth caravan sat outside the main door. From inside, I could hear the Old Man on the phone engrossed in conversation. His voice sounded strong.

He stepped out, looking ten years younger.

"Alright Jason. What are you up to?"

"Just dropped by. Understand you've left Katherine?"

"We've decided to remain friends. I thought it was for the best."

There was no regret in his voice, it was just business.

"So, what you gonna do now?"

He launched into an explanation of his plans. He was going to get Kate's place knocked into shape, put up some outhouses for storage, start bringing some stock in. He had a worker on the computer buying up furniture off some websites – Gumtree and Freecycle. Another worker would go out and collect, bring the goods here to be tidied up, repaired if needed, and then sold online for a good profit.

"We can make £500 a day easily," he noted.

I followed him around to the back of the cottage where a series of fridges and freezers were lined up, around to an outhouse where there were various chairs, fire surrounds, cabinets, and electric goods. A pair of workers were busy cleaning up the best for resale.

I smiled at his ingenuity. He sounded like his old self, and ironically, was doing what he'd started out doing in the seventies – buying and selling second-hand furniture. I hesitated to ask the next question, "Are you feeling okay? In terms of your health, I mean."

"None too bad; I'm sorting it. I've a man out in Spain sending me over some cannabis oil. This type is suited to my type of cancer – we've been researching it on the net. The oil will be arriving in just a few days. It could work miracles."

I nodded; this all sounded good.

"Added to that, I've managed to get hold of Long Hair. We're using Skype and he thinks he's got some reliable transport."

I winced a little and changed the subject.

"So… the buying and selling seems a good idea."

"It'll provide the capital to pay the exes. We just need to find five good items per day; it's quite simple."

I thought about asking more questions regarding the cancer but in truth, he looked well. So well, in fact, that I could no longer tell he was even ill. An hour later, I even drove away entertaining ideas of joining him once more. My sister Kate and half-sister Nellie, with a few others, were working with him. This could have been one last adventure, except I couldn't ignore the other things; he was making plans with Long Hair.

They most certainly would be importing cocaine.

Given his cancer, he could afford to take risks knowing he was unlikely to serve any future sentence. It might make him especially reckless and even more impatient than usual.

I returned home, thought it over and decided to stick to what I was doing.

* * *

WITH THE ARRIVAL OF the cannabis oil, the Old Man experienced something of an upturn. He again had the energy of a young man. Up at dawn, he bought and sold from morning till night with a small band of workers who bowed to his every whim. There was little talk of his cancer.

Some weekends, I would drop by for a catch-up. He would discuss his business deals, fireplaces and cookers, caravans and cars, a speedboat, some church pews, There was always something. All the while, though, in the background, I noticed how he continued to work with Long Hair on one last fortune.

I said nothing. He would do what he wanted to do, there was little point in discouraging him.

The main concern was his health, and on this point he seemed good. So good his illness became forgotten, rarely mentioned; to the point I no longer asked. His life was buzzing along like he could go on for some time, a year maybe, maybe more. It was around this time when things were on the up that I received a call.

"It's Pip."

"Pip?"

"Your Old Man gave me your number some years back. Thought I'd look him up next time I'm over."

"Pip...?"

"Pip Wells. Your Old Man's schoolmate. We used to knock about together years ago."

"Ah..."

It came back to me. Pip Wells was Philip Wells, the lad who was arrested with the Old Man when they were teenagers. One of the crowd, whom Margaret said, led the Old Man astray. Pip Wells was the local lad who went on to become a millionaire and retired to the Isle of Man.

"You're coming over?"

"Already here mate. How's Tony? I understand he's not well."

* * *

THE FOLLOWING AFTERNOON, I took Pip out to visit the Old Man. He had a gleaming Jaguar in burgundy, which he enjoyed driving slowly. He wasn't as I expected him to be. Mid-sixties, short burly and grey, he was modest in manner, cheerful in spirit. As we drove, he reminisced of old times and the scrapes they had got into. With each mile, I learned more and more as it became clear the Old Man as a teenager was the leader of a trio – himself, Pip and Rod Pepper. Far from being a teenager led astray, as Margaret had led me to believe, he was ever the leader, leading Pip and Rod down the wrong path.

"I remember we'd just robbed the TV shop around the corner from you. Made a bit and I thought we should leave it a while, but your Old Man wasn't having it. He wanted to rob HS Samuel in the town."

"The jewellers?"

"Yeah, and he was serious. He had it all figured out. We were to use a motorbike and sidecar. Arm ourselves with lump hammers; smash the main windows and fill the sidecar.

"'No Tone', I said. 'That's just…'"

"Did he try it with someone else?"

"No. Got caught around that time. Got dragged down the cop shop. It wasn't a good experience. Everyone knew about it… it was in the papers, and everyone read the papers back then."

He paused and cleared his throat.

"I wasn't proud of what I'd done. It was just something we did but… no… Not for me after that. I'd had enough."

"You did no more."

"No. I packed in."

We arrived at the Old Man's new unit.

Deep in the countryside, he had leased a large gabled unit. From here, he bought and sold on the internet. Cars came and went throughout the day: old items in, reconditioned items going out. They greeted each other like old mates with a nod and a hand-shake. The Old Man gave him a tour of the place, explaining what was selling, where the money was and where the business was going.

"When I become ill, Nellie or Kate will take it over. They've loads of experience and know the ropes."

"Kate's your daughter, isn't she?"

"That's right. She's at the other unit down the road."

I looked up at this lie.

Pip nodded and smiled, launched into another tale about the Old Man driving a bike into a lake so he could claim on the insur-ance. "Then a year later the lake was dragged, and they found it!" he laughed. "Police returned it to me, didn't they, Tone."

The Old Man acknowledged the event but showed little inter-est. He appeared more interested in the business at hand rather than memories of yesterday. I'd found out the same when I'd tried talking about the past.

He had no interest.

* * *

WE DROVE BACK in a less comfortable silence. I felt sorry for Pip and was disappointed the Old Man hadn't engaged with him more. Also, there was his lie – of the other unit. I'd later ask the Old Man of this, and he shrugged awkwardly, "Can't have him thinking this was it. Had to lie a little."

As we snaked our way down the lanes, Pip broke the silence and reminisced some more, displacing my key ideas regarding the Old Man as a teenager. I had been taken in by Margaret's ideal of the Old Man as a young boy who went the wrong way. Now I recognised this was her rose-tinted spectacles at work. By the time he'd met Pip, he already had an appetite for thieving, a disrespect for the law, and an ambition to think big.

At sixteen and seventeen, he was already that way.

Therefore, it seemed obvious to me that if anything that had sent him on the road to become a criminal, it had happened earlier. And as I was fast learning from my studies of psychology, it was childhood events and environments that explained people. And certainly, as far as the Old Man's upbringing was concerned, there must have been something there after all.

Most likely in the early years.

In those early years that my Aunt had long portrayed as perfect, there was one contradictory voice. I had, for as long as I could remember, avoided asking Mum about the Old Man. I didn't wish to stir up old memories. She had adored and loved him way back then, and still did.

However, when I had been able to raise the subject, she had said, "I'm sure his parents had split up for a while. They had not long got back together when I met your dad. I don't know why that was. He never spoke about it."

In time, this would prove significant.

CHAPTER 30:
THE FINAL YEAR

2015

NEW YEAR 2015, my brother and I were digging footings for a large two-storey extension. The weeks to follow would be cold and long, and my joints would frequently ache in the evening as I settled down to study. Often, I thought of the Old Man, who by now was ever on the move.

Despite being given weeks and then months to live, three years on, he was very much alive. Against protests from SOCA, he had been granted a passport. Consequently, he was frequently catching flights back and forth to Spain or disappearing offside to make Skype calls to Long Hair.

I dreaded to think what they were up to.

My festering worry was that the Old Man would develop a death wish towards the end; that those Skype calls to Long Hair would result in them being arrested somewhere out in the Atlantic with several tons of cocaine on board. An alternative scenario was him being arrested on another conspiracy.

Every few weeks I would drop by his unit. He would be in good spirits, confident as always. He had effectively returned to the life he had once known – of buying and selling, ducking and diving. He had a handful of employees who worked with him towards one last fortune.

What it was and what he planned to do with such a fortune, he never discussed.

Occasionally, I would overhear the hint of a drug deal but would choose to ignore it. By now I just hoped he wouldn't return to prison and would die a free man. Though we never referred to the cancer, it was there – under the surface. If he did talk about it, it was with a sense of control. He followed a stringent diet and took some cannabis oil each day. Initially, this coincided with a shrinking of the cancer and he was buoyed by the progress.

But on the next scan, it had advanced significantly.

Marriage No 4 came suddenly on the back of this. He bumped into an old secretary from back in the day. She became a worker and then wife within a period of just a few months. It appeared to have been as much a practical decision on his behalf. Sometime in the distant future, he would need to be cared for – if it ever advanced that far.

I wondered whether he would bypass the final stage. It would be easy for him to get a gun; go out by his own volition.

* * *

BY MARCH, the breeze blocks were going up and the roof work was moving closer. The days grew longer and milder. We spent lunch times in the Transit: me eating chips, David chain-smoking roll-ups. Occasionally the Old Man's name would come up in conversation, but there was a bittersweet undertone as to what might have been.

We would reflect on how he should have been the multi-millionaire he'd always dreamt of being, if only he'd made different choices. My brother believed he could have made it legally if he'd stuck to the cookers and shown more patience. He had become a criminal when it wasn't necessary.

Silence always followed these conversations.

By this time, steeped in psychotherapy, I had become convinced something had occurred in the Old Man's childhood that explained him. Maybe his parents had split up and it was linked to that. I didn't know, but I felt sure there was something.

Then one day, I received a phone call: the Old Man was driving around with a gun.

His daughter – our half-sister Nellie – had been shoved or threatened by a loudmouth from the estate. The Old Man had issued a warning, been ignored, and then simply snapped. He grabbed a revolver from somewhere and headed up to the estate. As it was, the loudmouth had swiftly gone AWOL. Faced with this, the Old Man visited the loudmouth's parents' home, spoke to them reasonably, pointed the gun at them both, warned them of what they or their son would be getting next time around.

This seemed out of character, and it rang alarm bells.

I recalled how my sister had known the odd abusive boyfriend. Back then, the Old Man had talked and warned, issued threats and more threats, but nothing had happened in the end.

Why was that? I'd wondered.

It was rumoured that his older brother Robert had slapped his wife around. I also recalled how in one or two prison letters, the Old Man had defended his marital mistakes, saying that he might not be perfect, but he never raised a hand to our mother or any woman.

It seemed an odd thing to write. *Why would such a thing need saying? Unless…*

A month later and another incident.

The Irish boyfriend of a niece threatened her with violence. Again, the Old Man snapped and issued an ultimatum. He gave him one day to leave the country, otherwise he would be kidnapped and killed whether here or on his return to Ireland. The man, who had recently awakened to the Old Man's Belfast contacts, left the country on the next ferry.

There was clearly something going on.

And so, it led me to the inevitable thought. My grandfather, that charming ex-army war hero who the Old Man held in such high esteem, *could he have been violent to my Grandmother?*

It might explain a few things.

* * *

BY JUNE, we were constructing the roof – a slow process with just the two of us. We hauled the timber up, and began to spend days on the scaffold. Each day from up high I would admire this house just the two of us had virtually built single-handed – with my labour and my brother's lifetime of skills. I hoped the Old Man might drop by and see what his two sons had built, but he was forever in Spain, wrapping up an important deal with Long Hair.

What could it be? Cocaine? Cannabis? Anything else?

We would later learn that thanks to his terminal cancer, he had wangled a cultivation licence from the Spanish Government to grow cannabis oil for health purposes. He and Long Hair planned to grow crops at several farms across central Spain. The oil would be smuggled to the UK where there was a great demand, though it was not yet legal.

On his trip to Spain, his lawyer had wrapped up the paper-work, and it was all ready to go. Before he returned, though, there was another task to fulfil.

One of his contacts had lost a boat load of cocaine when they'd been pulled by the Spanish Coast Guard. The parcel had been thrown overboard and remained at sea or washed up somewhere. The Old Man, for a percentage, spent several days up in a monoplane combing the coast for the washed-up parcel. By following the tides, he believed they were close to success.

It was at that point, there was a problem as severe pains struck.

He retired to a hotel for a few days, but his condition deteriorated. Too ill to travel, he remained stranded whilst he located a source of morphine to enable his return home.

Hearing the news, we stopped work and retreated to the van.

We sat in a long silence.

It had been almost four years. He was meant to have been dead some time back. Now the unthinkable lay before us.

On his return, he was to write the cannabis licences into his final will on the off chance he wouldn't be around much longer. This looked probable, though he insisted it was unlikely – after all, he had much to do. There were other deals on the go with some Irish importers; then some Dutch people were flying in from Rotterdam to discuss a deal. A month was all he needed.

He insisted the cancer would have to wait.

* * *

THE FOLLOWING DAY, I visited him at home. He lived at the end of a peaceful, leafy lane. His new wife told me to let myself in; she wouldn't be long. He'd just taken his morphine, so just be patient. I went in and I took a seat, waiting for his medication to settle.

I expected this to be a simple thing, but it was not.

He sat at the breakfast table, motionless. He noticed me but said nothing; just sat there. He had placed a bowl of soup and bread before him, but he didn't move. For more than ten minutes, he just sat there. He could not raise his arm, but his eyes were alive, waiting for the morphine to settle. I sat there and waited, expecting the effects to quickly subside.

After several further long minutes of silence, he finally spoke, slowly: "I'll eat it… in a few minutes."

I sat and waited.

More minutes passed and I watched him gazing at the soup – willing for him to move.

He finally spoke again, "Need…" He paused. "To take my jacket off first."

Another minute passed and then two. He didn't move. I watched on, not knowing what to do or say. The morphine dosage was far too high and overwhelming. I couldn't believe this level was required. I had seen him only last week, when he was still moving well.

Another long, unbearable minute passed, and I finally asked:

"Do you want me to help you take your jacket off?"

He didn't move. The moment passed in silence with no answer. At last, he slowly nodded.

I stood up, took a few steps across and lifted his left arm and slid the sleeve of his jacket off. I then lowered his arm, rested it on the table before him, pulled the jacket off his left shoulder, back and across to his right shoulder before pulling his right arm free from its sleeve. I lay his arm on the table next to his soup.

I hung the jacket up and sat in the seat opposite.

He didn't move.

The spoon lay just an inch away from his right hand. His eyes looked to it, and I could hear his breathing increase as if he was willing his hand to move, but it stayed still.

Should I offer to feed him, I wondered?

No. Don't be soft. He'll be okay.

I knew if I attempted to feed him it would be making a statement: that he was near the end – *and he certainly was not*, I told myself. I weighed up the other option: we could sit and wait for the morphine to reduce, for his strength to return and for himself to return.

The sound of a car door slammed outside.

I looked up to the surveillance monitor and observed his wife approach the front door.

"Nic's back."

No response.

I rushed around to the back door – to intercept Nic before she came any closer. I met her eyes, slowly shaking my head, "What have they done to him?"

Her face was blank.

"What have they given him?" I continued. "It's got to be too high – he was fine last week!"

She stared at me ghost-like – speechless. They'd been married just four months. He was meant to defy the cancer and keep going. I sat down, head in my hands, and feared the worst. He'd defied cancer for four years and now – just like that!

It had arrived.

* * *

THREE WEEKS LATER would be the day of his funeral.

He had been thrown by the speedy advancement of the cancer. His morphine had been reduced and in the final week he persisted in trying to complete some deals with the people from Rotterdam, but they would not happen. The cancer refused to back off. Within days, he was bed bound, though optimistic as ever. On our last visit he was upstairs in bed, talking well enough but conceding he was tired. On leaving, we promised we'd call by the next day after work.

"See you tomorrow, Jason," he said.

"We'll see you tomorrow, Dad," I called back up the stairs. And then I smiled. It had been many years since I'd called him Dad. They would be my last words to him. The following day, the morphine took over and he entered the final 48 hours. During that time, he lay unconscious and hopefully without pain. We took turns sitting at his bedside.

Then one morning, as I was about to head over to see him, came the call. He had died.

* * *

THERE WERE no local announcements, and few people knew he had passed on. Nevertheless, the church was full. Mostly family attended, with just a dozen or so local villains. Some plain-clothed officers waited outside the church, making notes.

Inside, I stepped up to the podium. I looked across the congregation of expectant faces, of his friends and family, his elderly wheelchaired mother, his present wife, a few ex-girlfriends, one or two old school villains stood at the back.

He deserved some words, but I had struggled with what they would be?

What was I to say? That he was a fine criminal? A great father? A virtuous man?

I opened my speech, cleared my throat, gazed out at a sea of faces and began to read my eulogy in the clearest words I could muster.

I outlined his life – the upbringing in Horncastle, his sharp mind as a teenager, meeting our Mum, marriage and fatherhood. I described the brilliant businessman of his twenties, of his passions, his drive, and his optimism, but then, alluding to his criminality, I spoke of his impatience and idealism that had often provided frustration. I drove towards the theme of the Gambler, which was how his barrister Charlie Benson had once described him. I adopted the metaphor and described his life in such terms, explaining, "that he lived his life not in order to accumulate profit but because he saw life as a game to be played... and that this game he chose, or this life he chose, was full of excitement, hard work, challenges, travel and camaraderie. He loved the excitement of this life that he made and chose to live it that way to the end."

At this point, my voice trembled, but I steadied myself and continued.

"The result was that he never stopped nor stood still. His life was a rollercoaster; a series of remarkable adventures that many of his friends in this room shared with him."

I allowed myself a look across the congregation of bowed heads, still and silent. My voice now strong, I pressed on and described how many people had said he should have written a book about his life, though they always said that it was too incredible to be believed. A few people smiled, perhaps thinking of the robberies, the smuggling, the counterfeiting and many other such things. Finally, I rounded off the best way I knew how:

"I leave the final words to our Dad. In 1978, whilst a young man at Leyhill, as part of a course paper he wrote about what were his strengths. He wrote that, *I have far more will power and enthusiasm than anyone else I know. If I find that I can see a use in doing a thing, then I can generate far more enthusiasm than the average person. By being able to do this, I find that some of the most difficult jobs become easy.'*

I paused and continued to the end.

"This spirit of optimism and enthusiasm he had back then, drove his life and made him the man we all came to know, love and admire. He will be missed by us all – and forever remembered."

A brief applause passed, and I stepped down from the podium and took my seat. My wife took my hand and squeezed it tight. I felt numb.

CHAPTER 31:
DISCOVERING ROSEBUD

2015

I WONDER what would have happened if the events I would uncover following the Old Man's funeral had come to light earlier. What would he have made of them? It seems both strange and tragic that only once he was gone did certain events rise to the surface.

It was November already, four months after the funeral. Somehow life had returned to normal, like it had to, I guess. Nevertheless, I had grown accustomed to calling by Margaret's and reminiscing about the Old Man. He'd left a void in both our lives and even with all his imperfections, I missed him being there. Often, I would stay too long and receive a text asking where I'd got to.

Such was the case that day.

She was nearing the end of an often-recounted tale. I was nodding along whilst mentally rehearsing how to kindly draw her attention to my need to head home, and then she said something unexpected.

"Just think, it was only a year before the other crash."

I looked up.

"That was far worse," she added. "Lucky we weren't killed."

"What crash?"

She looked my way and held back her next sentence. I frowned as I realised this was something new, "What car crash was this? I don't think you've ever mentioned a car crash before."

Her eyes widened and her voice climbed two octaves.

"I never told you?"

"No... I don't think so."

"About the car crash?"

I returned a blank look, "No. What crash was this?"

Her face brightened, "The crash your Grandad was in? Oh dear…" she shook her head gravely, "That was when his mate died! When we could have all been killed."

"First I've heard of this."

She frowned in thought, leant forward and checked the teapot with her palm. It was still warm. Whilst her mind churned away, she took my empty cup and poured a fresh one.

"It was in all the papers. Everyone knew about it."

I shrugged, "So when was this then?"

"When we were kids. 1958 I think."

1958?

This was news to me.

"I was eleven, Robert was twelve"

"And my dad?"

"He would have been nine, but he didn't come with us in the end. He stayed home." She sipped some tea, eyes lowered. "Funnily enough, your dad was on about the crash a few weeks before he died. When we were seeing the oncologist at the hospital."

Her forehead frowned as she strained to recall, "He was saying that it couldn't have been a brake failure… but I can't recall why."

My mouth was open, brows raised. In the fifteen years that I'd been visiting Margaret, she had never muttered a word about this.

"So, what happened?"

"Oh, it was nothing really. We were out in a little van your Grandad had just bought from Mam's relatives up in Horncastle. We'd just been to pick up his mate Stan from the Keresley Social Club. I remember 'cause whilst they went in for a drink, me and Robert were feeding apples to a horse in the field opposite. Then, when they came out, we drove off down the lanes. After driving for ten minutes or so, we were coming into Coventry when suddenly, Dad just lost control. The car swerved, hit something, rolled over and over, landed all crushed up on the verge.

"I must have blanked out for a few minutes… when I came around, I was lying on some grass. I got up, looked around, saw the car all crushed up. I went over and looked inside. Stan wasn't moving, his face a pool of blood. Even his ginger hair was blood-red. I came away and looked down at my blue velvet dress; it was shredded. Cuts and blood all over. I'd gone through the windscreen. I looked away. And suddenly over on the grass verge I saw Robert, walking about like nothing had happened. Not a scratch on him!"

She paused and looked ahead into the distance, "Oh, but then Dad…"

Her head shook slowly.

"Dad stayed unconscious. He was in a bad way, taken in an ambulance. By then, I was at someone's house being cleaned up, and Robert…well, he was fine. As I say, not a scratch on him."

She smiled and shook her head.

"After that, your Grandad was in hospital for a long time. I wasn't allowed to visit. Mam sent me to live with relatives up north; I was so traumatised by it all. It was a terrible business."

"And what happened with Grandad?"

"He finally came home, but he wasn't the same. The blow to the head had damaged him. He couldn't remember the crash at all." She paused, looked down a moment and continued, "Truth was he would lose his temper afterwards. He was angry with Mam, but then the accident had affected him. The doctor said so."

"Affected him how?"

"Well…" she paused to consider her words. "He would lose his temper… he could have a nasty temper and say such awful things, really nasty things to Mam. But it wasn't him; it was the accident. He'd had a blow to the head."

My mind raced through what she was saying. How had she not mentioned this before?

She carried on; there was more.

"Your Grandma and Grandad broke up for a while. We went to stay with family up in Horncastle and his temper was so bad. Then one weekend, Dad came up and spoke to Mam, and they decided to put it behind them."

I listened in disbelief.

Could this be...

* * *

NO SOONER had the doors opened, I grabbed all four rolls of microfilm and threaded the first reel of film into the machine's sprockets. After her recollection, she'd elaborated a little but not too much. What I had managed to draw from her was a little more regarding the date of the crash. It had certainly occurred in '58 because she said it was the same year of the Munich Air Disaster and her Eleven Plus. She hadn't seen the newspaper coverage of the crash, but it had appeared because she had heard relatives discussing it.

"I wasn't allowed to read it," she'd added. "I was too traumatised."

She'd also explained that my Grandad suffered amnesia and would never recall the events leading up to the crash. Not even in years to come would he recall a single thing.

"Did you ask him later?" I asked.

"No. We never talked about it. None of us did."

I studied the screen closely as the pages glided across the screen. Margaret had been reluctant to comb through the finer details, resistant even. I sensed a great deal of understatement in what she was saying as she rowed back from her early position of what was undoubtedly a dramatic childhood event.

"It didn't affect us really. We never talked about it, you see."

A man had died, and both she, her brother and father had almost been killed, and she was telling me it didn't affect them. How could it not?

Her parents had split up over it. Her father had nearly died. And she said he would lose his temper – which meant what exactly? I had prompted her to elaborate a little.

"When you say nasty, do you mean violent?"

"He hit Mam," she had blurted out. "But he was very angry, and Mam wasn't helpful – she didn't understand." Her face was defensive and desperate, "It was the accident – it damaged his brain! He couldn't help it."

A silence followed, during which I sensed there was more to this. Maybe a lot more.

For some time, I had suspected there must be some event in the Old Man's childhood that had affected him. Maybe this was it; something that had affected the entire family. I had been wondering for a year or more whether my Grandfather had been violent towards my Grandmother, and now it seemed there was something to that.

As I rolled through the February papers, the Munich Air Disaster passed across the screen and I was encouraged. This was the right year. And I might be within just a few weeks or so. I turned down the speed of passing microfilm to a slow crawl.

"Your dad had stayed at home – the lucky sod." she had said with a brief smile.

"But he would have seen and heard everything, wouldn't he?"

She shook her head. "No. Mam and Dad never let us see anything. They wouldn't speak in front of us. They had to protect us. Remember, they sent me away within a few days. I was so traumatised."

"But you said you were fine – and you remembered everything."

"Yes, but Mam wanted to protect me. She said I was in shock. So, she sent me away."

I nodded my acceptance and seeing her in distress, let the subject go; but in my mind, I could feel my brain processing it all, questioning and speculating. The Old Man's childhood wasn't this perfect world as she'd claimed all those years back – his dad had been violent, his parents had split up – and maybe there was more.

I'd gone past it.

My hand pulled back the lever and jerked it into reverse. I watched intensely as the microfilm slowly reversed direction and the pages slowly crawled back, until finally – a front page containing a large photograph of a crushed, overturned heap of metal slid into view.

I leant in closer.

Only the mangled wheels protruding from the wreckage suggested it was a vehicle of any sort. My first thought: *how could anyone have gotten out alive?*

Underneath ran the headline and article:

24th February, 1958
COVENTRY MAN DIES AS VAN OVERTURNS

A Coventry man was killed yesterday afternoon when the van he was travelling in skidded, overturned and was wrecked, at Kirby Corner, Canley.

The man, Stanley Gallimore (27) of Caravan, the rear of 83, Westwood Heath Road, died from head injuries. William A. Shipley (30), of 68 Kingston Road, Coventry, who was driving the van also received head injuries and was admitted to Coventry and Warwickshire Hospital. His condition was stated to be 'fair.'

Mr Shipley's two children, Margaret (10) and Robert (11) were also in the van. Margaret was treated at the hospital for cuts and bruises. The boy escaped injury.

Police were today appealing for witnesses of the accident.

There were several details of interest. Firstly, 'Fair' was the condition of my Grandfather, not in a coma, unconscious or critical, but 'fair'.

Secondly, they were calling for witnesses. Why was that?

They already had perhaps three witnesses – Grandad, Margaret and Robert – except my Grandfather would have amnesia.

I skimmed through the next few days of papers – to check if any witnesses did come forward.

Fifteen minutes later I'd advanced two weeks, was about to give up the search when I found a second cutting:

March 1st, 1958
INQUEST ON VAN VICTIM ADJOURNED
The article detailed the crash and how no evidence could be heard as my Grandfather was still seriously injured. There was no mention of Margaret or Robert, but by this point, Grandma in what I thought was an unusual act of caring for her, had sent Margaret away as she was 'traumatised'. Would she return for the inquest or remain traumatised I wondered?

I spun forward three weeks more and a third headline appeared:

March 14th, 1958
COVENTRY MAN'S DEATH IN CRASH WAS 'ACCIDENTAL'
A Coventry inquest was told yesterday that a van in which a Coventry motor packer met his death struck a grass verge, skidded 95ft, turned over, then travelled another 70ft, before coming to rest.

A jury returned a verdict of 'Accidental Death' on 27 years old Stanley Galli-more [...] however, Mr. Shipley who was seriously injured in the crash was too ill to give evidence, but his 11 years old son, Robert Leslie, also a passenger in the van was able to describe events just before the van struck the grass verge.

The boy said that just before rounding the bend the van started 'rocking.' The next thing he knew was that it was upside down. He blacked out, and when he regained consciousness he was lying on the road [...] The Coroner, Mr. C. W. Iliffe said the accident was probably due to the condition of the vehicle.

And so, the strangest thing.

Margaret hadn't given evidence; Robert had. And his version contradicted Margaret's recollection completely. She had mentioned no 'rocking' or any signs of a problem with the vehicle. He had also claimed to have blanked out when Margaret said she had seen him walking around without a mark on him. So why the lies?

To me, the reason why Margaret had been sent away seemed

less about trauma and more about making sure she was unavailable to give evidence. If she had, she wouldn't have mentioned rocking noises from the vehicle, but would have mentioned the earlier stop at the club for a few pints, and maybe their speed.

The vehicle had travelled 165ft in total. It must have been going some.

And then I recalled what Margaret had said, that the Old Man, after some forty years, was talking about this at the hospital. That he was saying how it couldn't have been the brakes at fault. Why had he been so sure? And why was it still on his mind?

In all these years, I had never known the Old Man show any interest in the past. My efforts to encourage him to do just that had come to nothing. But he was still questioning this crash and, what's more, he was doubting what he'd been told.

As was I.

* * *

HER FACE DROPPED as she read the article, "But that's wrong! It was me who blacked out, not him. He was fine!"

I studied Margaret's face. It was clearly the first time she'd seen the articles and it was obvious as to why: she disagreed with all of what was written, "There was no rocking noise. Nothing!"

Placing the articles down, she removed her glasses and looked across to me: "It was me who blacked out. I came around and saw Robert. He was fine – not a scratch."

"Did you know there had been an inquest?"

"No. I was away. Mam had sent me away."

A silence followed, and I hoped she was putting the pieces together.

"Your Grandad was ill," she added. "He couldn't remember a thing! He never would. He had amnesia, you see."

A minute passed, and I finally put it out there: "Do you think they sent you away so you wouldn't give evidence?"

She slowly shook her head, "No, no. I was traumatised. Mam sent me away for my own good. She was so worried."

"Would you not have been more comforted by staying?"

"No, Mam had a lot on. She was at the hospital every day and then – "

She looked down and away.

"You said the accident changed him…?"

She looked up, eyes shining, "He was so angry afterwards."

"You said 'violent' before."

She glared at me, surprised that I recalled this detail.

"Only for a while. The accident affected his brain. The doctor said so."

"And you said you had to move away?"

"But only for a while. I was back for my Eleven Plus." She sat back in her chair, "I know I was back because I did it late – in September. We were only away for a few weeks."

"But the accident was in February? That's not just a few weeks – that's more than six months."

She looked down at the date of the article, and began to mutter to herself as she did the maths, "It couldn't have been that long… no…"

She spent the remainder of the visit dumbfounded, as if her normally reliable memory had played a trick on her. It couldn't have been six months, she repeated, and tried to alter her calculations of time, but to no effect. Her parents, my grandparents, had split up for many months due to my Grandad's violent temper.

She refused to be drawn further as to the nature of this temper, or on the break-up. She'd not only dismissed the period, but had squashed it down to the smallest blip. Furthermore, the violence was dismissed as unimportant, after all – he had amnesia!

My mind suddenly jumped back ten years. When the Old Man had been awaiting extradition to Holland on the murder charge, he had initially planned to plead amnesia as his defence. I'd sent him papers on the condition to aid him in this and all the while, he'd never mentioned that this had been his own father's defence when he'd caused a man's death.

It was some coincidence.

And from what I could recall, amnesia was rarely permanent. Some memory usually returns, though the main incident sometimes remains lost. That is, if he had amnesia at all.

As the Old Man knew too well, it is easy to fake.

It might simply be that he was critically injured, took a long while to recover, and then learned of the inquest which had passed. It would be only then he would have learned how Margaret had been sent away to avoid giving evidence and his eldest son had stepped up to lie on his behalf.

And when he found out... he may have been angry. Fuming maybe.

Maybe his violence was understandable.

And in that light, wasn't Robert as an adult easier to understand?

As a boy, to defend his father and protect the family, he'd put any feelings to one side and lied to the inquest. He would have blood on his hands for ever after.

I wonder if the Old Man had known or suspected?

Perhaps.

One thing was for sure though: after the accident, the family had changed. They didn't talk about the accident, didn't talk about Grandad's violence, didn't talk about the break-up. Didn't talk about the past at all.

But had they not all been affected by it?

Robert grew up to be a smart but angry character. Abusive and sadistic – violent to his wife, but a hero to his mother.

And there was Margaret who had never got on well with Grandma who treated her with distrust. Even now, Grandma had few good words to say of Margaret, always keen to discredit anything she had to say, always stressing you couldn't believe what Margaret said.

Then there was the Old Man. How had he responded?

Always busy, whether boxing, art or motorbikes, always distracted. Never looked back, always forward, to a future that was grand, never small or modest, but one that would never be enough. Never enough money, never enough of anything.

And always he would display a gentlemanly way with women, protective and providing, polite and considerate. He was strikingly old-fashioned in this respect. Unsurprisingly, he occasionally showed contempt for those who were violent towards women.

It was this subject, when faced with it, that would leave him torn. He would reason and threaten but seem unable to act. It was only near the end there had been a change, and then it had been extreme.

On that first occasion, he had taken a gun and threatened the loudmouth's parents. The second time, he had threatened to have the Irishman killed.

Something in his psyche seemed to have snapped in that final year.

There appeared to have been more going on in his mind than I could have ever imagined. It seemed he was resolving the past. No longer accepting the unacceptable.

I reflected some more and then recalled the one person missing in this.

My Grandmother was very much still alive. Now eighty-eight years old, she was well. She had attended the funeral of the Old Man, took it in her stride, stoic and hardened, shedding no public tears. All those years ago, it would have been her who sent Margaret away. It would have been her who agreed for Robert to give evidence. It would have been her who would have kept my Grandad in the dark.

Even so, after all these years, would she be willing to recall any of this?

I decided to go and find out.

CHAPTER 32:
THE FINAL PIECE

THE BUZZER RELEASED the lock. I pushed the door open and made my way up the narrow stairwell, passing by her stair lift and onto a simple landing, which led to a sparsely furnished living room where she sat in a neat armchair. As I entered, my Grandma, eighty-eight years old, slowly rose and opened her arms.

It had been a few years.

We embraced and as she sat down, I noticed her moistened eyes. She wiped away a single tear and settled into her chair. On the coffee table before her was a teapot, two cups and some biscuits.

She smiled.

I smiled back, the best I could manage.

Visits had always been difficult. Mum and the Old Man's divorce had created a thirty-year gulf between us. In all these years, I had seen her just a handful of times – at funerals, my Grandfather's and more recently, the Old Man's.

I recalled her, but did not know her well at all.

Back in the day, she had been considered a hard and unfeeling lady who placed little value on my brother, sister and I; but that was all forgotten now, as she expressed sweet affection for a past long gone. Over the following hour we discussed such memories, of which we had few, and she expressed regret at how we had lost touch all those years ago. She explained, in a voice still sharp and proud, how they'd done their best and wished things had turned out differently.

"We gave up the house for you all," she reminded me. "Mortgaged it to help your father out with his businesses, and then he lost it." Her shining eyes looked into mine, "We did it all for you kids. We thought so much of you all."

It was impossible not to feel a twinge of guilt.

After a while, I steered the conversation back to our family history, and how due to my interest, Margaret had told me of the crash. She nodded as if this was the most ordinary of things, but added little. To prompt her memory, I explained how I'd managed to track down the news article.

Pleasantly surprised, she smiled and grabbed her glasses, and read it silently. I awaited her gut response, but there was nothing. She leant back, shook her head slowly, but showed no surprise.

"It was just an accident – couldn't be helped. Your Grandfather was in a bad way. In hospital for weeks and couldn't recall a thing – amnesia. And then Margaret, she was traumatised. Had to send her away."

She looked to me with large brown eyes and leaned towards me, close, her eyes glistening, "He was terrible after the accident."

I nodded sadly.

She paused, cleared her throat, raised her voice, "He... he... he would hit me!"

I looked up; she stared back, fearful.

"One time he arrived home. I opened the door. He stood there and punched me – straight in the face."

She blinked a tear away, leant forward some more, opened her mouth wide and pointed, "Knocked my front teeth right back!"

I tried to say something, but no words came.

She leant back in her chair, shaking her head over and over, "The accident affected him like that. In the end, I took the kids and went to stay with relatives – up in Horncastle. I couldn't stay with him. He was too violent."

I was still searching for words. I had suspected this, but to hear it so directly, and from a frail old lady who could no longer hurt a fly. She continued to explain.

"It was his brain. The specialists said so – it couldn't be helped."

I doubted this. "If it was his brain, then how come he was able to stop?"

"We talked; he came back. He got better."

A silence passed between us. I still didn't know what to say. I cleared my throat – it was dry – and attempted to retrace our steps. "Erm... the inquest. There was an inquest?"

"Was there?" she replied.

I passed her the inquest article.

"Oh... I haven't seen this before..." she said.

She read silently, and again I watched for her gut response, but there was nothing.

She lay the article down, "As it says, it was an accident."

"But Margaret remembers the crash clearly and said there had been no noises and that Robert hadn't been knocked unconscious at all, but that she had been."

"You shouldn't believe Margaret – she was traumatised. I had to send her away, you know."

I nodded, "Yes, she said you sent her away, but she said she felt fine and that –"

"That's Margaret for you – she makes things up. Would you like another tea?"

"Please," I stuttered, as her put down of Margaret lingered. She'd always been critical of Margaret, who had done no-one any harm, who always saw the best in people, even when they were undeserving.

I moved on.

"What about Grandad, did he ever recall what had happened?"

"Oh no, he never remembered a thing. He had amnesia, you know."

"But Robert remembered everything."

"Yes. Robert *was* a good boy. A fine son was Robert."

She smiled with pride, recalling her long-lost son. She saw nothing bad in Robert, only good; though as we talked, she opened up here too, as regarding the collapse of his marriage.

"I do think he used to knock her about a bit," she conceded. "But he was so nice was Robert, but after Helen left him, well..."

I bit my lip.

"He got into the drugs and... you know the rest. That's why I was so surprised your father got mixed up in all that. He had his whole life and —" she turned to me and smiled once more, "I remember your dad calling by once – dropped me a fridge freezer off – and the neighbour saw him. Well afterwards, she comes over to me and says, 'Who was that?'

"I said, 'That's my son, Tony.'

"'Oh,' she said. 'He looks just like a film star.'"

She chuckled to herself at this.

I smiled; she'd taken us away from the subject. I shrugged, "He sounds like he was your favourite."

"Oh no, no," she smiled," Robert was always my favourite. He was lovely was Robert."

I nodded with dismay and would have wondered why he was her favourite, but I think I now knew.

* * *

WAS THIS THE CHILDHOOD incident I'd long searched for? Was this the one event that might have explained the Old Man's life?

Maybe for me, it was.

The pieces all seemed to fit.

The crash and the events that followed had opened the door to a hidden past that went some way to explaining the Old Man's family. When seen against this one event, they were no longer such a puzzle – none of them were. Grandad, the ex-soldier, due to overconfidence and bad luck, was responsible for a man's death. Whilst he recovered, Margaret, the daughter who would have struggled to tell lies, was sent away; Robert the eldest son was instructed what to tell the inquest, so it would appear an accident.

He lied well, and by claiming to have blacked out, avoided any scrutiny. He had pleased his mother, saved both his father and the family's reputation. Even so, he would have noted the violence that followed, and maybe he felt he'd caused it. Robert would have watched his father explode in fury, in a violence that couldn't be explained to others, but Robert would have known why.

The inquest would leave my Grandfather's reputation scarred. The violence would pass, but he would have to accept what had happened and claim he had amnesia – to the dead man's family, to friends and workmates. It could never be taken back.

And what would the Old Man at nine years old have made of this?

Listening in on things but not being told much; noticing changes but being given no explanation; seeing his mother's bloody face and being told all was fine; hearing his father had been cleared of a man's death but knowing something wasn't right.

It would have affected him.

And perhaps he did hear a great deal. Maybe he did get a sense of his father being protected, of him avoiding justice. He may have overheard the covering up and the plotting, relatives adopting a code of silence. Maybe to him as a child, it was like a game, an introduction to 'Cops and Robbers', that game he would play throughout his life.

It's something I will never know for certain.

* * *

THE OLD MAN had been buried at a small village cemetery outside Coventry. His grave was on the front row by a picket fence which looked out onto a quiet road. It bore a wooden cross for the moment. The gravestone would come some months away when the earth had settled.

I stood and attended to my thoughts. If he had read the articles I'd found, if he'd known about the inquest, what might he have thought?

He might have just nodded in agreement, knowing that his brother would have done as he was told, and that Margaret – yes, she had to be sent away. It was important to keep one's mouth shut.

Maybe he suspected something was amiss, but had been practical – looked forward and not back, pretended all was fine.

To deny, in other words.

After the crash, the family would make a fresh start. They had moved to a new house, had two more children. A few years later, when the Old Man was wondering what he might do with his life, his parents would have been preoccupied with babies and nappies. He had been the youngest child for fourteen years, now he needed to grow up, get out there and earn a living. They seemed to expect that he would work in a factory, that he would be ordinary.

Being ordinary would always be unacceptable to the Old Man.

At that point, he appeared to have been ambitious, to be looking for an outlet. He cemented the new friends his mother disapproved of – Pip Wells and Rob Pepper – with whom he was soon robbing local shops and appearing in court. It was around this time he met my Mum.

She was unlike his own mother, and maybe that was the attraction. At the beginning, he seemed determined to be different from his parents. He disliked his mother's snobbery and his father's passiveness. He couldn't contemplate working in a factory all his life, nor being told what to do.

But something pulled him one way and something else another.

He had an irrational instinct that attracted him to an environment where people kept secrets, where a person had to be ruthless when he had to be, where people used authorities but never trusted them, where violence was common and a conscience did you no good at all. Like with the car crash, it was a world which led to a courtroom where you would attempt to subvert and cheat judgement before being handed a penalty you probably deserved. Above this though, what made this world worthwhile, and perhaps its most beguiling feature, was that along the way you could realise your wildest ambitions, live without accountability, make stacks of money and be whoever you wanted to be.

The aim of being a villain was supposedly to become a millionaire, but millionaires were careful people, and to be careful was against the spirit of being a villain. For the Old Man, being a villain was less about being wealthy and more about living a lifestyle of excitement and risk, like playing the game, 'Cops and Robbers'.

It would be a game he would play his entire life, long after others had stopped. More so, he continued playing long after it became apparent that he had talents elsewhere, that he was a flawed criminal, handicapped by his many contradictions.

He loved making money, would make millions legally and illegally, but ultimately waste it all. He prized freedom, loathed rules, but would serve more than 25 years inside the country's most regulated prisons. He worked alongside many violent criminals, but would loathe to employ violence himself, for he liked to be liked. Over time, as he wasted more and more money, and spent more and more years in prison, he would become an enigma no-one could fathom. Given all that happened throughout his life, I wonder whether he could ever have hoped to have made sense of himself? And in the end, had he tried?

I can still picture how, as a man of sixty-six riddled with cancer, he had grabbed a gun and headed off to confront the man who'd laid a hand on his daughter. And how he had threatened to have the Irishman killed.

Was this him attempting to resolve the past?

Up until then, had he always been avoiding that? Was that what business and crime to him were about? About never needing to look back. About always being busy. Always looking forward.

It had always been the answer he reached for.

Whenever inside, whether facing two years or ten years, he'd always been this way, making grander plans, always looking forward more intensely than ever, never back. However, in his final year, when there was no abundant future up ahead, he had looked back. And he had resolved to confront what he saw, and question what he had been told.

But in the end, maybe it had been too little too late.

CHAPTER 33:
CHOICES

A FEW YEARS LATER, and for most, life has moved on. Despite promises of staying in touch, few people do. They have their own lives to lead and have no desire to look back. For me, though, looking back is a habit I might never lose.

I still visit Margaret, but with each month these visits become less frequent. We'll drink tea, reminisce about the Old Man, laugh at some of the things he got up to. Occasionally these get-togethers are brightened by some news to share, and I wish the Old Man could have hung on a little longer to hear it.

His protégé, Ryan James, being arrested in Spain on large-scale drugs charges was one. The Old Man had always said he would fall heavily. Now he languishes in jail. I wonder whether he sees the Old Man as the best or worst person to befallen him? Meeting the Old Man certainly helped make him Britain's top drug smuggler, but he also faces the remainder of his life in prison.

Sad as it is, Raj, the ex-prison governor, I would not see again. Messages were sent along the grapevine, but there would be no response. His son Sunil served another sentence, this time for armed robbery. I understand he's now going straight. Tiff, the ex-boxer who caved under questioning, was fighting in a charity match last time I heard. I viewed it on YouTube; he lost but lost well. He was over forty but in good shape. McGlinchey, the cheeky villain who distributed *Smuggling Vacation* to UK prisons, passed away in his sleep not long back. Hundreds attended his funeral.

From overseas, the Old Man's pal Albert calls in every few months or so, but there is little news to be shared anymore. He is the only one who appears to have been a success in crime. Long Hair, the tech wizard who the Old Man planned to make one last fortune with, I have never heard from again. Maybe he's making that fortune by producing medicinal cannabis out in Spain. Sowerby, the heroin addict who aided the Old Man after he was shot, is still imprisoned in the Netherlands. He may never be released.

All the other names and faces are out there somewhere, but I'm sure I'll forget them in time as they matter less and less.

Closer to home, occasionally around the city, I still bump into an old face who knew the Old Man back in the day. It may be the mechanic who as a youngster recalled seeing the Old Man jump from the dock as police awaited to re-arrest him, or the old timer in the café who on realising my Old Man was Tony Spencer, walked over to shake my hand and expounded on what an remarkable man he had been, or the local lawyer, who when asked who he considered to be his most incredible client, answered, "without doubt, it was Tony Spencer."

One old face, who stood out from the crowd, was that of an ex-CID detective who knew the Old Man back in the day. He lives just a few miles away, in a comfortable semi on a corner I often drive past. I knocked on the door one day, introduced myself to Noel, a tall, grey-haired Irishman. He welcomed me in, and for a few hours regaled me with his memories of the Old Man.

He explained how the Old Man's second-hand shops were on his patch, and dropping by for a cup of tea was part of his itinerary. He recalled the absurd money the Old Man was making, the friendly nature, the generosity, the keenness to do a favour. Many officers like Noel would accept freebies back then. Mentioning his fence had been ravaged by a gale, the Old Man sent workers around to throw up a new one; told his cooker was playing up, he dispensed a worker to fix it; noticing an old classic bike lying neglected, the Old Man offered to fix it up.

This would throw up a red flag, as he explained.

"I was called into the Chief Inspector's office one day," he started. "I took a seat, and he asked me whether I owned a particular motorcycle with a certain number plate.

"Yes," I said.

"'Have you lent it to Tony Shipley by any chance?'

"I admitted I had. Tony was an ex-bike mechanic, 'He said he would fix it up for me.'

"'Do you know he's been following unmarked post office vans on your bike?'

"I didn't know what to say. It was my career in the balance.

"'Now get it back and have a word with him,' he said.

"So, I told your father. Reminded him of the trouble I could have got into. He laughed and apologised, but it served me as a reminder that I couldn't altogether trust him."

"And what happened with the post office van?" I asked.

"Got robbed the next week."

"And was it the Old Man?"

"Will never know, but with your dad, the police knowing what he was up to, made no difference. If he was going to do something, that was that. Us knowing just made it more exciting, I think."

This was all new to me. I had heard claims that the Old Man had taken part in robberies as a young man, but never heard anything to confirm this. I knew the second-hand shops had all been named after banks, but I had discounted the rumour they were named after the banks he had actually robbed.

"He was a big name even as a young man," he continued. "Knew the top people, those robbing the banks and post offices, those running protection, the club owners and loan sharks. Most of them were his mates back then. Your Old Man was different though; he was a good businessman, alright."

Like others before him, he talked of the cooker business and the fortune the Old Man was making and how he undertook a foolish insurance job, burning down the warehouse, the reckless act that brought it all crashing down.

"Should have made millions. But he fucked it up."

We talked some more, until finally I directed him around to the one question and an answer that I had been resisting for many years.

"So, to sum him up, do you consider the Old Man to be a villain or a businessman?"

It was an important question. For me, since I was a small boy, my Old Man had been a businessman who had become a criminal, but what was he really, and could I accept an answer either way.

He paused, frowned, rolled his tongue along the corner of his cheek and then looked back at me with an air of certainty.

"Your dad was a villain," he said. "He was a hell of a good businessman, but ultimately, he was a villain."

I nodded in agreement, satisfied I understood why.

It had been fifteen years since the shooting in Amsterdam, that time when I resolved to discover why he became a criminal. I had spent more than a decade looking back before arriving at an answer that satisfied me. And now whenever I hear such stories, the more it seems inevitable the Old Man was the way he was.

When I think of how he started out, everything now has an air of inevitability about it. Given the ideas he absorbed growing up, the grand ambitions, the love of secrets, the coldness of his upbringing, it seems he was designed for crime. He could have been a great businessman, he had the talent and discipline, and even though he made one or two fortunes, I can now see that he was always set to implode. He preferred chaotic villainy to disciplined business.

This had puzzled me for so many years.

I had spent my teens wondering why this was, unable to see his rationale, unable to recognise his character, always believing he intended to do the right and good thing when it simply wasn't his way. Even into my twenties whilst working for him, I struggled to accept his nature, believing that he wanted to be who I wanted him to be, not accepting that he liked his choices, he loved his life.

And then, throughout those years he was on the run abroad, my optimism was undiminished, as I had hoped for something good to happen, for some reform, a change in direction.

Looking back, this seems foolish now, but that's how hopeful I was back then. Only after the second Birmingham trial did I really begin to accept who he was. He may have been a businessman to me, but to himself he was a criminal. That was his choice and he lived it with no regret.

As for my own choices, whether right or wrong, I do accept they were mine. It may be that I spent a long time looking for something that wasn't there, hoping he would become the father I wanted him to be. For a long time, I think I probably needed to accept who he was with all his imperfections and grow up, except I didn't want to.

Following the Birmingham trial, I did start over and begin that process. Unfortunately, it would coincide with the Old Man's cancer diagnosis and eventually his passing. It was reflected in the eulogy I gave at his funeral. I had wanted to say what a fine father he had been, but recognised that I could not. He had been an incredible influence upon me, but he had not exactly acted as a father ought.

He had been my boss as much as he had been my father. A boss who encouraged me to join him in his adventures and ignore the risks. To join him in the game. But then whenever not working for or helping him, it was noticeable how the phone calls would slow and stop. There was no malice in his actions, that's just how he was. Ultimately, it would prove a loss to us both.

In studying psychology, the quote "Life is understood backward but must be lived forward" is often cited.

Knowing and understanding the Old Man's past made him easier to accept, the past easier to understand, and the future easier to shape into something different from the past. After many years of looking back, I at last find myself looking forward more. Knowing who the Old Man was, means I can now enjoy the stories, accepting him with all his flaws, marvelling at his occasional ingenuity, shaking my head at some of the foolish things he did, but no longer dwelling on the whys and wherefores.

Even so, life now is different.

With him gone, the world is an emptier place, though it still feels like he is out there. Up to some hair-brained scheme, a robbery, a counterfeit, importing or smuggling; for me, it feels like he will always be out there somewhere. For as far as I can recall, he has always been out of reach, away working and chasing deals, abroad or in prison, always busy, always on the move. Only difference now is that the phone calls have stopped.

Some days if I think of him, it feels like he'll be ringing in soon for his messages or to ask a favour, "I need you to grab £60,000 from Linx, then get it to Barcelona by Tuesday. Can you get moving and sort some flights?"

But the phone doesn't ring, and it never will again.

Nevertheless, life goes on.

* * *

AT BIRMINGHAM Symphony Hall, I stride onto the stage in robe and mortar, accept my graduation certificate, glance around a sea of a thousand faces and wave to Tariana positioned up high on the balcony. There ought to be a sense of pain that the Old Man can't be here – but there is not.

I know he would never have made it; he would have had too much on. Deals to make, places to be and lists to follow.

I've spent the last four years steeped in books, thinking and breathing psychology. It seems like I ought to go on to study a Masters to become a psychotherapist, but something else is calling me. There is one last thing I must do for the Old Man, though it is something he would never have requested.

It is to write his story.

In the Old Man's final years, a few people had remarked that he ought to retire and put his story down. He would laugh at the idea, perhaps thinking he had so much more to do. However, I recognise he would never and could never write a book; I could though.

And if the Old Man has left anything, it is the story of an incredible life.

A year ago, I began to write, and as I wrote I found that this was a responsibility he had left me, a gift if you will. To write his story in a way he never could, to reveal more than he ever knew, to understand more than he ever had. Ultimately, the aim of the story would be to explain who he was and why he was, two things he was always too busy to figure out.

The story would begin in Amsterdam…